Situ Panchen. Mahasiddha Ghantapa.
From Situ's set of the Eight Great Tantric Adepts. 18th Century.
(Collection of John and Berthe Ford.)

Karmamudra:

The Yoga of Bliss

Sexuality in Tibetan Medicine and Buddhism

Dr. Nida Chenagtsang

Edited by Ben Joffe
(Jigmé Dorje)

SKY
PRESS

Index of illustrations

Published by:

SKY PRESS

3640 SE Washington Street
Portland, OR 97214
www.skypressbooks.com

ISBN
9780997731989

Library of Congress Control Number: 2018940097

Editor: Ben Joffe
Design and Typesetting: Pearse Gaffney
www.mvdigital.nl

Yuthok and Vajravarahi
illustration by Anna Artemyeva

First English Edition
Printed on acid-free paper

Special thanks to all whose valuable contributions
made this work possible.

Contents

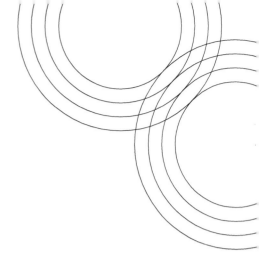

I would like to dedicate this book to all victims
of sexual abuse and especially to those who
have been abused in the name of spiritual
and religious traditions. May the pain and suffering
caused by sexual abuse swiftly cease in every
corner of this earth.

- Dr. Nida Chenagtsang

Mönmo Tashi Chidren

འདི་ན་སུ་དང་གང་གིས་མི་ཤེས་པའི།། མི་ཞིག་ཁྱེད་ལ་དགའ་
ཞེས་ཅ་ཅོ་འདོན།། རྡོ་རྗེ་མ་ཁྱོད་བསོད་ནམས་ལས་ཀྱིས་ནི།།
ཕན་དང་བསྟེང་ཞེས་གུ་རུས་ལུང་དུ་བསྟན།། ཀྱི་ཧོ་འདི་ནི་གསང་
བའི་བདེ་བ་དང་།། སྣང་སྟོང་འཕྲུལ་དུ་གོའི་ཆུབ་བདག་མ།།
ཐབས་ལམ་སྦྱོར་བའི་ལམ་གྱི་གྲོགས་མཆོད་དང་།། རྡོ་རྗེ་འཆང་
གི་ས་དེ་ལག་ཏུ་མཆི།། ཕྱི་ལོ་༢༠༠༤ ཟླ་ ༩ ཚེས་ ༢༤ ལ།

Here in this place, without anybody at all realizing it,
Someone is crying out loudly that he loves you,
Vajra Dakini, the Guru prophesized that
because of your merit and karma, you
and I would meet and be together – how incredible!
This is what is meant by the secret bliss and the magical
manifestation of appearances united with emptiness!
All-pervasive Lady, be my friend and partner on the
Path of Bliss, the path of union through means,
And the state of Vajradhara will be in our hands!

Prophecy
September 24th 2004

THE YOGA OF BLISS

Prefaces

Lam Drukpa Kunley (1455 - 1529)

Karmamudra and the Crazy Wisdom Tradition

I would like to greet all the readers of this book from Chimé Lhakhang, Drukpa Kunley's temple in the Punakha Valley of Bhutan. This great master, known as the 'Divine Madman,' came here from Tibet after he was completely enlightened, and helped to spread Vajrayana teachings throughout the country of Bhutan and to subdue wrathful demons. We can consider this place to be the birthplace of 'Crazy Wisdom' because Drukpa Kunley is remembered for his wild and outrageous behavior that transcended all social norms and broke through conventional thought patterns and fixations.

Drukpa Kunley is especially known as a great master of Karmamudra, probably one of the most famous masters of Karmamudra. When studying Karmamudra, we should understand it from two different perspectives: firstly on a literal, historical level and secondly on a more metaphorical or symbolic level. The first refers to the original classical practice as it has been taught and passed down over the centuries. Drukpa Kunley was truly a wild yogi who achieved realization and taught through his sexuality and other strange and unconventional means such as the hunting of animals and subduing of invisible demons with mantra and wrathful deity practices. This was not metaphor, but a very direct teaching that in 16th Century Bhutan was appropriate and highly effective. I fully understand and respect his method of transmission of the teachings.

Drukpa Kunley was a great master with a transcendent level of wisdom, skillful means, attainment, blessings, and power, he was free of negative emotions and therefore transcended the material dimension which is why he was totally free of all social conventions. At the same time, the people had immense and unadulterated faith in him. One story depicted on these temple walls tells of an old man who requested a mantra from Drukpa Kunley and recited it faithfully and ceaselessly for many years. This sacred 'mantra,' however, was in fact merely a string of dirty words that the master gave to this trusting disciple, but due to the blessing power of Drukpa Kunley and the unshakeable faith and diligence of the disciple, this old and uneducated man achieved rainbow body, the highest level of spiritual attainment when one's material body dissolves into light at the time of death. This is the true power of Guru Yoga. The combination of transcendent wisdom on the part of the master, and transcendent devotion on the part of the student is what made these Crazy Wisdom practices so effective during ancient times in a place such as Bhutan.

Unfortunately, in today's society, teachers lack the level of realization of the great masters of the past and students lack pure faith, making Crazy Wisdom methods dangerous and confusing. This is why today I think it is important that we understand Drukpa Kunley's stories from a more metaphorical perspective. There are so many crazy modern people that are using the name of Karmamudra, misunderstanding this great teaching, practicing incorrectly and using stories such as those of Drukpa Kunley as an excuse to engage in all sorts of unethical and harmful behavior which is damaging both to practitioners and to the teaching itself. Imitating the behavior of Drukpa Kunley while completely lacking in his wisdom is very dangerous.

One of my principal goals in writing this Karmamudra book is to clarify many wrong views about the practice. Of course, traditionally, this is a highly secret practice that is very difficult to receive and some may criticize me for publishing this book. But when we say that it is 'secret' many people think that Vajrayana has something to hide, something that is harmful for the public. This secrecy was originally meant to protect the tradition and to prevent unqualified people from having access to very high level teachings that can be difficult to understand and therefore prone to misinterpretation and misuse. However, it is my opinion that keeping these practices secret and clouded in mystique can be even more harmful, because without proper education and understanding about these practices, wrong views become rampant, especially in the age of internet and social media where all kinds of information spread like wild fire. So my book is really intended to provide clarification and increase transparency about Karmamudra practice which I think is very timely given the recent exposure of so many sexual scandals, both in spiritual and secular communities: in Dharma, politics, Hollywood, and at all levels of society. People have many questions and I have tried to answer these questions by addressing common misconceptions and clearly laying out the difference between true Karmamudra practice and sexual abuse.

If we understand the stories of Drukpa Kunley and Crazy Wisdom practices in a more indirect, subtle or metaphorical manner, we can see them as masterful teachings on how to work with our negative emotions and fears and to tame and slaughter the wild and dangerous demons of our own mind. Karmamudra is the most important practice for working with desire. Desire can be a very powerful positive emotion, but at the same time it has a very demonic force that can lead to many disasters and negative results on an individual, family, and societal level. When we lose control of our desire, our desire controls us and we become a slave to our cravings. Buddha taught that desire or attachment is the root cause of all pain and suffering, so in order to be free we must really understand this essential teaching and learn how to harness this extremely powerful force, how to work with this energy and use it as a tool on the path to enlightenment. It is very important for practitioners to understand why we need Karmamudra practice, how important it is, and not just to cast it aside or cover it up because it is controversial or has been misused. It is a teaching that can be incredibly beneficial spiritually, emotionally, psychologically, and physically, if understood in a proper way and not distorted.

I would like to thank all of my teachers and especially those who instructed me in Karmamudra: the yogi Lhanyön Rolpatsel (Akhu Lhamo) from the Rebkong *ngakpa* tradition whose story I tell in this book, and my beloved root teacher, the nun Ani Ngawang Gyaltsen who taught me the Six Yogas, Atiyoga, and Karmamudra in Lhasa, Tibet. I would also like to thank my dearest friend, Tshering Chöden whose support and blessings are behind every page of this book.

I'm very happy to be here today and to receive Drukpa Kunley's blessings for this book in the last days of the Fire Bird year, where the monks are performing a ritual to dispel obstacles in the coming year. I sincerely wish that this book will bring correct information, clarify doubts and confusion, and transmit the positive energy and wisdom of Karmamudra to the general public.

Dr. Nida Chenagtsang
February 14th, 2018
Chimé Lhakhang, Bhutan

Prayer wheel outside Drukpa Kunley's temple,
Chimé Lhakhang in the Punakha Valley of Bhutan

The plaque outside the temple walls reads:

"Lam Drukpa Kunley (1455-1529) was an enlightened Buddhist master who personified the true essence of Vajrayana tradition that is also known as 'Crazy Wisdom.' This is the profound wisdom that transcends the mundane cultures of religion.

Devotees fondly call Lam Drukpa Kunley the 'Divine Madman' because of his non-conventional and 'outrageous' style of teaching. He deliberately portrayed the image of a vagabond and wandered around the countryside, indulging in song and dance, alcohol and women, hunting and feasting. In reality, what it meant was that he was beyond the norms and conventions established by human society.

Lam Drukpa Kunley was a social critic that who taunted the hyprocrisy of the established orders, including the monastic order. Thus the use of his phallus as a 'flaming thunderbolt' weapon symbolizes the discomfort that society experiences when facing the truth. Lam Drukpa Kunley's most outrageous and sacred actions included the taming of a number of demons and demonesses that were tormenting the Bhutanese people. For example, he subjugated the infamous and much feared demoness of Dochula and buried her on the mound where Chimé Lhakhang was built in the late 15th century by his cousin brother, Lam Ngawang Choejey.

Lam Drukpa Kunley liberated generation after generation of Buddhists from cyclic existence. Buddhists from all over the world come to Chimé Lhakhang to pray for the survival and health of their children."

Request for the Blessings of Drukpa Kunley

འབྲུག་པ་ཀུན་ལེགས་མ་ཁྱེན་ནོ།

Drukpa Kunley, think of me!

རང་སྣང་དག་པའི་ཞིང་འདི།།
འོག་མིན་སྟུག་པོ་བཀོད་པ།།
རྗེ་རྗེའི་བླ་མ་མཆོག་དེ།།
འབྲུག་པ་ཀུན་དགའ་ལེགས་པ།།

In this spontaneously appearing pure realm
Of Ögmin Tukpo, 'Densely Arrayed, Below None'
Drukpa Kunga Lekpa
Is the supreme Vajra Guru!

རྗེ་རྗེའི་སྐུ་ཡི་གར་དེ།།
སྣང་སྟོང་སྒྱུ་མའི་ཕྱག་རྒྱ།།
རྗེ་རྗེ་གསུང་ས་ཀྱི་གླུ་དབྱངས།།
གྲགས་སྟོང་འཕྲུལ་གྱི་རོལ་མོ།།
རྗེ་རྗེ་ཐུགས་ཀྱི་རོ་བོ།།
འོད་གསལ་བདེ་སྟོང་ཟུང་འཇུག།

The dance of his Vajra Body
Is the illusory mudra seal of Form-Emptiness
The song of his Vajra Speech
Is the magically emanating music of Sound-Emptiness
The essence of his Vajra Mind
Is the inseparable union of Light and Clarity, Bliss and Emptiness!

ཐབས་ཀྱི་རྡོ་རྗེའི་མཆེ་ཆེན།།
ཤེས་རབ་པད་མའི་སྟུ་ཟབ།།
ལྷུན་སྐྱེར་བདེ་སྟོང་དབྱེར་མེད།།
འཁོར་བའི་འཆང་ཐག་རང་གྲོལ།།

The great Vajra-penis of Means
The Profound Lotus-vagina of Wisdom
Unite together in indivisible Bliss-Emptiness
And the bonds of samsara are spontaneously untied!

བླ་མ་འབྲུག་པ་ཀུན་ལེགས།།
མཁའ་འགྲོ་བདེ་ཆེན་བཟང་མོ།།
དཔའ་བོ་མཁའ་འགྲོ་འབུམ་ཕྲག།
བྱིན་རླབས་ཆར་ཆེན་ཕོབས་ཤིག།

Guru Drukpa Kunley
Dakini of Great Bliss
You hundreds of thousands of dakas and dakinis
Shower down your blessings!

རྣམ་རྟོག་སྤྱོག་ཆགས་མང་པོ།།
ཡེ་ཤེས་མདའ་མོས་སྒྲོལ་ཤོག།
ཉོན་མོངས་ལས་རླུང་འཁྲུག་དུས།།
ཤེས་རབ་པི་ཝང་དཀྲོལ་ཤིག།

Liberate the pack of wild animals that is conceptual thoughts
With the piercing arrow of your primordial wisdom!
When I am disturbed by afflictive emotions and karmic winds
Sound the soothing lute of your wisdom!

བདག་འཛིན་ལྕགས་ཐག་དཀྱུ་སྐྱིལ།།
བདག་མེད་རལ་གྲིས་གཅུབ་ཤིག།
གཉིས་སྣང་མུན་པ་མཐུག་པོ།།
ཕྱག་ཆེན་ཉི་མས་སེལ་ཤིག།

Sever the looping iron chains of self-grasping
With your sword of no-selfness!
Illuminate the thick darkness of dualistic appearances
With the sunlight of the Great Seal of Mahamudra!

ཐ་མལ་འདོད་ཆགས་ཆེན་པོ།།
ཤེར་རབ་དབང་གིས་སྨིན་ལ།།
བསོད་ནམས་ལས་ཀྱི་སྒྲོར་གྲོགས།།
མྱུར་འཕྲད་འོག་སྒོས་གྲོལ་ཞིག།

Having ripened all my great, ordinary desire
Through wisdom,
And having quickly met my consort through karmic merit
May I be liberated through the Lower Gates practice of Karmamudra!

སྨྱོན་པ་ཉི་ཟླའམ་སྔགས་པ་བདེ་བའི་རྡོ་རྗེ་ནས་འབྲུག་པ་ཀུན་ལེགས་ཀྱི་གདན་ས་འཆི་མེད་
དམ་ཁྲི་མེད་ལྷ་ཁང་མཇལ་རྗེས། ༢༠༡༤-༠༢-༡༥ཉིན་བུམ་ཐང་སྤུང་དུ་བྲིས།

Written by Dr. Nida a.k.a. the ngakpa or Tantric yogi Dewai Dorje, 'Vajra of Bliss' on the 15th of February 2018 in Bumthang, Bhutan, after he visited Drukpa Kunley's seat, Chimé Lhakhang.

This is a remarkable and unprecedented book. I would like to offer some context here for it, as well as some historical background for Karmamudra practice more generally, so that readers can appreciate just how special a book it is.

My involvement with this project emerged from my ongoing relationship with Dr. Nida, as part of my activities as both a researcher and practitioner of Buddhism. I am a cultural anthropology PhD candidate currently based at the University of Colorado and I am interested in the globalization of esoteric religions. My research focuses on Tibetan Buddhist non-monastic, non-celibate Tantric yogis and yoginis, religious specialists who are known a little more succinctly in Tibetan as *ngakpa* and *ngakma*. I first met Dr. Nida through his writing. As part of my research I had read and translated some of Dr. Nida's unusually comprehensive and accessible Tibetan language essays on ngakpa/ma history and practice, which he had written for non-specialist Tibetan readers as part of his efforts to preserve and promote *ngakpa/ma* traditions both inside and outside Tibet.[1] Himself a *ngakpa*, Dr. Nida is one of the most prolific Tibetan experts writing on Tantric yogic practices and practitioners today. As you will learn about in this book, Buddhism was established in Tibet through two distinct yet connected communities of religious professionals: the community of shaved-headed, celibate monks and nuns and the community of long-haired, white-robed Tantric householders or *ngakpa/ma*. While the former group of vow-holders uphold Buddhism by living and studying in monastic institutions at a remove (at least in theory) from the demands of worldly life, the latter pursue high-level Buddhist practice in tandem with raising families and engaging with village life and responsibilities.

---

[1] Dr. Nida and his brother are co-founders of the Ngakmang Foundation and Research Institute, a non-governmental organization devoted to supporting the historic Rebkong *ngakpa/ma* community in North-eastern Tibet, of which they are both part and which is one of the largest and longest-standing communities of householder yogis and yoginis in Tibet. More information in English about the foundation and its various activities can be found at www.ngakmang.org.

In 2016, while I was living and studying in India as part of my doctoral dissertation fieldwork, I had the good fortune of meeting Dr. Nida in person when he came to Bangalore to give some teachings on mantra healing to a small group of students. I was deeply impressed by his unaffected and kind style of teaching and his commitment to making Tantric Buddhism accessible to his audience. We hit it off immediately, and he expressed his pleasure with some of my earlier translations of his work, which I had shared with commentary online. With Dr. Nida's encouragement, I agreed to translate more of his writings on Tibetan medicine and Tantric yoga and these translations subsequently became part of the rationale for the development of Sky Press. This current book is quite a different animal from the translations that Sky Press has published to date. While it does in fact feature several original English translations of Tibetan texts which I prepared at Dr. Nida's request, the bulk of its contents consists of hours and hours of Dr. Nida's oral commentary, dating from roughly 2015 until the present. This commentary, recorded during public and private teachings, telephone conversations, and in-depth interviews, has been transcribed and reworked to form the unprecedented book on Karmamudra that you are reading right now.

The Path of Transformation:
Introducing Tantric Buddhism and Sexual Yoga

What then, is Karmamudra? Karmamudra refers to the ancient Tantric Buddhist practice of engaging in special, cultivated forms of sexual arousal and intercourse as a part of spiritual practice. Such Buddhist 'Tantric sex' has been an important if controversial part of the Tibetan religious landscape since Buddhism's arrival in Tibet in the eighth century. Known as the 'Path of Skilful Means' (*thab lam*) and as 'The Path of the Great Bliss of the Lower Gates' (i.e. the lower chakras or energy centers, *oggo dechen lam*),

Karmamudra uses powerful yogic techniques to work with human desire in a mindful way and to transform ordinary, worldly sexuality into a vehicle for spiritual advancement and liberation. Practitioners of Karmamudra cultivate and refine their sexual desire and pleasure in a non-dualistic way, shifting these away from fixation on self-and-other. In doing so, they are able to use the orgasmic state as a means of eliminating their mental afflictions and obscurations and as a springboard to recognizing the ultimately empty and blissful Buddha-nature of mind and reality.

For readers used to thinking of Buddhism as the primary domain of celibate monks and nuns, the idea that it could have anything to do with sexual intercourse may seem counter-intuitive or even shocking. Nonetheless, when Buddhism came to Tibet from India it came in both Sutric and Tantric and celibate and non-celibate forms. Tantra refers to a diverse set of religious practices, texts, and orientations which rose to great prominence in India from around the sixth century. Tantra's elaborate liberatory rites of initiation involving cosmological diagrams or mandalas embodying the perfection and ideal alignment of outer and inner realities, its practices of guru devotion, mantra recitation, techniques for the manipulation of body, breath and subtle energy, propitiation and visualization of often fierce and often female deities, and other special technologies for bringing practitioners beyond dualistic mind and appearances, came to have broad appeal. Its approaches were taken up and reframed at various points by Shaivites, Vaishnavites, Shaktas, Buddhists, Jains and later Muslims.

Tantric Buddhism or Vajrayana, the 'Indestructible, Non-Dual' Vehicle, makes use of such approaches within the broader moral and cosmological framework of Mahayana Buddhism. Here powerful, transformative Tantric methods allow for the actualization of the so-called Bodhisattva aspiration to attain Buddhahood – to 'wake up' and free oneself from suffering in order to help other beings do the same, with lightning speed and precision.[2] While Sutric approaches are exoteric, and tend to emphasize scholasticism and celibate monasticism, the esoteric path of Tantra emphasizes direct, gnostic realization through meditative practice and leaves room for careful engagement with sexuality and other ostensibly polluting, distracting or

---

[2] Tantra is said to hold unique soteriological promise. While other vehicles of Buddhism insist that it takes eons of rebirth accumulating merit and wisdom to achieve Buddhahood, the Tantric path presents the possibility of enlightenment within one human lifetime, in and through a single human body.

compromising elements of worldly life which Sutric orientated monastics are oath-bound to avoid. One way to understand the logic of this is with an analogy often used by Tibetan teachers to distinguish Sutric versus Tantric orientations (*do* and *ngak* in Tibetan, respectively): when a poisonous weed of afflictive emotion – anger, hatred, lust, pride, ignorance etc. – sprouts forth rapidly from the soil of our mind, the Sutric approach tells us that we should uproot it thoroughly and swiftly, that we should pull it out and disown it entirely. Once eradicated in this way, we should then plant the seed of a different kind of plant in its place. Having eliminated distracting, harmful emotions, we should cultivate mental stability, peace, clarity, virtue, and compassion instead. This is why the Sutric path is called the path of 'rejection, renunciation, elimination, turning back, or reversing' (*dok lam*).

Tantra takes a different tack. It too acknowledges that poisonous plants are potentially deadly, it too is concerned with producing stability, clarity, compassion and virtue. Yet whereas the Sutric orientation sees in poisonous weeds only disruption, pollution and a problem, the Tantric approach sees opportunity. Tantra is a medical or alchemical path. Just as a chemist can carefully and strategically cultivate toxic herbs to process them into powerful medicines provided they are smart, careful, and possess a laboratory and the requisite technical know-how, Tantric yogis and yoginis can make beneficial use of the active ingredients of their human mental poisons. By chemically refining their desire, anger, ignorance, pride, and envy they can distil something positive and beneficial out of what might otherwise plague or endanger them. It is for this reason that the Tantric path is known as the path of transformation or transmutation (*gyur/jyur lam*). It is this clever, pharmacological approach which Dr. Nida Chenagtsang explains with such rare insight and clarity in this book.

The 'yoga of bliss' or 'alchemy of desire' that is Karmamudra represents one particularly profound example of how potentially toxic elements of everyday, worldly life can be repurposed and redirected for the sake of liberation. That said, like other elements of high-level Tantra, Karmamudra has historically been kept highly secret. There are various levels of Indo-Tibetan Tantric practice and teachings. Contrary to popular representation, many of these require celibacy. That said, the Tantric texts and practices subsumed under the heading of 'Highest' or 'Unparalleled Yoga Tantra,' involve just the kind of alchemical engagement with impure or 'poisonous' emotions and experiences described above, and talk quite explicitly about sexuality as a tool on the path. As a Highest Yoga Tantra practice, Karmamudra is linked with the so-called 'Perfection' or 'Completion Stage' (*Dzogrim*) in Tibetan Buddhism. This stage of practice involves working with the energies and architecture of the subtle body and with highly refined states of awareness in very advanced ways. It is thus regarded as one of the highest echelons of esoteric Buddhism and has traditionally been off-limits for all but the most well-trained and elite practitioners. As Dr. Nida mentions in his foreword, over the centuries secrecy has helped to ensure that extremely powerful but easily misunderstood and misapplied Tantric Buddhist practices have been practiced and preserved safely and correctly, and have maintained their integrity. Yet it is also true that in the current moment, a dearth of reliable, general information about Tibetan Buddhist sexual yoga practices has enabled ongoing exploitation and abuse under the guise of Tantra. This has regrettably contributed to great misunderstanding and mistrust of Vajrayana teachings.

This book seeks to remedy this situation by providing reliable and clear information about Tantric Buddhism, and about what Karmamudra is and isn't. Rather than providing information about highly advanced practices that are beyond the capacities of all but a tiny minority of individuals, this book describes simpler traditional Karmamudra practices instead, ones that are intended for practitioners who lack the yogic and meditative training needed for these other levels of practice.

Countering Stereotypes: Patriarchy, Abuse, and Incomplete Pictures

As Dr. Nida explains in the chapters that follow, Karmamudra has become surrounded by a great many misconceptions and stereotypes. These misrepresentations of Tibetan Buddhist sexual yoga which Dr. Nida tackles at length in this book aren't just perpetuated by non-Buddhists or non-specialists, however. Scholars of Tibetan Buddhism have also sometimes promoted mistaken and one-dimensional views about Karmamudra. On the one hand, some scholars have claimed that while Karmamudra may have been more prevalent in ancient India, its execution and significance all but dwindled into oblivion in Tibet, where Tantric methods became thoroughly incorporated and regulated by monastic institutions (I address this claim a little further below). In light of this, they have suggested that Karmamudra is an obscure, virtually dead tradition with only limited relevance. Conversely, some commentators have proposed that Karmamudra is in fact alive and well in contemporary Vajrayana, yet they have concluded at the same time that in practice it amounts to little more than a patriarchal, cultural cover for enabling ongoing subordination, exploitation, and abuse of women by religious authorities. To bolster their arguments, proponents of this position often point to statements in Indian Highest Yoga Tantra scriptures which recommend virgin girls and marginalized, low-caste women as ideal consorts.

While blanket characterizations of Tantric sexual yoga as inherently disempowering for women have been roundly challenged by scholars (Allione 2000, Biernacki 2008, Gayley 2018, Jacoby 2014, Shaw 1994), it is true that 'Tantra' and 'Tantric sex' continue to be used as convenient justifications for abuse today. This book emerges in direct response to this reality, and one of Dr. Nida's primary motivations in publishing this text has been to demonstrate that Karmamudra can be practiced equally by men and by women, that it can be equally empowering for practitioners of any gender or sexual orientation, even if this has not always been the case historically. By carefully distinguishing between abuse and authentic practice, and between cultural mores and the essence and promise of the teachings, Dr. Nida presents a more egalitarian picture. Highlighting the contributions and achievements of female Karmamudra masters, he shows how sexual yoga has the potential to benefit all practitioners and need not further existing social inequalities.

Despite increased attention to female Tibetan Buddhist practitioners and Tantric yoga practice in academia, I have been surprised by the extent to which caricatures of Karmamudra persist among even highly qualified scholars. I once attended a meeting in which Tibetan Studies scholars had gathered to quiz a prominent, visiting professor about his new book of on Highest Yoga Tantra scripture. There were about fifteen scholars in the room, none of whom were Tibetan. At one point, the conversation turned to Completion Stage subtle body practices and the relation of these to sexual yoga. Noticing that some commenters had started speaking about sexual yoga as if it were a fairly static cultural phenomenon across time and Indian and Tibetan contexts, I intervened to suggest that were one to look at representations and styles of Karmamudra practice in Tibet across the centuries, one would see that they were in fact quite diverse. As an example, I pointed out that the Yuthok Nyingthig (the cycle of revealed teachings on which this book is based and which I discuss further below) presents a range of different sexual yoga methods which combine levels of Tibetan Buddhist practice in unique ways not seen in other texts. A highly-regarded non-Tibetan, American scholar-practitioner who has spent the better part of her life translating Tibetan Tantric Buddhist literature responded to my interjection immediately. "Huh!" she guffawed. "Those guys will do anything to get their rocks off!" Quip delivered, the rest of the room chuckled and the conversation moved instantly on to other things.

This comment amazed me. Sure, as a white, non-Tibetan scholar of Tibetan Buddhism I was no stranger to the curious way in which non-Tibetan Tibetan Studies scholars will regularly default to a kind of performative flippancy or levity when discussing technical details of Tantric practice and protocol as these relate to their research. I have witnessed scholars cultivate this sort of breezy disregard for Tibetan perspectives, authorities and priorities when they are in Tibetan-free spaces on numerous occasions. As a performance it seems to function as a distancing mechanism, and to index their ability as non-Tibetan scholars to 'see through' Tibetan categories and stipulations, even as they are rewarded for speaking glibly and making broad claims about Tibetan culture or 'the Tibetan imagination' and 'mindset' writ large. To be fair, I was also aware that the scholar who made this comment had spent years working to secure her authority as a female researcher in equally male dominated spaces of institutionalized Tibetan Studies and Tibetan Buddhism. And yet, I still could not believe that she could dismiss sexual yoga practices so casually as nothing more than elaborate mechanisms through which 'those guys' (i.e. male Tibetan lamas) could ensure they got laid. After the meeting, I found myself thinking again and again about how I would have felt hearing this dismissal if I was a Tibetan woman who happened to be the daughter of Karmamudra practitioner parents. About how I would feel to have a non-native expert reduce the potential context of my birth and my parents' entire partnership to a punchline about horny, patriarchal Tibetan men.

The commentary on Karmamudra that Dr. Nida provides in this book derives from his own experience as a highly trained non-celibate yogi and doctor, as a parent and a teacher. In many cases, non-celibate students of

Tibetan Buddhism have questions about sexuality and sexual yoga practice but their monastic teachers may not be equipped to address these in satisfactory or useful ways. The information in this book comes from Dr. Nida's involvement with a centuries-old community of house-holder Tibetan Tantric yogis and yoginis who practice Karmamudra in the midst of everyday life and realities. Their lives and sexual yoga practices are neither jokes nor one dimensional caricatures about esoteric boy's club conspiracies. Today, tragically, there is no shortage of stories of unscrupulous gurus manipulating and sexually abusing students but in contrast we hear the stories and voices of contemporary Tibetan Buddhist practitioners who are engaging with sexual yoga practices in healthy and responsible ways as part of their spiritual path only very rarely. Dr. Nida's text responds to this lacuna in a timely way. It seeks to bring Karmamudra down to earth without reducing its profundity. It addresses very real problems of patriarchy and the abuse of students and Tantric tradition without denying Karmamudra's complexity and its genuine potential to benefit practitioners at the same time.

Revelations and Revivals: A Brief Historical Detour

It should be clear that there remains a considerable lack of awareness – even among scholars – about the great diversity of practices that exist within Indo-Tibetan religious traditions and fall under the extremely broad rubric of 'Tantric sex'[3]. Tantric sex is not an a-historical, monolithic category. As mentioned above, Tantric methods spanned across lineages, cultural communities, and religious denominations. Shaiva Tantric sexual yoga texts and practices are multiple, internally diverse and have evolved in their own ways. They both overlap and differ from Shakta texts and practices, just as Shaiva and Shakta varieties are distinct from Vajrayana ones. Equally, Tibetan Karmamudra practices are also not necessarily reducible to their Indian prototypes.

Although Samuel (2008) and Snellgrove (1987) point to evidence in a text by Asanga for the possible existence of forms of Indian Buddhist sexual yoga practice as early as the fourth or fifth century CE, most scholars agree

---

[3] For a useful, albeit non-comprehensive summary of the considerable range of Tantric sexual practices that existed in Indian and Tibetan contexts by roughly the start of the eleventh century, see Hatley (2016).

that Tantric Buddhist sexual yoga only definitely appears in textual form in seventh and eighth century India. These early forms of Tantric Buddhist sexual yoga are found within the Mahayoga class of Tantric texts. Looking specifically at the Tibetan context, Jacob Dalton, who has studied some of the earliest extant Tibetan language Tantric texts found in the Dunhuang cave collection, has shown that the complex chakra systems and subtle body cartographies which are today associated with Tibetan Karmamudra developed as part of the formalization of Completion or Perfection Stage practices in the late ninth and tenth centuries, in line with the formalization of the third Tantric Empowerment as one involving sexual yoga practices.

Dalton explains that while Buddhist sexual yoga practices involving the manipulation of the subtle body may have existed for a long time as part of oral transmissions, at least as far as can be seen through textual evidence only:

"...later systems involved intricate arrangements of chakras and energy channels mapped across the body's interior. In the early Mahayoga texts, however, the technologies are simpler, the descriptions limited to the energies associated with sexual pleasure which rushes through the practitioner's torso." (2004, 10-11)

Dalton outlines how the development of Tantric Buddhism in general and sexual yoga practices in particular depended on a sort of interiorization of Buddhist ritual that had significant implications:

"The Tantric interiorization of Buddhist ritual was not a rejection of ritual. Nor was it a psychologization...This shift took place in the physical realm. Its beginnings can be traced to the first half of the eighth century, and the ritual technologies it spawned continued to develop through the ninth century. By the end of these two crucial centuries, a new ritual discourse of the bodily interior was in place. The Tantric subject had become the site for the entire ritual performance; the body's interior provided the devotee, the altar, the oblations, and the buddha to be worshipped." (2004, 2)

Such developments in Indian Buddhist practice were inherited by Tibetans, who began to make them their own. During the Tibetan imperial period which spanned the seventh to ninth centuries, Highest Yoga Tantra practices in Tibet were the sole preserve of religious and aristocratic elites, and their circulation among commoners was prohibited. With the collapse of the Tibetan empire in the late ninth century, state patronage and institutional monastic regulation of Tantric Buddhism foundered, and Tantric practices and perspectives percolated more broadly. While this period is remembered by later Tibetans as a period of fragmentation (*silbu dü*) – a 'dark age' of civil war, demonic activity and the degradation of the teachings – it was also a time when Tantra became thoroughly indigenized. Centralized monastic authority broke down, and while some monks fled to Eastern Tibet and maintained their vows, Vajrayana teachings were in large part preserved by *ngakpa* and *ngakma*, through hereditary transmission (Dalton 2011). The late tenth and eleventh century saw a renaissance of Buddhist culture in Tibet, and the resuscitation of large scale monasticism, which occurred in the wake of what is known in Tibetan as the *chidar* or 'later spread' or propagation of Buddhist teachings from India (Davidson 2005). As monastic institutions and practitioners came to dominate the religious landscape, Tantric sexual practices began to be undertaken in more symbolic forms. Although evidence suggests that Tantric Buddhist practices involving 'transgressive' engagement with impure persons and substances, frequenting of charnel-grounds and the practice of partnered sexual yoga likely originally emerged outside of monastic contexts and were undertaken quite literally by earlier Indian non-celibate practitioners (Davidson 2002, Onians 2003, Szanto 2010) over time in both India and Tibet such methods came to be increasingly reformulated for monastic, celibate use (Samuel 1994, Wedemeyer 2012). In Tibet, as Tantric empowerments or initiations came to be overwhelmingly transmitted and received by monks, the sexual yoga elements of these rites were de-emphasized and de-literalized in ways that allowed celibate religious professionals to participate in them without violating their vows.

Non-celibate styles of Tantric engagement persisted alongside more monastically oriented models, however. A smaller demographic of *ngakpa/ma* communities continued to practice Tantric yogic methods within the context of lay life, with many *ngakpa* and *ngakma* beginning their training during early childhood under the supervision of parents and other relatives. As it acclimatized to its new surroundings, Indian Buddhist sexual yoga naturally came to take on different meanings and associations in Tibet. In the Indian Tantric context, the power attributed to the ritual use of sex and sexual fluids, consuming of meat and alcohol, and consorting with corpses and low-caste women derived in part from a logic of transgression, from a strategic subversion of Brahmanical notions of purity (White 2003). Tibet's distinct socio-political context, which lacked any directly equivalent caste-system or set of social and dietary taboos to India, meant that sexual yoga inevitably came to take on a different flavour. One important way in which Karmamudra became Tibetanized and an integral part of Tibetan history and identity was through what is known in Tibetan as the *terma* or 'treasure tradition'.

Tertön or 'treasure revealers' are visionary prophets or saints in Tibetan Buddhist tradition. They are understood to be reincarnations of the original disciples of Padmasambhava or Guru Rinpoche. An Indian *ngakpa* and Karmamudra master thought of by Tibetans as a 'Second Buddha,' it was through Guru Rinpoche's Tantric yogic power that Buddhism was successfully established in Tibet. Before he dissolved his eighth century physical form, the great master is said to have hidden various 'treasures' all over Tibet and the Himalayas, with the intention that these treasures would be discovered by appointed persons at a later date. Guru Rinpoche left various treasures for safekeeping with guardian spirits in the sky, under the earth, in rocks and caves, and in the mind-streams of his closest disciples. Centuries after his time and into the present, certain individuals have claimed to have had powerful visionary experiences and past-life memories which have convinced them and others that they are reincarnations of Guru Rinpoche's elect. Attending to these visions, insights, and memories, these individuals have been able to follow the clues to unearth treasures left specially for them across space and time by Guru Rinpoche and his Karmamudra partner, the great female Buddha and princess Yeshe Tsogyal who Dr. Nida discusses in this book.

Treasures take various forms. They may be special physical objects or relics, statues, ritual implements, and so on, thought to have particular power to bless and help beings. Sometimes small scrolls written in cryptic celestial script will be discovered, which provide a basis for unlocking full *gong ter* or revelations that have been seeded in the minds of *tertön*, which are subsequently decoded and written down as new-but-not new revealed scriptures. Treasure texts are considered by those who believe in them to be direct and realized transmissions from the numinous. These revelations are even sometimes said to be superior to canonical Buddhist teachings that have been passed down orally and via copying and translation from Sanskrit, for two reasons: their directness and 'fatedness' removes the factor of human-historical error and degeneration, and the fact of enlightened beings having assigned specific treasures to specific times, people, and places means that treasures are uniquely suited to the needs, capacities and circumstances of their specific contemporaries. One of the most important practices for revealing treasures is sexual yoga. Just as Guru Rinpoche had his destined consorts with whom he engaged in Karmamudra in order to unlock the power needed to subdue Tibet's autochthonous deities and prime Tibet to become a Buddhist country, later generations of treasure revealers have their own karmic 'soul mates' and prophetic collaborators. Reunited across past lives, *tertön* consorts must thus work together to unlock one another's visionary capacities to fulfil prophecy and benefit beings.

In her recent book about the lives and love letters of Golok based Tibetan treasure revealer couple Khandro Tare Lhamo (1938-2002) and Namtrul Rinpoche (1944-2011), Holly Gayley (2018) underscores the importance of sexual yoga practices in treasure revelation and decipherment. She outlines a situation where a talented yogini was the primary initiator of Tantric partnership, where a woman was in charge and had considerable agency. She shows how ideals of selfless Tantric sex are navigated and actualized as part of Tibetans' everyday experiences as a thoroughly marginalized and disenfranchised ethnic minority in contemporary Communist China. By detailing how this Tantric couple envisioned and enacted a shared destiny to heal the damage done to Buddhism in Tibet under Chinese occupation and rule prior to and during the Cultural Revolution, Gayley challenges stereotypes of female consorts as exploited tools of men. Moreover, she underscores the way in which authentic Tibetan Karmamudra is not just about personal realization, longevity or gain but is predicated instead on altruistic intention. As a mechanism for creating continuity with specific culturally meaningful pasts in the face of trauma and upheaval, Karmamudra in its specifically Tibetan forms is implicated in greater visions of large-scale, collective healing and social upliftment. This capacity of Karmamudra to be of benefit to both individuals and their larger societies is precisely what Dr. Nida emphasizes in this book.

Ancient Teachings for Current Problems: The Special Qualities of the Yuthok Nyingthig Tradition

Understanding *terma* is important for appreciating the nature of this book in other ways. Quite significantly, all the texts and teachings on which the instructions in this book are based are treasure texts. In Chapter One of this book, Dr. Nida notes that many scholars of Tibetan Buddhism read injunctions relating to sexual yoga in important Highest Yoga Tantra scriptures and then imagine that they then know exactly how Karmamudra works on the ground, that taken together these statements represent the entirety of Karmamudra practice. Dr. Nida reminds us however, that there are centuries-old, living, oral traditions relating to Karmamudra in Tibet. Specific lineages, regions, and religious communities have their preferred texts and styles of practice, and as Dr. Nida demonstrates, oral-lineage interpretations and emphases may diverge markedly from standard formulas repeated in foundational texts. Given that *terma* are understood as more targeted teachings, intended for specific times and places with specific problems, it should come as no surprise that particular families and communities in Tibet have come to rely on the approaches and advice of specific *terma*.

The main source of Karmamudra teachings for this book is an extensive cycle of revealed teachings known as the Yuthok Nyingthig or the 'Heart-Essence of Yuthok'. These teachings were transmitted via visions by the Dakini or Tantric goddess Tsomo Palden Treng to *ngakpa* and physician Yuthok Yönten Gonpo the Younger (1126 – 1202), one of the fathers of Sowa Rigpa or traditional Tibetan medicine. Yuthok the Younger subsequently taught these revelations to his close disciple Sumtön Yeshe, who made notes based on Yuthok's direct oral instruction. After this, Yuthok edited these notes himself and these came to comprise the first edition of the complete teaching-cycle of the Yuthok Nyingthig. Called in full 'The Heart Essence of Yuthok, the Sunlight of Compassion, the Dharma-cycle of the Blessings of the Practice of the Guru that Dissolves all Suffering and Darkness,' Yuthok's set of revealed practices were later included in the 'Nectar of

Good Qualities' section of the Mahayoga cycle of teachings in the Rinchen Terdzö, the so-called 'Treasury of Precious Terma' or collection of revealed scriptures assembled by Tibetan scholar Jamgön Kongtrul Rinpoche in the late nineteenth century. Yuthok the Younger was part of a hereditary lineage of traditional Tibetan doctors and *ngakpa,* and the Yuthok Nyingthig mirrors his own overlapping domains of expertise as a realized Tantric yogi, meditation master, and physician.

The Yuthok Nyingthig is a complete collection of teachings on Tantric Buddhism. It includes instructions on every aspect of the nine vehicles of the Nyingma or 'Ancient Translation' school of Tibetan Buddhism. It offers rich yet remarkably concise instructions on preliminary practices, Guru Yoga and Dakini procedures, all the six traditional Tantric yogas mentioned in this book, every aspect of Mahamudra and Atiyoga or Dzogchen meditations, protector deity practices, daily practices, sundry Tantric rites of healing and exorcism, and of course Karmamudra. While it predates the formal *rimé* or non-sectarian movement launched in Eastern Tibet by some seven centuries, its instructions are presented in a consistently and strikingly non-sectarian manner. A tradition of Vajrayana for working medical professionals, the Yuthok Nyingthig acknowledges the potentially diverse sectarian backgrounds of its chief target audience, and stands as a spiritual complement to the exoteric curriculum taught in the Gyüshi or 'Four Medical Tantras,' which form the foundational textbook of Tibetan medicine. As such, it comprises the only comprehensive set of Higher Yoga Tantric practices involving the Medicine Buddha in Tibetan Buddhist tradition.

Importantly, the Yuthok Nyingthig teaches two forms of Karmamudra practice. A 'classic' version of sexual yoga which requires elaborate training in subtle body 'channels-winds' (*tsa loong*) and inner heat or Tummo yoga practices, and a 'Karmamudra for Dummies,' a more entry-level practice for yoginis and yogis without such expertise (*tsa loong ma jangpai naljor pho mo*). Before I met Dr. Nida and began studying and practicing the Yuthok Nyingthig, I had no idea that such a thing was possible. I also had no idea that the Yuthok Nyingthig taught unique condensed *ngöndro* or Tantric preliminary practices, or that it included a special level of such procedures that incorporated explicit concerns about social justice and upliftment into Buddhist practice. There were a lot of things I didn't know. When I first heard that Dr. Nida was teaching about seven-day *ngöndro* retreats and was offering instruction in other Yuthok Nyingthig practices that I had never heard of, I was suspicious. I initially imagined that Dr. Nida was somehow dumbing down traditional practices to pander to the interests of foreigners thirsty for Tantric exotica. After I met with Nida, picked his brain, received initiation into the Yuthok Nyingthig lineage, and began to study and practice its teachings, however, I came to understand how wrong my original perceptions were. I developed a deeper appreciation for Dr. Nida's mission, motivation, and inspiration. Yuthok is said to have attained the 'rainbow body' (*jalü*), or full Buddhahood at the point of death where one's body shrinks and dissolves into multi-coloured light. It is said that in his omniscience, Yuthok foresaw that in later times practitioners would find themselves saddled with considerable obstacles in the practice of Vajrayana. For this reason, he recorded for posterity a collection of teachings that included various versions and levels of traditional Vajrayana practices, suitable for students of diverse capacities. He transmitted comprehensive yet condensed Tantric practices that working, lay practitioners who lacked the time or resources to engage in prolonged, difficult and expensive training and retreats could integrate into their lives and use to benefit themselves and others.

Prior to the twenty first century, the overwhelming majority of practitioners of the Yuthok Nyingthig in Tibet were highly qualified traditional doctors, who for the most part would have had considerable training in Tantric Buddhist meditation and ritual and would have already been involved in other lineage-practices when they came to implement Yuthok's teachings. Today, however, things are little different. Dr. Nida's promotion of the Yuthok Nyingthig can be understood in light of the profound benefits he himself has experienced as a lineage-holder and practitioner of the tradition. At the same time, his promotion of the tradition is motivated as well by his appreciation that Tibetans and non-Tibetans alike are today facing just the sort of obstacles to practicing Vajrayana that Yuthok prophesized. Many practitioners of Tibetan Buddhism around the world today are not monastics but are instead busy lay people with families, day jobs, and limited training and opportunities. Embodying an ideal of integrated Tantric and medical practice (*ngak men zoongdey*), the special practices of the Yuthok Nyingthig can be understood in terms of Yuthok's unique commitment to uniting the earthy empiricism, humanistic realism, and 'worldly' concerns of medicine with the profound view and lofty goals of Tantric Buddhism.[4]

Earthy Mysteries: Lelung Rinpoche and Erotic Visions of Real Life

Yuthok is not the only influential Tibetan adept who presented an accessible and down-to-earth style of sexual yoga practice. In 2016, while we were in the midst of working on other projects, Dr. Nida contacted me to ask if I could produce a full and thorough translation of a Tibetan text he had in his possession. The text in question was another revealed *terma* text and it dealt explicitly with Karmamudra practice. It described teachings that had been received in a vision by an eighteenth century monk-turned-*ngakpa* called Zhepai Dorje, otherwise known as Lelung Rinpoche or the fifth incarnation of the Lelung reincarnation line in Tibet. Dr. Nida granted me permission to read the text and I set about translating it. I had never read anything quite like it before. In the grant proposals I had written to secure funding for my research about *ngakpa/ma* living in exile, I had clearly stated that although I was deeply interested in the social histories and politics surrounding the circulation of esoteric knowledge and expertise, I would refrain from focusing my attention on personal or technical details of *ngakpa* and *ngakmas'* Tantric yogic practices. At the time, I did not feel that it would be especially necessary or appropriate for me to ask Tibetan lamas about these topics as a researcher – certainly, lamas were under no obligation to humour me and any questions I might have as a scholar and non-disciple about anything at all, let alone the intricacies of secret Tantric practices.

Yet, fast forward several months, and here I was being asked by a Tibetan *ngakpa* who had become one of my key research interlocutors as well as my spiritual teacher to do what I had initially set out to avoid – to engage with, analyse, and translate esoteric material about Tantric yoga practices and to ask direct questions about them. Diving into Lelung's text, I was immediately struck by the extremely down-to-earth way in which Nyima Zhönnu ('Youthful Sun'), the Dakini or Tantric goddess who relayed these visionary teachings to Lelung spoke about such matters. Before meeting Dr. Nida and encountering Lelung's text, Karmamudra had seemed to me like an impossibly remote practice. In my limited understanding, Karmamudra was something practiced exclusively by figures of mythic proportion, almost-and-already-Buddhas whose level of spiritual accomplishment positioned them

---

[4] For more information about the distinct features of the Yuthok Nyingthig, see my translation of Dr. Nida's essay titled 'The Importance of the Yuthok Nyingthig, or its Twelve Uncommon and Special Characteristics,' (Joffe 2016).

far above and beyond the realities and limitations of quotidian, human life. And yet here was Nyima Zhönnu transmitting remedies for dampened libidos composed of real-world ingredients, here she was transmitting practical Tantric sex instructions that took for granted that some practitioners may well be engaging with Karmamudra without perfect prior training in more advanced Completion Stage subtle energy practices. While Lelung and his goddess Youthful Sun's subject matter and language were rich, sublime, and evocative, their instructions were hardly the stuff of idealized hagiography. Here was pragmatic and auto-biographically informed advice, meant to be applied by and to benefit properly prepared readers. I was fascinated and awed. Finishing my preliminary translation, I was left with a number of questions and Dr. Nida encouraged me to do my own investigations into Lelung Rinpoche's remarkable career and to write down some of my subsequent reflections for the public. I quickly prepared an essay discussing Lelung's life and the text which had inaugurated my entry into Karmamudra and this project, and published it on my research blog (Joffe 2016b).

Medicine for Every Patient:
Teaching Karmamudra Responsibly and Accessibly

A translation of Master Lelung's *terma* appears in the appendix of this book, along with a range of other texts specifically selected by Dr. Nida to demonstrate the great vitality, profundity and diversity of Tibetan Karmamudra teachings. This translated traditional material strikes a somewhat different note to Dr. Nida's colloquial tone in the body of the book. Although these texts include practical instructions, readers should not mistake them for DIY Buddhist Tantric sex manuals. Practicing Tantric Buddhism is not like buying and assembling furniture from IKEA. As Dr. Nida explains in significant detail in Chapter Four, individual Tantric practice texts or sadhana can only be safely and successfully practiced under the guidance of a qualified personal teacher or guru, after one has completed specific preparatory exercises (*ngöndro*) and received special Tantric transmissions known as *wang* (empowerment or initiation), *loong* (reading transmission) and *tri* (direct, personal instruction) that are specific to that practice. Two different Tibetan Buddhist practitioners may both do the same broad category of Tantric practice – Dream Yoga, *Tummo* or Karmamudra, for example – but the way they will each implement the practice will be specific to the lineage they have been initiated into and the individualized instructions they will inevitably receive from their teacher. This is one of the most unique aspects of Tantric Buddhism. As Dr. Nida explains in Chapter Two, such tailor-made strategies and vital, personal relationships are at the heart of Vajrayana and are part of what make it so powerful and special.

While the practices that appear in the appendices of this book are 'bracketed' and cannot be used straight off the page or fresh out the box, the simple suggestions, visualizations and breathing exercises drawn from the Yuthok Nyingthig that Dr. Nida outlines in Chapter Four can be practiced by anyone. This book introduces and sketches out the terrain of Vajrayana for general readers so that if they decide to venture into Tibetan Buddhism or Yuthok's tradition they can do so in an informed way. At the same time, it provides readers with methods through which they can begin to engage with desire, sex, and orgasm more mindfully, regardless of who they may be or whether they end up seeking Tantric empowerment or a guru. In teaching more accessible styles of traditional Karmamudra practice instead of emphasizing more advanced and prohibitive practices, Dr. Nida seeks to address contemporary students' needs and realities in an appropriate way and to bring his Tantric and medical expertise to bear on current problems responsibly. In doing this, he draws inspiration from spiritual forebears like Yuthok and Lelung who both opened up Karmamudra in their own ways. Both these adepts and their respective treasure Dakinis taught that it was possible for less trained practitioners to engage with Karmamudra safely at their own level, provided they were properly educated, a view that Dr. Nida shares.

Dr. Nida's teaching in this book of simple esoteric Tantric yoga practices that can be safely and usefully applied by less initiated and experienced readers is far from some idiosyncratic innovation on his part. Physicians in Tibet have prescribed simple Tantric yoga techniques as therapies for their non-yogically trained patients for centuries. For example, Tantric yogic practices like *nejang* (physical exercises involving self-massage and breathing) and *yookchö* (so-called 'stick therapy' which involves tapping repeatedly on key points on the body with specially prepared rods) have been recommended and applied by physicians over many generations. Notwithstanding the fact that *nejang* exercises were first developed as special supportive practices within the context of the highly esoteric and advanced procedures of the Kalachakra Tantra or that *yookchö* practices arose in the context of Tantric virtuosi's self-treatment in retreat, Tibetan yogi-doctors recognized these methods' more immediate medical efficacy and value for ordinary individuals and applied them accordingly. Rather than representing some sort of dilution, degradation or cannibalizing of esoteric techniques, such reorientations testified to practitioners' compassion and deftness at mobilizing their Tantric expertise to benefit beings. They were also fully in keeping with Tantric scriptures' own dual concern with both the ultimate, soteriological and more immediate, 'temporary' outcomes and benefits of yogic practices. This medical orientation pervades the Yuthok Nyingthig and animates this book. Dr. Nida explained this approach to me once during a chat we had in 2016 in Amdo, Tibet about an earlier translation project. When lamas teach Dharma as 'religion', as they most typically do, Dr. Nida said, they tend to speak of the 'worthy' or 'karmically fortunate' (*kaldenpa*) student. By contrast, when a great physician and *ngakpa* like Yuthok transmitted Dharma, it was as medicine. When Dharma is taught as medicine no patient can be turned away for want of a cure. Instead, medicine is dispensed judiciously, in the proper form and dosage, for all and any who suffer. Priests may minister to supplicants based on religious affiliations and qualifications after all, but compassionate and dedicated doctors can make no such distinctions.

First of its Kind: Some Final Notes on How this Book was Produced

As Dr. Nida notes in Chapter One, today there are all kinds of introductory books available on Tibetan higher yoga practices like Dream Yoga, Atiyoga, Mahamudra and so on. Tibetan teachers around the world have seen fit to offer accessible information on these topics and yet there remains resounding silence and consistent awkwardness and confusion around the topic of sexual yoga. Tibetan Tantric Buddhism identifies four primary conditions or states of consciousness: waking consciousness; deep, dreamless sleep; dreaming; and orgasm. Lamas have made various traditional meditative techniques aimed at working with each of these states as springboards to realizing the ultimate nature of non-dual mind available to students at varying levels, but as Dr. Nida observes in this book, traditional methods for working with orgasmic consciousness have been strikingly neglected. Students all over the world have sex and experience sexual desire and orgasm in ordinary, thoughtless ways every day. These experiences continue to contribute at worst to students' suffering and at best to only temporary happiness. If safe and simple methods for working with these experiences in more mindful and realized ways are available, why not offer them in an appropriate fashion? This is a question that this book asks and answers.

Today many books on the subject of 'Tantric sex' are available. These range from dense texts about traditional Asian religions written by professional academics to more popular, how-to guides on New Age 'sacred sexuality'. While the former are often highly specialized and theoretical and so dense as to be impenetrable, the latter often cobble together distinct histories and traditions of practice in a confused and misrepresentative way. This book steers between these extremes in a refreshing and timely fashion. Dr. Nida draws expertly on his initiated, lineage-based knowledge while maintaining an accessible style and a focus on the practical value of traditional practices throughout. His book represents perhaps the first text ever published to address the topic of Tibetan Karmamudra for a general audience. I have full confidence that it will bring enormous benefit to readers everywhere.

In closing, I would like to offer a few words about how this book was written. After enlisting my help in producing a translation of Lelung's *terma* in May 2016, Dr. Nida shared with me an early draft of this text which he told me he and some of his students had been working on for some time. Dr. Nida felt strongly that a book on Karmamudra, especially as taught in the Yuthok Nyingthig, was sorely needed but at that point the text was still a fairly jumbled and discordant collage of hastily written raw transcripts, bullet-point lists, and blocks of text cut-and-pasted from Dr. Nida's other publications. A lot of the material that Dr. Nida was keen to incorporate into the text was also scattered across multiple files. I recognized the value and uniqueness of all this material immediately, but knew that it would need to be significantly overhauled and reorganized if it was ever going to take on a form that would do justice to the amazing insights it contained. The earliest draft of the book did not have a single or coherent voice. Some of the transcribed material was less transcript and more summary; some of it referred to Dr. Nida in the third person, while other portions reproduced Dr. Nida's comments as direct speech. A lot of crucial information was also contained in transcripts of question-and-answer sessions connected with particular teachings, and needed to be integrated into the main body of the text. Chapters were ill-defined or non-existent and most of the material had yet to be thematically organized. In short, things weren't pretty.

Nonetheless, thoroughly convinced of the book's importance and potential I agreed to take on the task of editor as a side project alongside my ongoing translation and doctoral work. One of Dr. Nida's immediate concerns was that his English be edited for clarity and flow. Students who have had the good fortune of attending Dr. Nida's teachings will know that he is an extremely capable and engaging English speaker. Nonetheless, even the most brilliant and electrifying spoken words can lose much of their power and clarity when transcribed directly onto paper. Along with concerns about register, structure, and intelligibility, Dr. Nida also wanted to ensure that his book would be comprehensive in scope and useful and accessible for the widest possible spectrum of readers. My work as an editor and translator for this book was undertaken on-and-off between May 2016 and March 2018. The bulk of the material found in the chapters that follow was developed out of transcripts of teachings and Tantric empowerments that Dr. Nida gave in Oradea, Romania in April 2014, in Amsterdam, Holland in May 2016, in Boulder, Colorado in June 2017, and in Topanga, California, U.S.A in December 2017. The Oradea and Amsterdam recordings represent two days' worth of introductory teachings on Karmamudra and sexuality which Dr. Nida conveyed to small groups of students along with Yuthok's more condensed empowerment. I was not physically present at either the Oradea or Amsterdam teachings. While I personally transcribed recordings of the teachings given in Amsterdam, parts of the Oradea teachings were transcribed by other students of Dr. Nida and were already included in the body of material present in the earliest draft of the book which I received from him. Teachings in Boulder and Topanga in 2017 were delivered as part of Dr. Nida's transmission of the full set of empowerments for the entire cycle of practices in the Yuthok Nyingthig. I attended both of these multi-day empowerments in person. As it happened, Dr. Nida provided unusually detailed commentary on Karmamudra during the Topanga event and these insights proved especially useful for fleshing out portions of this book.

I took personal notes and made recordings during both empowerment events and transcribed relevant sections of Dr. Nida's commentary with help from Christiana. Transcribed material was coded thematically, carefully edited, and re-arranged extensively.

The aforementioned material was supplemented further with transcribed commentary drawn from several hours' worth of semi-structured interviews that Christiana and I conducted with Dr. Nida individually and together, in person and over the telephone. As part of these question-and-answer sessions, I was able to ask Dr. Nida a number of questions about gender and the subtle body and lesbian, gay, bisexual, trans and intersex practitioners. Dr. Nida is remarkably outspoken in his support of LGBTI practitioners and is quite comfortable discussing topics like homosexual desire. As a queer person, I was very grateful that I had the opportunity to make my own inquiries about the usefulness or relevance of Karmamudra for non-straight, non-cis-gender practitioners. I have encountered many queer people who believe that traditional Tantric sexual yoga is an inherently and irrevocably conservative and heteronormative practice, and that it has nothing to offer them or to do with their lives and experiences. While this book does not explore same-sex sexuality or questions around gender in any kind of exhaustive detail, I am confident that the crucial insights that Dr. Nida provides on some of these issues will be of great use to LGBTQI readers. Few Tibetan lamas have acknowledged LGBTQI practitioners in their work as directly as Dr. Nida does in this book, and the considerable efforts he makes in promoting a less male-centric and more inclusive vision of Karmamudra will undoubtedly be of great value and interest to sexual and gender minority practitioners.

Along with interviews, I also translated sections of some of Dr. Nida's Tibetan-language writing on topics like the *ngakpa* tradition (Chenagtsang and Drolma 2015, Joffe 2017) and Kamasutra (Heruka/Chenagtsang 2014a, 2014b), which I then used to round out parts of the text. All translations in the body of the book and in the book's appendices – apart from the translation of Yuthok's Song – are my own, and were executed in close consultation with Dr. Nida. I have tried throughout this text to preserve as much of Dr. Nida's unique style of speaking as possible, while still transforming his direct speech into a shape suitable for paper. Dr. Nida and I made the early decision to have all material in the body of the text in the first person, with the hope that it would lend the book a more colloquial and engaging flavour. I will leave it up to readers who know Dr. Nida to determine how successfully I have managed to capture his characteristic lucidity, creativity, and frequent hilarity in print. At points, Dr. Nida requested that both Christiana and I prepare paraphrased versions of some of his statements and asked that we fill in small gaps in the text in our words according to his instructions. In all cases, I have aimed to maintain a reasonable level of uniformity in style and expression. In a further effort to preserve such uniformity, I have also relegated all my own commentary to footnotes. Section headings are for the most part my own invention, albeit thoroughly inspired by Dr. Nida's words.

When it comes to transcribing Tibetan technical terms, we have refrained from using direct Wylie transliteration. Knowing that non-specialist readers will likely find this confusing and counter-intuitive, we have opted instead for roughly phonetic and hopefully intelligible renderings throughout. In a few notable cases (for e.g. Karmamudra, Mahamudra, Atiyoga), Dr. Nida prefers to use Sanskrit technical terms in place of their Tibetan equivalents. Although the Tibetan name for Karmamudra – *lekyi chagya* – is a direct translation from the Sanskrit, the term Karmamudra seems to be more widely known and used among non-Tibetan speakers than *lekyi chagya*. This seems to be in keeping with broader trends in the global North, in which Sanskrit technical terms have come to be widely favoured over Tibetan ones for many converts. With sincerest apologies to Sanskritist readers, we have decided not to include diacritics for Sanskrit terms in this book. We have left more familiar Tibetan terms like Dzogchen, as well as Tibetan proper nouns, unitalicized. Other technical Tibetan terms appear italicized and without English-style pluralizations. Sanskrit terms are unitalicized. Citations appear in the body of the text and in footnotes as (Author Year, Page Number) and full references are listed in the bibliography at the end of the book. Tibetan texts appear there in Wylie but when cited in the body of the book I have rendered authors' names in English.

This project has been a demanding but enormously rewarding one. I feel deeply blessed that Dr. Nida would entrust a task like this to someone as minimally qualified as me, and I am profoundly grateful that I have had the privilege of playing a part in bringing such an important and ground-breaking work to fruition. Since 2016 until the present, Dr. Nida has made himself constantly available to answer my questions, to go over translations, and to provide precious oral commentary and advice relating to both this book and my life. Except when in retreat, it has been rare that he has ever been more than a few hours and a few voice notes away. The attentiveness and support he has shown me has been incredible and is all too easy to take for granted. I thank him from the bottom of my heart for his enormous kindness and I have no doubt that by the time they finish reading this book, readers will too. This text is positively brimming with precious insight into Vajrayana and even readers who have no intention to pursue 'mindful sex' in any significant way will come away from it informed and enriched about Buddhism and their own human potential. I would like to express my deepest gratitude to Christiana and Pearse for the enormous amount of work which they have put into making this book a reality. Christiana and SKY Press joining in on this project gave it new focus and momentum, and I doubt that I would have ever been able to complete the charge that Dr. Nida gave me without her crucial assistance. I bow my head with utmost reverence to the great yoginis and yogis of the past, present, and future who have preserved and will continue to preserve with purity and positive intent the great teachings of Karmamudra, the Path of Great Bliss-Emptiness. May this book bring boundless benefit to beings!

སྨྲ་རྒྱལ་གཡུ་ཐོག་པ་ལ་ཕྱག་འཚལ་ལོ། མཚོད་དོ། སྐྱབས་སུ་མཆིའོ།།

Ben Joffe (Jigme Dorje)
March 29th, 2018
Denver, Colorado, U.S.A.

I am incredibly honored to have had the opportunity to work on this important project with Dr. Nida Chenagtsang and our fantastic SKY Press team. I would like to say just a few brief words to acknowledge the hard work that has gone into bringing this book to completion:

Karmamudra: The Yoga of Bliss has gone through several incarnations since Dr. Nida's original wish to publish a book on the subject many years ago. Various people's contributions have supported this process along the way, but without the work of anthropologist and translator Ben Joffe (Jigmé Dorje), this could not have reached the academic standard that it has. His excellent translations of the Karmamudra texts included in the Appendices place this book in the historical context in which it belongs, and his work in editing and weaving together all of Dr. Nida's numerous written and oral teachings on the subject in such a seamless and cohesive way was an immense task. He remained in direct communication with Dr. Nida all throughout the process, clarifying any doubts or confusions, verifying the translations, as well as receiving transmission, instruction, and empowerment in the Yuthok Nyingthig tradition in order to further his own understanding.

As always, I would also like to thank Pearse Gaffney for his beautiful graphics, incredible patience, and his involvement and interest in this book from the beginning, long before SKY Press even existed.

This subject is as important as it is potentially controversial, and I believe there is not a more appropriate time to address the topic openly, nor a better person than Dr. Nida to clear away the many wrong views that surround it as well as bring light to its blatant misuse. His training as both a physician and *ngakpa* (non-celibate Vajrayana yogic practitioner) as well as his full immersion within both traditional Tibetan and modern Western cultures gives him a unique capacity to approach it from multiple perspectives: spiritual, psychological, medical, historical, and societal. He is able to offer invaluable advice to both Vajrayana Buddhist practitioners

Publisher's Acknowledgments

and to non-practitioners alike, always pointing towards the ultimate goal of Karmamudra (and all authentic spiritual practices), while at the same time not undermining the more relative and healing benefits that proper education in sexuality and the practice of Karmamudra can provide, both for individuals and for societies as a whole. His intention in writing this book is unquestionably altruistic and I sincerely thank him for giving SKY Press the opportunity to publish this remarkable book.

I encourage all readers of this book to suspend judgment and preconceived notions about the topic and open their minds to the multiple layers of meaning that are contained within these pages. Much more than being a book about sexual yoga practice, this is an excellent overview of the Vajrayana tradition as a whole and about the variegated teachings and techniques for working with one's own body, energy, mind and emotions through deepening levels of awareness. This is a book about inner transformation, empowerment, compassion, and ultimately about freedom.

Christiana Polites
SKY Press, March 26th, 2018 in Portland, Oregon
www.skypressbooks.com

For information about Sorig Khang International, Foundation for Traditional Tibetan Medicine, and to view Dr. Nida Chenagtsang's international teaching schedule, please visit **www.sorig.net**

INTRODUCTION

Generating Bodhicitta

སེམས་བསྐྱེད།

Generating Bodhicitta

བདེ་བའི་མཆོག་གྱུར་བདེ་མཆོག་ལྷ།།
དབྱིངས་ཀྱི་བདག་ཉིད་རྣལ་འབྱོར་མ།།
ཡེ་ཤེས་མཁའ་འགྲོ་ཚོགས་ལ་ཕེབས།།
གཉིས་སྤྱོར་བདེ་སྟོང་རོལ་པར་མཛོད།།

God of the most supreme of supreme Bliss,
Yogini who is the embodiment of the expanse of Emptiness,
Come to this gathering of primordial wisdom dakinis,
And revel in the Bliss-Emptiness of union!

བླ་མ་གཡུ་ཐོག་ཡབ་ཡུམ་དང་།།
རྟ་ཕག་ཡི་དམ་ཡབ་དང་ཡུམ།།
ཡེ་ཤེས་མཁའ་འགྲོ་དཔལ་ཕྲེང་མ།།
རྩ་གསུམ་མཆོག་ལ་སྐྱབས་སུ་མཆི།།

I go for Refuge to the three supreme roots:
To the Guru Yuthok in union,
To the *yidam* or Tantric meditational
deity consorts, Hayagriva and Vajravarahi,
And to the wisdom Dakini Peltrengma, Glorious Garland Goddess!

བྱང་ཆུབ་སེམས་མཆོག་བསྐྱེད་ནས་ནི།།
ཐབས་ཤེས་ལམ་ལ་འབད་པར་འགྱུར།།
འགྲོ་ཡོངས་བདེ་ཆེན་ཡེ་ཤེས་མཆོག།
རྗེད་ཕྱིར་སངས་རྒྱས་ས་འགྲུབ་ཤོག།

Having generated bodhicitta, the supreme mind
that aspires to enlightenment for the sake of others,
May I exert myself on the Karmamudra path of Method-and-Wisdom!
May I attain the state of Buddhahood
So that all beings may discover the supreme primordial wisdom
of Great Bliss!

སྤྱན་སྐྱེས་བདེ་བ་གདོད་ནས་སྐྱེས།།
ཡང་དག་དོན་ཆེན་ལུས་ལ་གནས།།
རྩ་རླུང་ཐིག་ལེའི་རྡོ་རྗེའི་ལུས།།
བསམ་གྱིས་མི་ཁྱབ་དཀྱིལ་འཁོར་མཆོད།།

Spontaneous, innate Bliss arises primordially,
The great authentic truth abides in the body –
I make inconceivably (vast and precious) mandala-offerings
To the Vajra Body of the channels, winds, and drops!

སྔགས་ལ་དད་ཅིང་དབང་ཐོབ་ལ།།
བླ་མའི་བྱིན་རླབས་སྙིང་ལ་ཞུགས།།
སྦྱང་དང་ཉམས་གོམས་ལས་བྱུང་བའི།།
ཉེར་མཁོའི་གདམས་པ་བརྗོད་ལ་སྤྲོ།།

With faith in Tantra and having obtained the empowerments,
With the Guru's radiating blessings having entered my heart,
I happily express these needed instructions,
Born from training, meditative experience and mastery (in the practice).

Opening verses from my 'Treatise on Desire'

CHAPTER 1

Clarifying Confusion

We can think of the precious teachings on Karmamudra as a golden temple of knowledge and practice. It is my belief that instead of us just saying that there is a golden temple within Tibetan Vajrayana but then leaving the door to this temple firmly closed, we should open that door. The true aim of the Vajrayana teachings is to help others. It is altruistic. If our altruism is real, then why leave the door closed hiding all the gold inside?

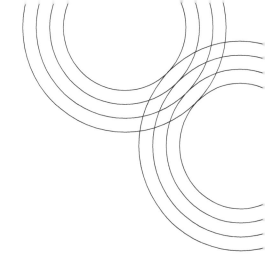

Karmamudra today

What is Karmamudra? *Karmamudra* is a Sanskrit word with two parts. The first, *karma*, means 'action' or cause-and-effect and the second, *mudra*, means a 'seal' or a special ritual gesture. In Tantric Buddhism, the karmamudra or 'worldly action seal' refers to a sexual companion, a physical partner with whom one has sex as part of one's spiritual practice. So, simply put Karmamudra – or *lekyi chagya* in Tibetan – refers to a Tantric sex partner. But Karmamudra is much more than just physical intercourse. Karmamudra is a profound kind of meditation, it is the art of orgasm and bliss. It is a special practice designed to teach us how to become more mindful during sex and orgasm.

Orgasm here refers to much more than just physical orgasm. Although physical orgasm can be very powerful and strong it is often very short. When our orgasms are limited to these short-lived physically focused experiences we miss the fact that there are important subtle energy aspects to orgasm as well. When we have sex merely with the objective of achieving a physical orgasm the result is rougher and more limited compared to the many very subtle and refined sensations we can enjoy if we have sex in a more mindful way. If we are able to feel these sensations, instead of coarse mundane orgasms, we can access orgasmic states which are more powerful and longer lasting. The subtle feelings associated with these states have the potential to transform our mind. Experiencing them can transform negative emotions of anger, sadness and fear into positive and life-affirming energies instead.

Reading this, you might be asking yourself: If this is true, why isn't everybody practicing this art? This is of course a nice idea but there are challenges involved in teaching Karmamudra today. Many Tibetan masters say that the true tradition of Karmamudra is dead. They say that this teaching is all but lost and extinct in Tibet, that it is no longer practiced. They also say that Karmamudra is a highly secret practice – no one other than the most advanced practitioners really know (or *should* know) anything about it beyond what is written in the old texts which are very difficult to understand and off-limits for most practitioners anyway. These teachers argue that since ordinary people do not have the capacity to comprehend or practice Karmamudra, it should not really be spoken of at all. It is true that there are many misunderstandings about Karmamudra today. Many non-Tibetans think that Karmamudra is the same thing as the Kamasutra and that it is nothing more than exotic sexual postures or sensual indulgence for its own sake. They think that Karmamudra is just about enhancing physical pleasure and gratifying worldly desires, that because Karmamudra involves physical intercourse and sensory stimulation, that that is all it is about. To make matters worse, when non-Tibetan scholars have written about the practice of Karmamudra they have sometimes represented it as little more than a Tibetan Buddhist boys' club, where high lamas engage in secret practices with no other purpose or possible outcome than the exploitation of young women.

This book aims to correct these and other misunderstandings about Karmamudra. It explains how Tantric Buddhist sexual yoga has been and is practiced in Tibet, and describes how it can be practiced today and in the future. It is a book based on my own experience as a student and practitioner of Tibetan yoga and Traditional Tibetan Medicine. In the sections that follow I will explain and contextualize some of the above claims and objections about Karmamudra and clarify some of the misconceptions and myths that currently surround this art.

We can think of the precious teachings on Karmamudra as a golden temple of knowledge and practice. It is my belief that instead of us just saying that there is a golden temple within Tibetan Tantric Vajrayana Buddhism but then leaving the door to this temple firmly closed, we should open that door. The true aim of the Vajrayana teachings is to help others. It is altruistic. If our altruism is real, then why leave the door closed hiding all the gold inside? It is important that we respect and preserve the tradition and the authenticity of the temple's tradition yet for a number of reasons I think that it is also imperative that we open that door. It is my hope that this book will help start this process in the clearest and most beneficial way possible.

*"The true purpose of Karmamudra is altruistic.
To practice Karma-mudra authentically we should be
guided by a compassionate and selfless motivation. In
Buddhism, this motivation is called bodhicitta.
To practice Tantra with bodhicitta means that we use
powerful techniques to better ourselves so that we can
help others. Given that Karmamudra was developed as
one such technique, I think that today it is important
and beneficial for us to open up the subject."*

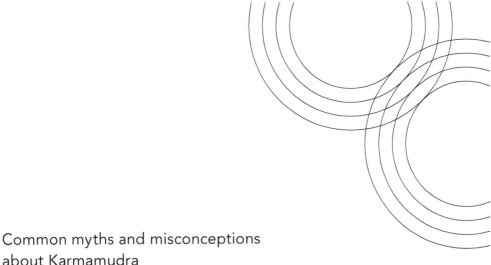

Common myths and misconceptions about Karmamudra

Misconception 1:
Karmamudra is so secret that it can never be discussed

To understand how we can benefit from practicing Karmamudra today we need to understand both who can practice and the different ways that Karmamudra can be practiced. We also need to appreciate the ways that secrecy has been used throughout history to both protect and to abuse precious and easily misunderstood teachings.

Sometimes, when people learn that I teach Karmamudra they will ask me, "How is it possible that you can even *talk* about Karmamudra at all?!" They have heard and believe that Karmamudra is a completely secret teaching. When this happens I ask them in turn, "If Mahamudra and Dzogchen are also secret practices then why are there so many books on these other secret Tibetan teachings published today?" It is true that Karmamudra as well as Mahamudra and Dzogchen were traditionally very advanced and secret teachings, but it is also true that much has changed regarding the transmission of such teachings in the world today. Other people will say that Karmamudra is not just a secret topic but also a *forbidden* one and will again wonder how it is that I can even discuss it. Again, I reply that Dzogchen or Atiyoga has traditionally been an even more advanced and restricted teaching than Karmamudra yet today it is discussed publicly all over the world. Already there are so many other teachings available in print on Mahamudra and Atiyoga. These great and secret teachings have already been made public, so why not Karmamudra? That is my question. It was also a question posed by my nomad yogi Karmamudra teacher in Tibet, who you will learn more about in the pages that follow.

Even experienced Vajrayana practitioners can have strange opinions about what is and is not appropriate to discuss. It is generally believed that

Karmamudra is a very secret teaching – that virtually no one can see it, no one can touch it. This is a very big misunderstanding! The extent to which practitioners today think that Karmamudra is completely off-limits to them was brought home for me when a student of Tibetan Buddhism once told me that he would do 'normal' Vajrayana meditation in other aspects of his life, but when it came to the 'sexual part', to what he did in the bedroom, he would practice Chinese Taoist sex techniques instead. I joked with this man, "It sounds like according to your style of Buddhism, sex is a sin that can only ever bring negative karma!" It is really quite amazing and amusing how many strange ideas many people – including some Buddhist masters – have about Karmamudra. As we will see below, Vajrayana can be applied to every aspect of our human lives. Wanting to separate sexuality from our spiritual practice says more about us and our own hang ups than the teachings themselves.

Misconception 2: Karmamudra is a lost or dying tradition

Secrecy aside, some sources and teachers also say that in the Tibetan tradition Karmamudra has been lost over time and that today it is a dead or dying path of practice. This is false information. The truth is that Karmamudra is still alive and well. It is still practiced in my home community of non-celibate, non-monastic Tantric yogis or *ngakpa* in Tibet and it is still very much a living practice in the Yuthok Nyingthig tradition of Vajrayana, the tradition from which the practices described in this book are derived.

Some people claim that the reason Karmamudra teachings have supposedly been lost is because they are too difficult to practice. Many traditional Karmamudra texts say that you need to master complicated yogic exercises as the foundation for Karmamudra and this has led many people to think that Karmamudra is far too demanding for any ordinary person to accomplish. Most of these exercises have to be done when you are young because just like with acrobatic and gymnastics routines, they become more challenging with age. One such yogic exercise mentioned in the texts and which is often brought up in discussions about Karmamudra is called the *Vajroli* mudra in Sanskrit. The *Vajroli* mudra is a kind of urethral suction technique that requires strong control over the uro-genital muscles. The texts say that when a male practitioner urinates, before the urine even touches the floor, he should by flexing his muscles be able to suck it up again immediately back into his bladder. Some texts also say that a male practitioner should be able to draw a whole container of milk up through his penis. Similar demanding requirements are listed for women: female Karmamudra practitioners should be able to suck milk up into their bodies through their vaginas as well. According to these texts, it is only once you have obtained this ability that you can practice the true Karmamudra. This is why many masters today will point to Tibetan Vajrayana tradition and say, "Oh! If you can't suck back your urine, if you cannot drink milk from your genitals, you're not qualified to do Karmamudra! These days no one is qualified to do Karmamudra!"

This is typical of a lot of exclusionary and false dogma that has historically surrounded Karmamudra. There are many texts that promote the idea that you can only practice Karmamudra when you have reached a certain level of yogic muscle training and that is the reason why some people have come to believe that Karmamudra is virtually impossible to practice and must therefore be a "lost" tradition. These sorts of reactions are typical of people who have heard a few things about Karmamudra, but not a lot – people who maybe read some texts, maybe one or two, then said: "Okay, that's it, I know exactly what this is all about!"

If you look at all the different oral and written teachings on Karmamudra however, you will see that there are many styles and levels of Karmamudra practice and not all of them require you to be an amazingly gifted sexual yogi-athlete. Karmamudra is not just about difficult or uncomfortable ascetic practices. It is something very powerful and very joyful. Its aim is very precise and I think that it is a genuine pity that up until now so few people have had access to its teachings. The goal of this book is to introduce readers to practical and safe styles of Karmamudra practice that do not require prior training in Tantric yoga. The teachings and practices included here deal with experiences and methods that almost anyone can access as part of their everyday life, and which they can apply at their own level according to their own capacities.

Misconception 3: Karmamudra is the same thing as Kamasutra

These days, many people have heard about the *Kamasutra*, the 'Treatise' or 'Commentaries on Desire'. One of the most persistent and common misconceptions about Kamasutra is that it is a Tantric teaching. Like the Tantric practices of Karmamudra the teachings of Kamasutra are Indian in origin, but unlike Karmamudra, Kamasutra has a samsaric or worldly rather than spiritual focus. If Kamasutra is the 'Art of (Worldly) Sex' then Karmamudra is the 'Art of (Spiritual) Orgasm.'

In the 19th century there was a Tibetan master, a famous monk by the name of Ju Mipham Namgyal Gyatso. Ju Mipham was a great scholar and a very renowned master from the Nyingma tradition, the oldest school of Tibetan Buddhism. Ju Mipham wrote a ground-breaking book called *The Treasure Loved By Everyone* in which he discussed Kamasutra and Karmamudra together. He made his book public and explained that he had written it for his yogi and yogini students who were studying and practicing Tantra. Some of you might find it a little ironic that a monk wrote an instruction manual on how to have the best worldly and spiritual sex, but trust me, when you read the book you see that that doesn't matter. It is a very good book! Master Mipham makes a connection between Karmamudra and Kamasutra - he notes that Kamasutra is something very samsaric, something you can enjoy in your normal life, and Karmamudra is something more spiritual, something not like worldly life. What is so interesting is that he said you can bridge these two. What Mipham explained is that if you read and train in Kamasutra first then that will help you when you come to practice Karmamurdra. Learning about Kamasutra provides you with greater understanding about relationships and offers an ancient and valuable education about sexuality and sexual intercourse.

This book is not about Kamasutra and I will not be providing instructions in Kamasutra here. Like Master Mipham though I do recommend that everyone who would like to learn about Karmamudra reads and studies some Kamasutra teachings. The most extensive Tibetan adaption of Kamasutra was written by a controversial and brilliant Tibetan scholar called Gendün Chöpel in the early 20th century. Gendün Chöpel made his own translation of Indian Kamasutra texts and borrowed from Master Mipham's teachings. He also drew on his own personal experience, on the sexual experiments he conducted after he disrobed as a monk. Jeffrey

Hopkins has translated Gendun Chöphel's important text into English under the title, *Tibetan Arts of Love* (2000). I recommend that students read this book as their homework. They need to read it for one year. Cultivating sexual desire and bliss is an art and requires study. In Chapter Three I will talk some more about how previous Tibetan experts have treated Kamasutra and Karmamudra as two distinct but complementary approaches. These masters explain how the worldly or karmic system of sexual cultivation of the Kamasutra can be integrated with the Karmamudra approach to sex to improve one's practice.

Misconception 4:
To practice Karmamudra you need to have many sexual partners

Many people assume Karmamudra is some kind of excuse for promiscuity. Sometimes, you meet individuals who claim that the practice of Karmamudra or what they are calling Tantric sex allows them – or even requires them! – to have sex with many partners and to participate in orgies. Even some respected scholars dismiss Karmamudra as a sort of cultural cover for male lamas to go around and fulfill their urges to have sex with many different women. But when we look at traditional sources we see that this is not the case. Centuries ago, the great Tantric yogi and founder of Traditional Tibetan Medicine Yuthok Yönten Gönpo directly responded to practitioners who thought doing Karmamudra meant having many different partners. Yuthok's explanation about this in the Yuthok Nyingthig, Yuthok's special collection of texts which is the basis for the Karmamudra teachings described in this book, is very clear. Since Karmamudra is a profound spiritual practice and not ordinary sex, certain key conditions are necessary to practice it successfully. One of the most important of these is that both partners be properly qualified for the practice and completely spiritually compatible with one another.

So the truth is that it is actually quite difficult and rare to find even one partner that you can really practice Karmamudra with, let alone two, or four, or sixteen! In his comments on this, Yuthok criticizes male practitioners who resort to magical rituals to 'hook' female partners to them, and who think that they can practice Karmamudra with anyone they feel like. He shows the foolishness of this approach in quite a funny way. Here is a translation of his words:

"The [range of] methods for determining which women are the best sort of Karmamudra partner[5] may well exceed imagining, but having listened to the direct advice of the guru(s) [I can tell you] here that the oral lineage teachings are as follows:

Extraordinary pleasure or bliss arises merely by seeing the form of the girl in question, by hearing her voice, by smelling her scent, or touching her body. She has faith and interest in the teachings of the Secret Mantra. She expresses happiness, smiles and so on just by seeing the yogi who does the practices. If you rely on someone like her as a partner then regardless of whether she is young or old, your meditative experiences and realization will increase. However, if seeing, hearing, thinking of or touching your partner doesn't bring joy and she has no room in her mind for Tantric teachings you should avoid her, whatever her age may be. If you make stabilizing your inner 'white portion'[6] your main practice or priority, it is a fact that you will attract a Karmamudra partner endowed with [proper or good] subtle channels to yourself automatically.

Even if you 'hook' a partner to you using ritual substances, mantras and meditation, if she doesn't beam while looking at you with the sheer force or 'sweet fragrance' of bliss, if she doesn't express great joy in any way whatsoever the instant she sees you as a result of the karma and aspirations of [both of your] previous lives, then no matter how much you exert yourself in these measures nothing will come of it. [Conversely], if [you both] show expressions of bliss or ecstasy [upon meeting], you will accomplish your aims irrespective of how skilled you are in [such magical] techniques. Not understanding how to set up the profound disposition in which outer, inner, and secret auspicious links or conditions [are all aligned, these sorts of Tantric yogis] get involved in all kinds of little rituals and then get frustrated and lose faith in the oral instructions. They themselves have made the teachings useless and then they go after [and blame] their meditational deities [for their failures] instead!" (Gönpo, 2005)

---

[5] Here Yuthok literally says 'for determining who is a *rigma* or 'awareness lady' belonging to the Padma or Lotus Family.' In Tibetan Buddhism, Karmamudra partners are classified according to the five families of Tantric Buddhism. Women who exhibit the signs or marks of a Lotus family Dakini are traditionally said to make the best partners for Karmamudra practice.

I like this explanation from Yuthok very much because he shows clearly that Karmamudra is not about having lots of different sexual partners. He also makes it clear that for yogis who have received proper oral instruction in Karmamudra and who truly know the practice, the age of a Karmamudra partner is much less important than the spiritual connection you share with them. This is a very important point. Many scholars talk about passages in Tantric Buddhist texts which say that the ideal Karmamudra partner should be sixteen, a virgin, from a particular kind of family and so on, and then think that they understand what Karmamudra is. "Oh yes, that's what Karmamudra is, oh, yes, now I've got it!" This has contributed to stereotypes of Karmamudra, where scholars say that it is nothing more than a spiritual justification for older male lamas to have sex with very young girls. But Master Yuthok reminds us that the scope of oral teachings and practices relating to Karmamudra goes way beyond just what we can see written down in texts. Many scholars don't know about this, about how Karmamudra is lived in practice, even though they like to write about what Karmamudra is or isn't.

With Karmamudra, it is not that you *must* only ever have one partner, but that the practice should not be used as an excuse to have a lot of sex with many different people. This goes for both men and women. Some people hear stories about Indian Tantric practitioners meeting in groups in secret with prostitutes and think that Karmamudra is all about orgies and casual, group sex. But the reality is that Karmamudra does not really mention or support the idea of casual sex at all. There are some Tibetan Buddhist gurus today, both male and female, who have sex with many of their students and call it Karmamudra but I think that these teachers do not really know what Karmamudra is and simply want to have sex with attractive young men or women. Some of the stories you hear about what these teachers do with their students also suggests that they don't really have much idea about how to have good quality or consensual sex either – sometimes some people are thirsty and they just have to drink water right away. But of course the problems start when such teachers get a lot of power and start abusing it and demanding that their needs be met. All sorts of suffering follows.

---

[6] This refers to the white, lunar *thiglé* or 'sexual energy drop' which is part of subtle, Tantric anatomy. These concepts and methods involving them are described in Chapters Three and Four of this book.

While many historical and legendary Karmamudra masters have had many partners, and while there are many male and female gurus who have sex with many of their students today under the guise of spirituality, the simple answer is that you absolutely do not need to have many partners to practice Karmamudra. This point was clearly made by a great Karmamudra practitioner from my home *ngakpa* community in North-Eastern Tibet, Khamla Namkha Gyatso. He admitted that, were he to count them all, it was true that he had had many, many Karmamudra partners. He experimented a lot and he received so many *terma* or revealed treasure teachings but in the end he still said that it was very difficult to find the perfect match. He explained that there are so few Karmamudra partners whose channels will truly match your own, in most cases they don't match or match poorly. When the parts of your and your partner's subtle anatomy or energy bodies go together and when your mentality matches, then your practice goes together too. When all the parts of your subtle body go together, when they match like this, your *thiglé* or 'energy drops' attract one another invisibly. So that's why sometimes even if you're far apart from each other, if the other person is thinking of you, this kind of energy is there, you can feel each other, you are connected.

Karmamudra is not a justification for having many partners. Even though today, like I said, many teachers are going around saying "Oh I'll teach you about Karmamudra, about all these secret things, let me have sex with you" and so on, I think students have to think carefully about this. This is not only a question of their teacher's reputation and qualifications but also their intentions. Engaging in risky sex with many partners can become a medical concern when STIs (Sexually Transmitted Infections) are involved. But even if these teachers say 'Don't worry, we'll prevent sexually transmitted diseases using a condom,' blah blah blah, there is still what we call *dip* in Tibetan or subtle pollution to think about. If you're having sex with one random or incompatible partner after another you can pick up lots of this kind of subtle pollution and there's the risk that your channels will get blocked. When the channels are blocked, *thiglé* and other parts of the subtle anatomy cannot flow well, so this can have a negative effect on your yogic and Karmamudra practice. So having many Tantric partners is not really the correct or advisable way to do things even if you know about sexual yogic practice.

Misconception 5: Karmamudra is patriarchal – it exists only to exploit and abuse women and to empower heterosexual men

Many masters across the centuries have had very real and sensible reasons for maintaining so much secrecy around Karmamudra and for limiting their descriptions of it to a symbolic level. The topic of sex is a very sensitive one. It can and has been all too easily misused, misinterpreted, and misunderstood. Secrecy has helped protect the teachings. Unfortunately, it has also sometimes been used as a cover for manipulating and abusing uninformed and vulnerable individuals.

To my mind, if we say that Karmamudra teachings are so secret that we cannot ever discuss them then we seal Karmamudra up and this can be just as dangerous as talking about Karmamudra or other Tantric practices too freely. Sealing things up like this creates opportunities for misinterpretations. One of the biggest misunderstandings about Karmamudra is that it is just a practice for men, that it is some kind of secret boys' club where men just focus on retaining their semen, on extending their lifespan and vitality at the expense of others, and on taking advantage of women. If you search for the term Karmamudra on the internet, you will find some very bad and misleading articles about it. Many of these articles focus on Karmamudra as a patriarchal institution, one that exists only to exploit and hurt women. These articles often accurately identify possible misuses of Karmamudra but they usually do not talk about the true aim or power of Karmamudra and why we use it as a spiritual practice.

The true purpose of Karmamudra is altruistic. To practice Karmamudra authentically we should be guided by a compassionate and selfless motivation. In Buddhism, this motivation is called bodhicitta (Sanskrit). To practice Tantra with bodhicitta means that we use powerful techniques to better ourselves so that we can help others. Given that Karmamudra was developed as one such technique, I think that today it is important and beneficial for us to open up the subject. Talking more openly about Karmamudra can help with the problem of sexual scandals which regularly take place in religious communities. In the past and still today, some masters have used the term Karmamudra to trick female disciples into having sex with them. Such masters benefit from the veil of secrecy which surrounds Karmamudra. Since most people are highly uninformed about the specifics of genuine Karmamudra practice, this ignorance can be worked to abusive teachers' advantage. Some Tibetan and non-Tibetan masters might say: "Oh, don't worry, we can do Karmamudra! What I'm telling you to do might seem strange but it really is Karmamudra! I am your guru, so you have to do what I say and keep it secret," blah blah blah, on and on. Chances are that what those masters are calling Karmamudra ends up being very short and bad sex, that it turns out to not be Karmamudra at all. If you have a basic understanding of what Karmamudra really is and how it works, however, then you can't be deceived or abused by others.

In the past, secrecy helped special practices like Karmamudra remain pure and protected them from being misunderstood. Today, however, secrecy has given rise to both misunderstandings and abuses. One of the most common questions I am asked is "Why are you teaching Karmamudra publicly?" I was once criticized by a Tibetan master, who said, "Oh, you are teaching Karmamudra?! You are opening the secret, that's dangerous!" He then went so far as to say that by doing so I was destroying Vajrayana tradition and that I was harming all sentient beings. While I listened to and respected his concern and criticisms, when he said that last phrase I thought to myself, "Wow, that's maybe a little bit too much!" I'm completely fine with others criticizing me – I wasn't angry with his criticism, I certainly didn't get defensive or fly into a rage and yell at him about how I was going to kill him or anything like that! I could understand his thinking and where he was coming from, and it was no problem for me. As you'll read about later, I myself had to learn to deal with my own cultural anxieties and ingrained ways of thinking when I first started thinking about how best to teach Tantric Buddhist ideas and practices to different audiences around the world. But when this master said that I was "harming all sentient beings" that was when I really thought, "Oh my God! Do you understand what you're saying?!" I call this spiritual paranoia. If someone thinks I'm teaching something wrong, then they should come to my class, listen, and then decide: is this something harmful, or is it something beneficial, something so simple and fundamental?

Some people get the idea that when I teach I'm criticizing other teachers and their teachings yet this is not the case. I'm not against anyone, I'm not saying anyone must change their practice. My intention is not to criticize any specific target, teacher or tradition. What I wish to do is give earnest students information to improve their understanding. Sometimes I receive strange letters from people who say, "I know you are against this master, this teaching" etc. This is quite bizarre because this has certainly never been my intention. What is important in spirituality is clarity, to practice based on thorough understanding. We do not need to create divisions or to cause fights. If a student suspects that I am criticizing a teacher or a tradition, they are of course welcome to ask me. If a student asks me for my opinion on some other traditions, I can certainly tell them what I think. But I will not try to tell them that I'm right and these other traditions are wrong. I am merely teaching what and as I have been taught, and I can only ever offer my personal perspective based on my own experience and what my teachers have taught me. My own teaching is not rooted in opposition to any school or teacher.

As it turned out, this teacher who criticized me ended up being his own worst enemy. I later discovered that although this master who critiqued me was acting outwardly like a monk, he was doing all kinds of strange things with ladies behind closed doors. That was when I thought, "This is just ridiculous!" For me, that kind of behavior is completely hypocritical and fake. You have a title, you are a reincarnation etc., you try to convince people that you're a disciplined monk in public but then you change your dress and hang around with ladies and do all kinds of things. That's not the behavior of a genuine lama who cares about not causing suffering or spreading discord among Buddhist practitioners. On top of that this lama told me, a teacher who is not and has not ever been a monk, that I was "harming all sentient beings." He said that publicly too. I didn't much mind the criticism but it was the hypocrisy that concerned me. He said, "Yes of course you can teach, I know you are qualified in Karmamudra, you can teach your students, but bring a small group to a mountain retreat, to some hidden place." That was his suggestion for me. It is true that that is how Karmamudra has traditionally been taught. In the next chapter you'll read some of my thoughts on why it's not always possible or advisable to teach in this way. One main point that we can draw from this story though is that some teachers, and male ones in particular, can sometimes have vested and less-than-noble interests in secrecy.

Traditionally, Karmamudra has been described from a very male-centric perspective. Historically, the Karmamudra system was designed for men and many of its goals were men's goals. One of the reasons I think this was so is because in previous times there were simply just more male practitioners – this had to do with the gender inequalities and specific obstacles or barriers that women who wanted to practice Vajrayana faced in Tibetan society. If one investigates thoroughly, it is clear that Karmamudra includes methods that females, males and even intersex people, of whatever sexual orientation[7] can practice individually by themselves, or with a partner as part of sexual intercourse. Yet even though Karmamudra is applicable to different genders' bodies, health and pleasure, men's priorities and perspectives have dominated.

Even with this gender bias, however, we still have several examples from Tibet of accomplished female practitioners of Vajrayana. These female role-models are extremely important. We Tibetans believe that the first Tibetan to become a Buddha through the Vajrayana, the first Tibetan person to achieve spiritual liberation was Yeshe Tsogyal. Yeshe Tsogyal practiced Dzogchen or Atiyoga as well, but the foundation of her practice was Karmamudra and it was through Karmamudra that she obtained liberation. It is well known that Guru Padmasambhava gave many teachings and accomplished many things in Tibet and that Yeshe Tsogyal respected Guru Padmasambhava as her teacher and represented him in Tibet really strongly. All the work Yeshe Tsogyal did on Padmasambhava's behalf is less acknowledged though. You know the proverb: behind every successful man there is a great woman. I think it's fair to say that Padmasambhava was so successful in Tibet in large part because of Yeshe Tsogyal. She was truly great and the reason I mention her here is that she was the first person who practiced Karmamudra in Tibet, so I think her story and example is both excellent and crucial. Despite Yeshe Tsogyal's importance, when she is not shown in sexual union with Padmasambhava as his Karmamudra partner, Yeshe Tsogyal is often represented in paintings as a much smaller figure writing down teachings off to the side of Guru Padmasambhava, who is a lot bigger. Personally, I hope that one day it will be just as common and accepted to see Buddhist centers with huge Yeshe Tsogyals and small Padmasambhavas!

It is really important to realize that Karmamudra is something that can be practiced equally by men and women. In Tibetan Vajrayana feminine energy is very important. In Tantric Buddhism we have the concept of Dakinis, of which there are two kinds: 'Primordial Wisdom' Dakinis and

---

[7] For a fuller discussion about Karmamudra practice and sexual and gender orientation, see Chapter Four.

'Karma' or 'Worldly' Dakinis. Wisdom Dakinis are enlightened, whereas all woman, no matter their state of realization are Karma Dakinis. In Nepal and some parts of India if you say the word Dakini people get scared – in colloquial forms of the languages there 'Dakinis' are thought of as witches, but in Vajrayana Dakinis are the perfect practitioners, they are the enlightened ladies. Learning about historical female figures who practiced Karmamudra can help us appreciate how Karmamudra can be practiced by both men and women and used not just to exploit but to empower the latter.

Yeshe Tsogyal was the most famous female practitioner but we also have maybe the second-most famous female practitioner, Machik Labdrön. Yeshe Tsogyal didn't have any children - she had Karmamudra partners but no children. Machik Labdrön on the other hand had three kids and she did Karmamudra as well as the Chöd practice for which she is most famous. So we can think of Machik Labdrön as the second-most important female or lady guru of Karmamudra. Another more recent great female practitioner of Karmamudra was the nineteenth century yogini Sera Khandro. She was an incredible practitioner and treasure-revealer, a kind of Tantric prophetess who revealed hidden teachings. Her revealed treasure text or *terma* on Karmamudra which is connected with the Tantric goddess Vajravarahi is really so amazing. You can find a translation of a teaching song about Karmamudra by Sera Khandro in the Appendices of this book.

It is easy to look at Tibetan culture and history and to dismiss a Tibetan Buddhist practice like Karmamudra as something patriarchal and harmful, like some scholars seem to have done. We know that Karmamudra has been abused. But if you really look at history it will become clear that there were at least a few important scholars, practitioners, and teachers in Tibet who were concerned about gender equality and were thinking carefully about the relationship between religious ideals and cultural norms. In his book on Kamasutra, Gendün Chöpel advocated for the improved position of women. He noted how in ancient Nepal, if a woman was raped, afterward the woman was required to thank the man who raped her for doing so. Gendün Chöpel denounced these sick and perverted attitudes. He talked extensively about the importance of equality between men and women. That's why I say he is a feminist. In fact, I don't think it would be inappropriate to describe him as the founder of or first fighter for sexual freedom in Tibet.

Another famous erotic yogi Drukpa Kunley, has many funny stories in his autobiography. Most of them are about sex. His are some of the most famous openly portrayed stories of Karmamudra. Some of his behavior and the stories about him are very strange and a little difficult to interpret. But in one chapter in his biography he addresses the importance of women very clearly. According to Vajrayana there are fourteen root Tantric vows[8]. One of these main vows is that men should not insult women, that they should not treat women badly, they should not bully women, they should not even say one bad word or joke about women, and so on. The chapter where Drukpa Kunley discusses women and mentions this vow is a small one in his book, but he nonetheless expresses just how important women are in a great and profound way.

In the 17th century Lelung Zhepai Dorje was the leading proponent of Karmamudra practice. Significantly, Lelung Zhepai Dorje wrote his Karmamudra texts through and for his female disciples. In fact, it was one of his female disciples who asked him to write and circulate information about Karmamudra in the first place. Lelung's practice and approach is very unique. He says really openly that Karmamudra is for both male and female practitioners. Lelung Zhepai Dorje was once a monk and was recognized as a *Tulku* or reincarnated master. In his autobiography, he recounts his amazing dreams, in which he communed constantly with protector deities and spirits. He was very psychic and could see the future from when he was a boy, which allowed him to foresee both political and spiritual problems. Lelung was trained as a monk from a young age but changed his mind about his monastic lifestyle after he had a dream one day. In his dream, he met a Wisdom Dakini named Nyima Zhönnu, which means the 'Youthful Sun'. This Dakini became his teaching or visionary treasure Dakini and she gave Lelung Karmamudra teachings in his dreams. She warned Master Lelung that if he didn't do sexual yoga practices he would die prematurely and have many obstacles. Accordingly, Lelung went on to extend his life and become a great Karmamudra master. Nyima Shönnu and Master Lelung practiced Karmamudra together in the dream-state and as a result Lelung's mind was opened up in a different way[9]. Lelung's writing style is very direct, very 'naked'. And just like his writing style, he talked and taught about sex really nakedly too. What is noteworthy here is that Lelung taught Karmamudra to female as well as male disciples. He gave specific suggestions to his female

---

[8] See Chapter Two for more information on Buddhist vows.

disciples and at least two of his texts appear to have been written at the request of his female students.

These female practitioners' examples and stories show us how Karmamudra is not just for men. When we read about their lives we realize that Karmamudra is not just about some top-secret practices where men take young girls as sex partners for their own benefit. Practitioners like Yeshe Tsogyal took their own male partners and set the terms of their own spiritual and sexual relationships. What is interesting though is that even with these possibilities, the overwhelming majority of Karmamudra instruction texts are still addressed to male readers. Even when a text is revealed by a woman, its instructions may still be phrased in terms of men's bodies and perspectives. My own belief is that if Karmamudra is only designed for men or pitched at men's needs, then Karmamudra practice is not yet perfect. If you really look at the way that Karmamudra is designed I think it actually fits more with women's biological and sexual capacities than with men's (more on this in Chapter Five). Although in the past Karmamudra may have been treated as a practice of, by, and for men the approaches found in it align very well with female sexuality and with women's sexual needs and tendencies.

I think that Nyima Zhönnu and Master Lelung hoped that Karmamudra could be a source of empowerment for women. 'Tantric sex' does not have to mean the exploitation of women by male teachers. There's a story that involves Master Lelung which I quite like. During his lifetime Lelung's influence was so great that he even became the main guru to the then political leader of Tibet, Lhazang Khan. Lelung was also a student of the great Nyingma master and founder of Mindrolling monastery Terdak Lingpa, whose own revelations and practices he took up and developed. Terdak Lingpa had a daughter called Mingyur Paldrön who was a great and sought-after teacher in her own right. Dakini Mingyur Paldrön chose to live a single, celibate life during which she devoted herself to advanced religious practice and retreat. According to some sources, at one point, Master Lelung approached her and told her that she was karmically destined to work with him and help him further his activities as his spiritual consort and Karmamudra partner. But Dakini Mingyur Paldrön turned down Lelung's offer. For this great female Dzogchen adept to turn down an offer like this coming from someone like

---

[9] A translation of one of Nyima Zhönnu's instructions on Karmamudra, given to Lelung through a vision in a dream, is included in the Appendices.

Master Lelung – someone who was involved with her father and his activities, and had the support of the highest political authority in Tibet - was really significant. I really like this story about Mingyur Paldrön because it shows us that just because a big lama tells a woman that she must have Tantric sex with him – even a lama like Lelung who in my opinion was a legitimate and brilliant practitioner – she is not obligated to agree. Mingyur Paldrön preferred to focus on Mahamudra and Dzogchen and to live a celibate life. Maybe she was too stuck in the Sutric view to appreciate Lelung's activities but regardless of what we might think, the most important point is that she was not swayed in her goals by the priorities of powerful men. Dakini Mingyur Paldrön had the power to refuse Lelung, and that is very important.

Karmamudra includes methods that people of all gender and sexual orientations can practice individually and together. It applies equally to both women and men's bodies, health, and pleasure. The inner part of Karmamudra involves working with complementary energies which are sometimes described as 'male' and 'female' energies, but these things are equally a part of every person's constitution. While the idea of Karmamudra may have been used to exploit and disempower women up until now, there is no reason it should today. In the past cultural conventions and biases have prioritized some practitioners over others, but there is no need for us to continue this in the name of tradition. Karmamudra offers everyone the chance to come to know their own nature and to work with and transform their desire.

Misconception 6: Karmamudra is about lofty and abstract spiritual things, it has nothing to do with ordinary people like me

When we look at Tibetan religious art, we see that images of male and female Buddhas in sexual union are important and pervasive. Students who ask about these images – which are referred to as *yab yum*, or 'Father-Mother pose' in Tibetan – are often told that these pictures have nothing to do with actual sex or sexuality at all. Many teachers will say that these images are merely symbolic. They will explain that because these images are esoteric representations they ought not to be interpreted literally. Rather than indicating actual sexual intercourse, they will say, Buddhas and deities in sexual union symbolize the union of compassion and wisdom, bliss and emptiness, male and female energies and so on – they are a representation of the indivisibility of binaries whose unification points to the non-dual reality that is the basis of all phenomena. These points are all true of course, but these images of sexual intercourse are more than just abstract symbols.

I once gave a talk on Karmamudra in London and during the question and answer portion of the teaching a man took the microphone and said that all the Tibetan union Buddhas had nothing whatsoever to do with sexuality. When this man said this, I asked him, "How do you know?" "I have studied Tibetan Buddhism with a teacher for three years," he said. "These Buddhas depicted in sexual union don't have anything to do with actual sex." "Your teacher must be a monk," I said. He nodded. "But you are not a monk?" He nodded again and I suggested that this man read and study a bit more widely. I got the feeling that maybe he was a little shocked by my response. Symbolically speaking, the sexual union of these Father-Mother Buddhas does stand for the union of compassion and wisdom. But teachings about the union of compassion and wisdom, bliss and emptiness and so on are all a part of Karmamudra itself, which does in fact involve sexual intercourse. If we are true practitioners of the Highest Yoga Tantras, we cannot say that union Buddhas from the Chakrasamvara, Kalachakra and Guhyasamaja Tantras are merely symbolic, they are something much more. It would be a real pity if we were to leave the union of compassion and wisdom as illustrated in the *yab yum* posture on a purely symbolic level. Teachers' insistence that *yab yum* is merely figurative and has nothing to do with physical sex distracts us from the fact that these images are for and about us, they are for and about human beings, they are linked with our lives.

This is important to understand. Sex is a part of human life, and Karmamudra is about working with our everyday sexual desires to transform ourselves. Often, when we talk about things like the Six Dharmas or Yogas of Naropa people hear these names and think "Wow! That sounds like something really esoteric, like something really secret and exotic!" But if you're truly familiar with the Six Yogas, if you really understand them, then you'll know that these yogas are all about human life, about the human mind. They are for and about *humans* and the human condition – they are not for Buddhas or enlightened beings. Karmamudra and Tantric iconography cut to the heart of our embodied human experience. Karmamudra targets us humans and our desires in a very profound way.

So, what is this human life of ours, what is our condition? When we wake up and go about our lives, we have all kinds of experiences, feelings, and beliefs. We invest in people and things, in a certain idea of ourselves and others. This is why we have Illusory Body yoga – this yoga deals with all of our waking time, with the things we do and invest in during the day. Likewise, by harnessing the warmth and vitality linked with our metabolism, *Tummo* or Inner Heat yoga is also connected to our waking life. Conversely, when we go to sleep, we have Dream yoga and Clear Light or Sleep yoga. And when we die, we have the yogas of *Bardo* or the intermediary state between rebirths, and the yoga of *Phowa* or the transference of consciousness at death. So we have three important parts of our life: day-time and night-time experiences and experiences connected with death and dying. And these are all about human life. The deities and Buddhas are beyond all that, they are beyond the ups-and-downs of day and night, they are beyond death. If the Six Yoga teachings were about deities, then why would any of these things be necessary? The deities are beyond the sun and moon, they are beyond time and space, so why would they need these things? These yogas are specifically designed for us, for humans, and the sexual yoga of Karmamudra is no different. The basic building blocks for Tantric transformation are things we all share. We risk missing this point if we treat Tantric yoga as something that is just for a bunch of high-up men with top-secret methods that allow them to do special or magical things. If you really understand Vajrayana, then you'll realize that it's so much connected with *you*, with your everyday heart, with your mind, with your life.

7) Almost no one is qualified to practice Karmamudra

The classic or traditional Vajrayana approach to Karmamudra alluded to above requires that one absolutely have a good base in the practice of *Tummo*, the yoga of inner heat, before one can practice Karmamudra. Mastering *Tummo* grants one the ability to raise one's core body temperature and generate great amounts of heat (and bliss) on command. Like the practice of Karmamudra, mastering *Tummo* requires involvement in a lineage and training under a qualified teacher. This traditional requirement implies that would-be practitioners of Karmamudra should be accomplished in *tsa loong* and *trul khor*. *Tsa loong* refers to advanced meditation techniques involving the subtle channels and winds (described in Chapter Three) while *trul khor* are special physical movements and breathing exercises associated with these practices.

These methods form part of what is known in Tibetan Buddhism as *Dzogrim*, or the 'Completion' or 'Perfection Stage' of Highest Yoga Tantra practice, where practitioners visualize themselves as Buddhas in sexual union and manipulate their subtle energy bodies in advanced ways to transform their body, speech, and mind. To master the Completion Stage requires extremely specialized training in *Tummo* and *tsa loong* as well as a certain amount of time and resources for extended retreat and spiritual instruction. Historically, only a handful of highly advanced spiritual elites have practiced these techniques in their fullest form. As a result of this, most Tibetan masters today will say that Karmamudra is not for ordinary people. They will explain that Karmamudra is out of bounds for the majority of people, who lack the karma or qualifications for this high practice. They will point out that the average person is simply too uninformed, too inexperienced, too lazy, too undisciplined, too busy and maybe even too poor to do all the Completion Stage retreats and practices needed to master them.

Now, if we look at the basic life obstacles of our modern times, what do we discover? More and more people are too poor, too busy, too lazy or too distracted to devote themselves to spiritual practice. Master Yuthok Yönten Gönpo, the founder of Tibetan medicine and the original revealer of the Yuthok Nyingthig teachings had a vision of the future. He saw and prophesized that in times to come people would have great need of effective teachings but would not have the means or facilities to practice in the classic way. Thus, due to Master Yuthok's great compassion and altruistic heart, we have been given two methods of Karmamudra in the Yuthok tradition. On the one hand, we have the traditional way, which requires extensive training in *Tummo, tsa loong, Dzogrim*, and so on. On the other, we have another way, one suitable for people without training or experience in channel-and-winds yogic practice. The latter are the practices that are explained in this book.

Historically, most people have taken the classical approach to Karmamudra and have mastered *Tummo* first. *Tummo* is its own practice, with its own aims and benefits, but it is also a kind of preparation or base for Karmamudra. *Tummo*, like Karmamudra, is all about *detrö* or the union of bliss and heat. The methods for manipulating and transforming the white and red *thiglé* or energy drops found in *Tummo* practice are very similar to those in the self-cultivation approach of Karmamudra (*ranglü thapden*). *Tummo* is the same kind of self-training – you train your own body, and then once you're very good at *Tummo* and generating bliss-and-heat then you do Karmamudra. In Tibet many people are trained in *Tummo* but then they don't do Karmamudra, they just stay at the level of *Tummo*. With *Tummo* you cover self-cultivation, but you don't have the method of practicing or cultivating with another's body (*shenlü thapden*), so that's *Tummo's* limitation. Naturally, if you're trained in *Tummo*, if you have trained your own body, then Karmamudra is easy, you've trained, after all. The problem however is that everyone gets stuck on these things, on the idea of proper procedure and end up thinking there is or should only be one way to practice. Yuthok's answer to this is perfect. He said, 'If you're trained in *Tummo* and *tsa loong*, then great, you can do Karmamudra in this way. But if you're not trained in these things then also fine, you can practice like this, in another way. He explains that it is similar to training a new horse. There are two approaches: either you train the horse from the ground, systematically, so that eventually when you get on it to ride, it is broken in and amenable, or you train it with your feet, as you go. But even with these two possibilities, you have people who will say "No no no, to ride a horse you have to do one hundred days of training in this, three years of retreat in that, and then you can do this, after which you do this, this, and this." This is a very thorough approach but sometimes it can mean that the possibility of horse-training remains little more than a theory for most people. Both Yuthok and Lelung teach Karmamudra directly – they do not ask less advanced students to accomplish so many complicated practices.

Today there are several fake *tsa loong* teachings out there. These are coming from both Tibetan and non-Tibetan masters who are just taking out bits and pieces from different traditions, which they are combining with materials from here and there and their own quite arbitrary ideas. Thus, if you do practice *tsa loong*, it is better that you do so in a traditional way and learn it authentically, from an authentic teacher. In any case, when people say that Karmamudra is so difficult, that it is lost, that it is not practical I am left feeling perplexed. Of course Karmamudra is practical! All people – barring a few who have specific medical concerns or are asexual – have sex or want to have sex. So how then is Karmamudra, a practice that uses and refines sexual desire, not "practical"? One sad consequence of this type of misguided thinking is that we come to believe that the only sex we can ever have is samsaric or worldly sex, which is stupid. Worldly sex and desire bind us to samsara, but there is another way. If we know how, we can use sex differently, we can use it as an opportunity and method on the path to freedom.

Karmamudra is thus extremely important for humans, who are so full of desire. Vajrayana teaches that as humans we experience four major states of existence or consciousness. There is the waking state, the state of deep (dreamless) sleep, dreaming, and the fourth one is orgasm. As mentioned above, Vajrayana has developed special practices or yogas for working with these states, for using them to experience our own nature, to heal our suffering and help beings. Every day we wake up, every day we have deep sleep, every day we dream, and today many people around the world are practicing Illusory Body Yoga, *Tummo*, Clear Light and Dream Yoga at various levels. People all over the world are also experiencing the fourth state of orgasm everyday, so why don't we practice Karmamudra every day? It is one more opportunity. With Karmamudra we are targeting the fourth consciousness or mental state, just like how with the waking states we have Illusory Body yoga, for dreaming we have Dream yoga, and so on. So many practices are based on the awake state, but the orgasm part is somehow ignored, it has been neglected.

Four States of Consciousness			
Waking State	Deep Sleep (Dreamless State)	Dream State	Orgasm State

The great bliss of non-duality and non-conceptuality we can experience through Karmamudra is part of ourselves. The problem is that so many people have sex and orgasms yet they don't experience or recognize that and this is why they are so stressed and have so many problems. One reason I wanted to publish this book even though many people have reservations about revealing information about Karmamudra is because I believe that people deserve to have access to information that can help them get benefit from this fourth state which is such a fundamental part of their human life. I know that many people will buy this book and will skip past all my explanations and commentary and will try to do Karmamudra partner practice even

The Yuthok Nyingthig system of practice as portrayed in the form of a tree.
The roots of this tree are the Ngöndro (preliminary) practices, out of which grow the three branches of Kyerim (Creation Stage practices), Dzogrim (Completion Stage practices which are divided into the two branches of the Six Yogas and the Two Mudras) and Dzogchen (Great Perfection)

though they are not committed to really doing full Karmamudra practice by following all the steps, doing retreat, and so on. Whether or not I publish anything about Karmamudra people will still be having sex and orgasms. The state of orgasm and sexual desire is with us all the time, so there should at least be some accessible information – approaches based on Karmamudra principles – that can help people work with it wisely and in beneficial ways, even if they are not committed practitioners.

Yuthok's tradition is a non-sectarian one and is a mixture of the old and new schools of Tibetan Buddhism. In the Yuthok Nyingthig tradition, all the important practices of Vajrayana are presented together concisely and their sequence and relationship to one another is clearly laid out. This is especially true in the case of the Completion Stage teachings, which in the Yuthok Nyingthig have two main divisions. The first is the training in the Six Yogas of Naropa, mentioned above. The second consists of the Two Mudras: Karmamudra and Mahamudra. There is a long chapter in the Yuthok Nyingthig about Karmamudra and only a very short one about Mahamudra. Why should this be, especially when today Mahamudra is discussed and taught so much more readily than Karmamudra? The reason is that, as the great Indian Tantric teacher and philosopher Saraha said, "without Karmamudra, there can be no Mahamudra". Saraha is the 'grandfather' of Mahamudra, so we know he knew what he was talking about. In the Yuthok Nyingthig tradition, this is very clear: Yuthok says that until you lose sexual desire, you practice Karmamudra. Then, once your sexual desire has dissipated due to ill health or advanced old age, or if you are a monk or a nun, then that is when you should practice Mahamudra.

Yuthok's point here is that when it comes to Vajrayana we should practice according to our actual abilities and circumstances and not just abstract ideals. If we have the ability (that is to say, if we have sexual energy, sexual desire), then we should use it for Karmamudra. We should not waste this opportunity, this amazing resource. If your Karmamudra is very good, the result will eventually be Mahamudra. Yuthok's way of presenting Vajrayana thus has a very important psychological aspect, one we need to appreciate to make sense of his approach to the teachings. Yuthok was a doctor and his genius was that he approached Dharma like medicine. He was working with patients and with ordinary people, and as a doctor he knew that a person's psychological health is very important. Without solid psychological and physical health and fulfillment, we will never make true progress in the Dharma. So Yuthok designed different teachings that suited a range of different mentalities and needs.

Over the years students have continually asked me to teach Mahamudra and Atiyoga. But then when I do teach them, many students find Mahamudra too basic, too boring. I have encountered many young people in particular who think that meditation is boring which is something that can definitely happen. According to these students' mentality, sitting like a stone, not doing anything, not thinking anything is boring and as a result they are not connected with the practice and make no inner progress and get discouraged. That's why when it comes to teaching the Dharma it is crucial that we understand a person's mentality. Yuthok said that if you talk about sex, no one will say it's boring, not even monks and nuns! No one will get bored or be lazy in their practice. Some might think that a meditation you have to do three times a week is a lot to ask. But when it comes to Karmamudra, even if you are lazy, your body wakes you up in a palpable and undeniable way and says, "Hey, it's time to practice!"

I think this is at the heart of Yuthok's approach: he understood sex and Karmamudra as a doctor, as someone who knows that desire must be understood in terms of individual psychology. In Karmamudra practice the first thing we address is how to make use of our desires. Sexual desire is the most powerful form of human desire. It is innate. Rather than repress this desire, we should acknowledge how very powerful an energy it is. Yuthok's tradition encapsulates the essence of *jinlab nyurwa* or 'swift blessings'. The Yuthok Nyingthig describes Yuthok as 'all Buddhas in One'. It is a very essential and condensed teaching, which is really valuable, since it is so easy for students to get lost in the incredible range of Vajrayana teachings, which can become just another kind of delusion and struggle. Yuthok's methods are aimed at the lazy, busy, and poor so we really do not have any excuse to not better ourselves and our lives through them! We should do our best to do these practices at our own level and achieve results. Through Karmamudra we can learn how to harness and then transform this sexual energy and how to transform other aspects of our mind in turn. As a result of practicing Karmamudra's well-defined methods, we can come to experience bliss, pleasure and joy in all aspects of our lives.

When some people who are not familiar with Yuthok's uniquely condensed and accessible teachings hear about my teaching activities, they misunderstand and think that I am merely cutting corners for Westerners, for 'modern' practitioners who lack the appropriate caliber and training. My statements here do not only apply to Westerners and these quick and adaptable teachings are not my own invention. They are Yuthok's own instructions, which he revealed through his compassion and clairvoyance because he understood the limitations practitioners would face in the future. Not only Westerners, but people throughout Tibet and the rest of Asia, my friends, other Tibetan doctors, people all over the world, they too do not always have the time to practice in the classical way. My Tibetan doctor friends are so busy – they see so many patients every day and then by the time they get home they are so tired and lazy and don't want to do intensive practice. In 2001 my brother and I published the full Tibetan text of the Yuthok Nyingthig in a regular Western-style book format. Prior to this the text had only been available in classical Tibetan pecha form, and wasn't particularly affordable or very easy to carry around. So my efforts to promote Yuthok's approach are not just for Westerners but for Tibetans and other people as well. The circumstances of our current degenerate times are exactly the same for Tibetans and non-Tibetans.

Any person of any age and gender who is serious in their practice can be trained in Karmamudra. Yuthok's simpler, more accessible form of Karmamudra is an easier and safer teaching to adapt. Some traditional texts say that if practitioners are over thirty or forty years old then they are too old for Karmamudra practice. Master Lelung says this too, and that is one thing that I disagree with him about. These days this is an outdated idea, but in ancient times this age limit made sense – in ancient Tibet and India by the time you were in your thirties and forties you were often already a grandparent and it was generally thought you were too old and depleted to practice Karmamudra. Back then access to good food was not guaranteed but in our case, we have a rich diet. These days the period of our thirties and forties is the prime of many of our lives, we have a lot of rich and enjoyable experiences, so Karmamudra can go on until we lose our sexual and sensual desire completely and if you are properly trained, you will never lose it. In his own text, Yuthok states that humans up until the age of seventy – or maybe even older by today's standards – can still have a strong libido. Yuthok himself got married and only bore children at a very advanced age. This reminds me of one time when I was joking with my Karmamudra teacher in Tibet. "Master," I said, "It says in the texts that by the time you're thirty or forty you're already too old to practice Karmamudra, and you're seventy! It's too late for you to be doing this!" My teacher joked back, "Hmm. Maybe the masters who wrote those texts were impotent!" If you have a healthy body and mind and still have sexual desire, Karmamudra techniques can be useful for you.

The main point of this book is to introduce readers to Tibetan Karmamudra practices and to Yuthok's Karmamudra 'without yogic training' approach. This text is intended to be beneficial to everyone. Throughout this book I give techniques derived from Karmamudra practices that anyone can use to work with their sexuality and desire in a more healthy, mindful and deep way. I will not be explaining the main practices of Yuthok's system in great detail in this book. For readers who want the complete teaching on these practices and who wish to do them fully and properly then special preliminary practices, initiations and transmissions are required. These are explained in Chapter Four.

The Future of Karmamudra

Today, as a result of developments in our human society, monastic institutions are decreasing. Monastic society may have had a golden age in the past, but now it is becoming less and less prominent due to social, cultural and economic developments and changes in people's mentalities. Monasticism is no longer a really viable option for many people, and on top of this, people's desires and samsaric attachments are only becoming stronger. For these reasons, lay forms of Buddhist practice and couples practice will be very important in the future. Karmamudra will be an essential practice in times to come.

Master Lelung explained that sexual desire is naturally powerful and it can therefore be turned into an opportunity, a method on the spiritual path. He described Karmamudra as a joyful, easy and speedy approach. For this reason, I really think now is not the time to just say, "Oh, Karmamudra, that's top-secret!" Now is not the time to dismiss Karmamudra and frank discussion about it, only to have some gurus then come along and say on the one hand, "Oh this sexual thing I want to do with you, it is Karmamudra, I promise!" while claiming on the other that "Oh no, Karmamudra has nothing to do with real people's sex lives at all!" All this does is add to our confusion and we have more than enough of that already. All it does is allow self-serving teachers to remain unaccountable and get away with all kinds of things. Lelung's tradition and Yuthok's tradition go together. Like Master Yuthok, Lelung said you don't necessarily have to worry if you're not trained in advanced yogic techniques – both teachers said there was a way you could go safely into Karmamudra without these. It is my belief that today is the perfect time for more people to learn about what these special traditions really involve. We are living in a world of ever increasing desires and sexual dysfunction and suffering. We need this practice now and we will need it in the future.

CHAPTER 2

Sutra and Tantra:
Renunciation and Transformation

*No matter what Buddhist practices you do, training
and transforming the mind is always the ultimate goal.
Whatever you are doing, if there is no inner change,
if there is no inner transformation then this isn't truly
a Buddhist practice.*

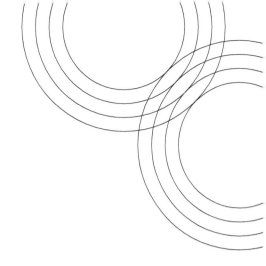

Introducing the Buddhist Path

A lot has been written and said about Tibetan (Tantric) Buddhism or Vajrayana[10] - but what is it, really? When we talk about Buddhism, we can identify two systems or streams of Buddhist teachings, the Sutric tradition and the Tantric tradition. The word 'Sutra' most commonly refers to texts describing the words and activities of Buddha Shakyamuni, the former prince by the name of Siddhartha Gautama who became enlightened under a tree in India more than twenty six centuries ago. Shakyamuni is sometimes called the 'historical Buddha'. This is to distinguish him from the many 'cosmic' Buddhas who are also important in different Buddhist traditions, but who exist beyond ordinary human time, space or perception and who were not historical figures in the same way as Shakyamuni.

At one point in the Sutras, the Buddha is asked to sum up the essence of the Dharma or the Buddhist teachings. This is what he said:

> *"Do good things as much as possible.*
> *Avoid bad things as much as possible.*
> *Tame or control your own mind."*

This is the entire Buddhist Tradition, in a nutshell: do good, don't do bad, and control your mind. The mind is the source of all actions and reactions, all deeds and misdeeds.

To completely "tame your own mind" is thus the most important aspect of the Buddhist tradition. Many other religions emphasize doing morally good things and avoiding immoral acts too, and pronouncements about what counts as virtue and non-virtue are a common thread that runs throughout the world's spiritual traditions. Buddhism's special contribution

---

[10] Vajrayana is the Sanskrit name, whereas the Tibetan term is *dorje thekpa*.

is that it describes in such an incredibly direct and precise way how to "tame your mind". In order to accomplish this, the Buddhist tradition offers many different types of meditation, like meditations for relaxing and calming the mind, abiding mind or *shamata* meditation to strengthen and focus the mind, insight or *vipashyana* meditation for perceiving the basic nature of phenomena, various forms of meditation involving visualization, and many more. The goal of all these meditations is to help you to tame your mind.

Inner Transformation: the Fundamental Goal of Buddhist Practice

No matter what Buddhist practices you do, training and transforming the mind is always the ultimate goal. Perhaps you are doing special Buddhist ritual practices or specific meditations. Whatever you are doing, if there is no inner change, if there is no inner transformation then this isn't truly a Buddhist practice. Without inner transformation you are cheating yourself, and maybe cheating others too. There is a proverb that says: 'You understand Dharma, but Dharma doesn't understand you'. For example, you might talk on and on about meditation, but meditation doesn't know you. That's one example where there is a lack of inner transformation. No amount of intellectual understanding can make up for a lack of inner cultivation and transformation. There are so many religious and spiritual traditions but Buddhism is unique in that it offers precise antidotes to our mental poisons, our personal psychological afflictions. Globally, the number of philosophies, theories and systems of thought that exist or have existed are endless but if they don't facilitate some kind of beneficial inner transformation, they are not useful nor helpful. That's why in order to actually 'tame your mind,' you need some precise techniques to transform your mind and emotions.

Buddhism in the Eye of the Beholder:
Experiencing Mini-Buddhahood Everyday

There are many different definitions of Buddhism one can hear today. Today many people say, "Buddhism is not a religion, it's a philosophy" or "it's a way of life." Others insist that Buddhism is a religion. For religious people, Buddhism can be a perfect religion and for philosophers, Buddhism is indeed a philosophy. Personally, I find this all a little funny. There are so many teachers now who are saying that Buddhism isn't a religion, it's a philosophy, but when you come right down to it, the issue seems to be that these particular teachers are philosophers, while people who think of Buddhism differently and want to call it something else, are not. I think you can understand Buddhism in many different ways. If you are a philosopher, that's great, Buddhism offers so many philosophies, it *is* a philosophy. But on the other hand, if you are religious, then of course Buddhism is a religion. You use your faith and your prayers and so on, there's no problem. Then again, if you are more like a therapist or a psychologist you can think of Buddhism that way too. Incidentally, that's the part I gravitate to most as a doctor of Tibetan medicine – I see Buddhism as a perfect form of psychology since it deals with how to work with the human mind. His Holiness the Dalai Lama says that Buddhism is a science very often too and many scientists today find Buddhism to be compatible with their perspectives. This is because Buddhism offers this Dharma view of the cycle of cause-and-effect, which is mainly what science is concerned with. By definition science wants to understand what the cause-and-effect of phenomena are. Science says that there are no miracles, that everything can be explained and that's exactly what Dharma teaches, that everything can be explained through cause and effect. So, if you're a scientist, you can see Buddhism as a science too, and in fact in Tibetan Buddhism is an 'inner science'.

Ultimately though, whether you conceive of Buddhism as religion, philosophy, psychology or science, the final goal is always the same. Regardless of your position, you as an individual have to wake up. Even if you think of Buddhism as being about religious doctrine or practice the final goal is still experiential. You have to gain your own realization and in the end you have to wake up from even religious beliefs. It is the same if you think of Buddhism as a philosophy: you still have to wake up. There are so many philosophers who get lost in their theories. I've heard that many philosophers today are depressed. The truth is that real life and theories are different and it is the same thing with psychology. If we see Buddhism as a psychology, it must ultimately be the sort of psychology that helps us to wake up from our mental problems and our psychological issues, it must not remain only theory.

Today so many people suffer from depression, but in some cases our mental suffering is really a question of waking up to the nature of things. Sometimes a sudden new insight or realization is enough to dispel depression. This sort of waking up from our delusions and illusions, these moments of realization are like a sort of mini-Buddhahood. Ultimately, we can attain full Buddhahood – one day we will wake up and know that even this life is in essence an illusion, like a hallucination, and then we are free. For Buddha Shakyamuni it took six years to wake up from this life. This is similar to ordinary dreaming. Sometimes we experience different levels of dreaming. You are dreaming and then you wake up – you think you are really awake but it turns out you are in another dream, then you wake up in that dream only to find yourself in another. There are layers of dreams. Becoming a Buddha and becoming awakened also involves different layers of awakening. Nonetheless, if you are depressed and you are able to wake up and shift out of that state into a state of innate peace and happiness then you have already experienced a kind of mini-Buddhahood. Then, maybe once you have experienced that mini-Buddha experience once or a few times, that might help to wake you up from anxiety, which in turn might help to wake you up from panic attacks, and so on.

Sometimes, very young babies are like little Buddhas, they are totally shameless and fearless. The reason why they are shameless and fearless is that they haven't started any 'love stories', and narratives about self, need, desire, lack, fulfillment, and so on in their minds. When we are very young the whole world is our toy. We can play with anything. We are very free. But when we become adults we become the world's play-thing. We become life's toy. Some people say that in order to practice Buddhism you have to become an intellectual or you have to become very religious or so on. But the real point is that we can see for ourselves how we feel, we can see what our tendencies are. Buddhism is like a beautiful location that appears differently to different people. It is a garden or a forest, a beautiful beach or any other imaginable natural landscape. It is up to each of us how we feel about this location. If we feel that one specific habitat is our home, then it is our home.

If you feel good about it, if it seems like a beautiful location to you, then that is what it is. We really don't need to put Buddhism into some kind of standardized box and say, "THIS is Buddhism!" Whatever way we find our home in Buddhism I think what is really most important is that we know that every day we can achieve some part of Buddhahood, we can experience this awakening from our problems and our mistrust, our miscommunication and misunderstanding, which are the foundation of all human conflict. If one day we really awaken from miscommunication and misunderstanding then everything becomes okay and there is no conflict. That's a little taste of Buddhahood too. So that's why we shouldn't think of Buddhahood as just this one big waking up from samsara. We have to pay attention to the small wake-ups, to the mini Buddhas, day and night.

Sutra and Tantra: Distinguishing the Two Traditions

In the Sutric system, the main way people devote themselves full-time to the Buddha's core teaching is through monastic discipline. By becoming a celibate monk or nun, individuals ideally disengage from worldly responsibilities and distractions so that they can focus on cultivating virtue and avoiding wrongdoing and so that they can learn to subdue unruly emotions and negative states of mind which produce suffering. Lay people can also engage in these activities but monks and nuns are professional tamers of the mind. For good reason then, many people today think that monks and nuns are the epitome of Buddhism. Monasticism and celibacy are undoubtedly vital aspects of Buddhism. They are not, however, the only path. In addition to the Sutric tradition of monastic renunciation and monastic vows there is also the Tantric tradition or Vajrayana.

When Buddhism arrived full-force in Tibet from India in the eighth century C.E. it came in the form of both Sutra and Tantra. By that time, Buddhist Tantra was being practiced in India by both celibate monks and nuns and by *ngakpa* and *ngakma*, non-celibate non-monastic Tantric specialists. One such Indian *ngakpa* called Padmsambhava is revered as the father of Tibetan Buddhism by Tibetans. We Tibetans think of Padmasambhava, whose name means 'The Lotus-Born One,' as a Second Buddha. We commonly refer to him as 'Guru Rinpoche,' which is a hybrid Sanskrit-Tibetan title that means 'The Precious Guru'. At first sight, the iconography, ritual practices and yogic techniques associated with Buddhist Tantra can seem a little strange, unexpected or even scary to many people. Without proper understanding, special images of Tantric deities drinking blood, engaging in sex, and trampling on corpses are easy to misinterpret. Without context, these things can seem very disconnected from the celibacy, detachment and restraint people usually associate with the Sutric path. It's important to understand that Tantra *is* the essence of Buddhism, however. It is all about taming and transforming your mind. Tantra is often thought of as a very direct and powerful expression or actualization of Mahayana Buddhism, which is centered around the cultivation of bodhicitta. Tantra offers a series of tried-and-tested methods – by using these methods properly we can make quick and dramatic progress on our path towards

Buddhahood and can be of great benefit to others.

The concept of Tantra is crucial for understanding the Tibetan Buddhist system. Nowadays, especially in the West, many people think 'Tantra' just refers to exotic, 'Eastern' sexual practices. The reality is that Indo-Tibetan Tantric traditions encompass a wide range of practices which have been passed down from generation to generation and which cover all aspects of human life, not just sex. Tantra is above all about integrating spirituality and awareness into every part of our life. This can be seen clearly when we look at the terms for Tantra in Tibetan. There are two words in the Tibetan language which are used to translate the Sanskrit word 'Tantra'. The first of these, *gyü*, literally means a 'thread', 'chain' or 'continuum' and it is also the word for a 'lineage of teaching'. The meaning of Tantra is thus strongly connected to the idea of a system of transmission of the Vajrayana tradition's teachings. This idea of continuity across time is very important. If a teaching comes from an unbroken lineage then this preserves the purity and originality of that teaching. Crucially, this sense of 'continuity' or 'continuation' refers both to the transmission of the knowledge across generations in an unbroken stream from teacher to disciple, and to the goal of maintaining a pure and unified continuity of awareness and mindfulness throughout the different states of human consciousness – waking, dreaming, deep sleep, dying and orgasm.

The other term for Tantra in Tibetan is *ngak*, which means 'mantra'. Like 'Tantra,' the term 'mantra' has many esoteric explanations but the direct meaning of this Sanskrit term is 'that which protects the mind'. Recited and visualized mantras are important tools in Tantric practice for preserving the focus and stability of the mind. Mantras protect the mind against all those different distractions which draw us away from recognizing and staying with our mind's pure nature. They connect us with the innate qualities and potential of our mind. We can thus think of the meaning of 'Tantra' as a 'transmission lineage' or continuum of teachings which provide us with a 'proper or authentic education' in the nature of the mind.

So what exactly distinguishes the two traditions or orientations of Sutra and Tantra then? Popular portrayals of both Hindu and Buddhist Tantra sometimes make it seem like the Tantric tradition is all about orgies and pure indulgence. Sex and desire are an aspect of Tantric practice but it is important to understand that the Tantric tradition is about much more than just having sex. Tantra refers to a particular approach to working with and transforming the mind, one which is different from the Sutra approach. While these systems are distinct, they involve the same core tenets and have the same goal. Some people can be confused when they learn that in Tibetan Buddhism it is entirely possible and appropriate for monks and nuns to practice Tantric techniques while remaining celibate. It is also totally acceptable and absolutely essential that non-monastic specialists or *ngakpa/ma* study and practice Sutric teachings fully and with dedication as well.

In Tibetan Buddhism the relationship between Sutra and Tantra is described in terms of the 'Three Vows' or *Dompa Sum*. These three vows are the Individual Liberator vow(s), Bodhisattva vow(s), and Secret Mantra or Tantric vow(s). The Individual Liberator vow is often associated with monastic vows and the Vinaya, which are the traditional codes of conduct for monks and nuns. As a vow it is sometimes said to correlate with the Theravada vehicle of Buddhism, which is the form of Buddhism found in countries like Sri Lanka, Cambodia, Thailand and Burma. The Bodhisattva vow relates to and refers to one's commitment to act as a Bodhisattva in the world, which means that one aspires to achieve Buddhahood not for one's own sake but in order to free all sentient beings from suffering. The Bodhisattva vow is associated with Mahayana Buddhism, the form of Buddhism found in Japan, China, Korea and Tibet. 'Secret Mantra' or Tantric vows relate to the special vows one maintains as part of practicing the secret or esoteric yoga, meditation, and ritual practices that are part of the Tantric path. In Tibetan Buddhism, Tantric vows and practices come out of and are inseparable from a Mahayana Buddhist Bodhisattva intention. Even though Tantric vows are most strongly related to the Vajrayana or the 'non-dual mind' vehicle of esoteric Buddhism they are still firmly connected to the previous two sets of vows.

We can roughly distinguish Sutra and Tantra according to the following charts:

I. SUTRAYANA (Sanskrit), 'The Sutra Path or Vehicle'; Do (Tibetan)
Most associated with monastic practitioners, i.e. monks or nuns
Exoteric - does not require empowerment/initiation to practice
Path of renunciation of afflictive emotions
Avoidance of causes of suffering (mental poisons)
Cure through antidotes (allopathic approach)
Mahamudra as highest mudra practice

I. TANTRAYANA/MANTRAYANA (Sanskrit) 'The Tantra/(Secret) Mantra Path or Vehicle'); Ngak (Tibetan)
Most associated with non-monastic/house-holder practitioners
Esoteric - requires empowerment/initiation to practice effectively
Path of emotional transformation
Direct confrontation and transmutation of the causes of suffering (mental poisons)
'Like Cures Like' (homeopathic approach)
Karmamudra as highest mudra practice

In Tibetan Buddhism, both monastics and non-monastic Tantric yogis are expected to hold all three sets of vows properly when practicing Tantric techniques. Holding Tantric vows does not invalidate or supersede monks and nuns' Individual Liberator vows which require celibacy, and just because *ngakpa* are not monks and have families does not mean that they aren't still committed to the basic precepts and aren't concerned with the teachings of the Sutras and with moral virtue. The great *ngakpa* and Karmamudra master Dudjom Rinpoche explained these points as follows:

"When the light of the lamp of the teachings of the Buddha illuminated the realm of darkness that was Tibet from its very ground of being, the monastic Abbot Shantarakshita, the Tantric master Padmasambhava, and the Dharma King Trisong Detsen themselves directly decreed that the sangha or community of Buddhist practitioners was to be [divided] into two sections: the Sutric community of shaved-haired monastics and the Tantric community of long-haired yogis or ngakpa/ma. This constitutes, as the well-known expression goes, the 'two sangha communities which were an object for offerings or reverence for the King,' both of which endure to the present day. While there is some slight difference between these two communities of monastics and ngakpas in terms of their dress, the external markers they exhibit, and the specific ritual activities they perform, both groups are completely alike in how they observe the three sets of vows and practice both Sutra and Tantra in an integrated way so as to develop the spiritual qualities of inner realization."
(Dorje, 1979)

Misbehaving and Married 'Monks':
Distinguishing Between Practice and Abuse

These days, there is a lot of confusion about who can practice Tantra and who is practicing properly. Today's students, both in the East and West are often confused by the many different ways that different Buddhist teachers and practitioners dress and how this relates to their vows and their behavior. In Tibetan Buddhist contexts there are two levels of monastic vows: *Getsul* and *Gelong*. *Getsul* or *Getsulma* refers to monks and nuns who hold some monastic vows, while *Gelong/ma* is a monk or nun who holds the full set of monastic vows. It is very important to understand that *gelong* and *getsul* are *never* allowed to have sex as part of their vows, under any circumstances. Even if these monastic vow holders also practice Tantra and keep Tantric vows alongside their monastic ones, they may never engage in actual physical sexual intercourse with someone and still be considered to be upholding their monastic vows correctly. The reason it is important to explain this is because these days there are many teachers who say they are monks but they aren't really. They wear monks' robes externally but internally they are having love affairs with girlfriends and go around telling ladies that they can bless them through special sexual practices and so on. These teachers try to hide their behavior. They publicly claim to be monks, but then they engage in sex, often with their students, in secret. They publicly pose as monks and claim that they are observing monastic vows of celibacy but then they will justify their sexual exploitation and abuse by saying that they are actually 'Tantric monks' and that what they are doing is okay. These individuals will tell all sorts of different stories and will try to deceive women by saying that what they're doing is okay because they wear 'special robes' etc. For them, wearing monk's robes is just a strategy, it is just for show. You see this very often in China, where many people still have a lot of respect for Buddhist monks. Publicly claiming to be a *gelong* while having sex in secret is terrible misconduct. Teachers like these will use their name or status as so-called *tulkus* or reincarnated lamas to get away with this kind of bad behavior and to mislead their followers. Cases like this seem to be really spreading throughout Tibet, China, Bhutan, Nepal, and India, and many different places. Sexual scandals exist all over Eastern spiritual communites, in the same way that they do in the Christian church, and sexual misconduct is very common within the circles of high level lamas.

I'm not the only one who thinks this is a serious problem today. His Holiness the Fourteenth Dalai Lama has also pointed out the dangers of this sort of behavior. Below you can read translations of advice that the Dalai Lama gave on this subject in 2009 and 2014, during two separate visits to Ladakh. You can see that he makes it very clear what kind of behavior and activities are allowed for monastic and non-monastic practitioners in Tibetan Buddhism. In his 2009 explanation he points out the dangers of *kyamin sermin*, practitioners who are 'neither lay nor monastic':

"The community of monastic renouncers became the chief holders of the Buddha's teachings [in Tibet]. Whether one is a male or female monastic it is extremely important that one maintains an excellent standard of practice. There wasn't any tax collector at all who came and said 'you need to become a monk or nun'. It was something that you took on individually, of your own accord. Since you took this up and you got into this, practicing with a high standard is really important. Still, many times becoming a monk can have no benefit. Sometimes one encounters individuals who are neither lay nor monastic, who based on their clothes look like they are monks but based on the families that they have look like lay people.

Not one nor the other, kyamin sermin like this are not good. Conversely, to practice in a pure fashion means to do so in accordance with the two religious communities that are said to have been established when the abbot [Shantarakshita], the Tantric master [Padmasambhava] and the Dharma king [King Trisong Detsen] came together long ago: namely, the so-called 'white robed, willow leaf-shaped dread-locked community' [of non-celibate Tantric yogis or ngakpa] and the 'saffron [robed] monastic renouncer community' [of monks and nuns]. If you have a family and children it is best if you are a member of the white robed, dread-locked community [i.e. that you practice as a ngakpa] and if you desire to remain a member of the saffron-robed monastic renouncer community then once you have been ordained you must preserve monastic rules and discipline properly.

Therefore, all of you need to think carefully about this. It's really important that everyone, from the highest lamas to their communities of monastic disciples be very careful in this..."

In another speech in 2014 the Dalai Lama explains how the sexual misconduct of monks cannot be excused through claims about Tantra:

"In the past in India due to members of the Buddhist sangha's material greed and their failure to preserve the Tantric tradition properly the Buddhist teachings deteriorated. These causes and conditions are entirely and exactly the same as those that affect us Tibetans. I've said to several friends previously that it is wrong that when respected teachers or lamas go back on their vows people say that they've taken Tantric consorts (sangyum), but when monks have reneged on their vows and have gone back to being ordinary lay people they are called 'dralok'[11] and have to be kicked out of the monastery.

Ultimately, taking a consort should be something special and particular, something out of the ordinary. If it is not and it ends up becoming an excuse to make one baby after another like a pig having piglets then it completely loses its meaning. So for us to use Secret Mantra or Tantra as a pretext for such behavior and for people in general society to say 'Oh [don't worry] the lama has taken a Tantric consort' isn't okay. For example: there's a nunnery in India, where when I asked 'What are some of the most amazing or wonderful

---

[11] *Dralok* is a general term for ex-monk in Tibetan but it has a rather derogatory flavor and often implies a monk has broken his vows of celibacy.

accounts you can tell me about nuns here rendering service to the Buddhist teachings?' The nuns said 'We are extremely fortunate that many among us have become the Tantric consorts of lamas'. Lamas who couldn't stay lamas and who were unable to preserve their vows became dralok with these nuns.

Through this, for no good reason at all and due to blind faith or superstition these practitioners, even while they say they 'Go for Refuge' [to the Buddha, Dharma and Sangha, i.e. profess to be Buddhists] remain in error. I say this really honestly and frankly. Many of you here are nuns. And in any case, if the Secret Mantra turns into wanton or dissolute conduct there is great danger of the Tantric tradition being discredited and called into disrepute..."

In Mongolia and Buryatia where I sometimes teach, many 'monks' are married. These practitioners are usually just called 'lama' – teacher or guru – by their communities. They are almost exclusively from the Gelukpa school of Tibetan Buddhism, which is the main Buddhist tradition in these countries. Yet even though the Gelukpa school strongly emphasizes monasticism, they don't claim to be either this fake category of 'Tantric monk' or *ngakpa*, a non-celibate Tantric vow-holder, which is a legitimate category. Everybody knows these lamas are married. This situation is a result of the history of Soviet occupation in these countries. During the Soviet period, Buddhism and religions in general were persecuted and many monks were forced to disrobe. Today monastic institutions are not so developed in places like Buryatia, so you have people like these lamas who wear robes that look a little bit like monks' robes for public events, or when they perform rituals or give teachings but who then go back to wearing normal non-religious clothes when they are going about their lives and spending time with their families. When these teachers go out for their ordinary business they appear like ordinary lay people and are fully integrated into society. Technically speaking these practitioners are what are known in Tibetan as *genyen*, or devout laypeople. This situation is okay because while these lamas may look like monks they are not actually monastic vow holders, nor are they claiming to be.

Holders of *genyen* or 'Approacher of Virtue' vows takes refuge in the Triple Jewels or Buddha, Buddhist Teachings, and Buddhist community (Buddha, Dharma, Sangha) and commit themselves to permanently up-holding the five basic precepts of Buddhism: 1) to not kill 2) to not steal 3) to refrain from sexual misconduct (however that might be defined in context)

4) to not lie and 5) to avoid intoxication. These vows are often supplemented with three extra vows which are observed on full and new moon days: 6) to not eat at inappropriate times/after midday 7) to refrain from dancing, singing, make-up, jewelry and other forms of entertainment and self-adornment and 8) to not sleep on high beds. Devout laypeople who hold these vows may also practice complete celibacy on new and full moon days. These lay disciple vows are typically seen as falling under the umbrella of the different degrees of Individual Liberator vows. In countries like Mongolia and Buryatia where monasticism has weakened, married *genyen* lamas with religious training do the jobs that might be performed by monks and *ngakpas* in other places. When they wear robes in public the communities they serve understand this. They are not trying to deceive anyone or pretending to uphold vows that they are actually breaking. Technically, *genyen* are not allowed to wear the same clothing as *getsul* or *gelong*. In this case, these Mongolian and Siberian teachers use monks' robes as a kind of public uniform to signal their religious expertise. In cases like these, we see that the monastic tradition has already transformed in these local contexts.

When it comes to *ngakpa*, there are also special forms of dress that are meant to mark *ngakpa* commitments and status. *Ngakpa* in Tibet who are full-time village ritual experts may wear their white robes and red and white shawls all the time, while other *ngakpa* and *ngakma* may only wear their *ngakpa* robes when they are performing rituals. If *ngakpa* do other work besides rituals they may wear ordinary laypeople clothes in these other context. In exile, in the Indian context, the *ngakpa* community is maybe a little smaller and less well-known or understood. As a result of this, *ngakpa* who do wear their special form of dress at all times may sometimes be teased or criticized. This criticism is quite unfair – after all, if *ngakpa* wearing their appropriate uniform is 'showing off' then surely every monk and nun are showing off too? This issue of social opinion and criticism is significant here. As the Dalai Lama implies, there is a lot of stigma associated with being a disrobed or 'ex-monk'. Tibetan monks in India and Western countries who disrobe – who legitimately return their vows without breaking them through misconduct – are often ashamed about telling their families that they have returned to lay life. Because of their fear of being criticized by other Tibetans in their community, even when these ex-monks are married and have kids they may pretend for years that they are still monks. I know of several monks who have moved to the West and have disrobed but will put their robes back on when they return to visit their families in Tibet. These monks aren't bad, they haven't done anything wrong, but they are afraid of being judged by others.

We can thus see that understanding the precise differences between the Tantric and Sutric traditions is very important for a number of reasons. The better people understand how Tantric and Sutric practices and vows are different and also combine together, the better they can protect both the teachings and themselves from being harmed, exploited and abused.

Avoidance versus Transmutation: The Poison Path and the 'Like Cures Like' Approach of Tantra

If a heterosexual nun sees a very attractive man or a heterosexual monk spies a very attractive woman, the Sutric path teaches that they have to imagine the person who is the object of their desire to be very old, stinky or revolting, to think of them as a corpse or skeleton. Other instructions say that you can also imagine yourself as a skeleton or corpse too. This negative thought or mental counter-measure helps to reduce desire and to remind the person experiencing it of the momentary, composite and impermanent nature of their bodies and impulses. This is a very famous Sutrayana example of how to block desire, especially sexual desire, using your mental power. I once heard a story about this common example, one which is quite revealing. A Tibetan monk-lama was once giving teachings on desire to some students and someone in the audience asked him what he does when he feels desire for a woman. The monk teacher explained how he used the above method and imagined women as old and stinky. There were many foreigner women attending this teaching and when they heard this they became very upset with this monk. They objected: "We are beautiful ladies!? Why are you thinking about us as disgusting stinky skeletons?!" Of course they were angry – this monk's statements seemed misogynistic, they were shocked to learn that a teacher they respected was imagining them in such an unsavory way. But the monk didn't understand their complaints – from his point of view this was totally natural. This was simply the Sutrayana Buddhist tradition. This is one particularly disastrous example of cultural misunderstanding. One of the ladies who was angry about the lama's comments came to me and complained about what the lama had said. She was so upset and was demanding some kind of explanation, so I was a little nervous! Thankfully the explanation was simple enough: "Don't worry," I told her, "He was just talking about Sutrayana. In the Tantric path things are exactly the opposite! In Tantra, let's say you're sixty years old – Tantric practice will make you seem like you're twenty years old – Tantric practitioners don't see your wrinkles, so don't worry!" The woman looked at me with surprise, "Oh! Are you joking?" she said. "No!" I told her, "It really is like that!"

You might be wondering, just like this woman did, what I mean by all this. One of the most important concepts in Tantrayana is 'pure vision' or 'pure appearances', which is called *daknang* in Tibetan. Pure vision means thinking and seeing positively in an unconditional way. To have pure perception of yourself is to have it for others. The Tibetan master Patrul Rinpoche explained that the essence of Vajrayana is *daknang*, to prefer to think positively about others. To view them as vibrant, as powerful, as good – as pure expressions of realized mind and Buddha nature.

Dealing with Desire: Spirituality, Suppression and Sickness

When I was young I read some of these Sutric texts that speak so badly about women, and I didn't like them very much at all. They disturbed me. Ultimately, we all come from our mothers, younger me reasoned, and so if it was true that women were so impure or inferior then that must mean our own source was also negative. No man comes from a man, after all. I was really confused and worried about this until I came to appreciate that these texts were for monks, and were designed to discourage them from desiring women. Of course, the problem is that even these strategies don't always work, they don't necessarily stop monks' desire. The monks' Vinaya approach may have worked in the past, but today there are enough examples to show that this kind of demonizing of women doesn't automatically spell the end of men's desire. The sexual yogi Drukpa Kunley pointed this out when he joked about the prevalence of homosexuality in Tibetan monasteries as far back as the 15th century: "You say you dislike women, but you really just like other monk's asses!" In joking like this, Drukpa Kunley spoke publicly about something Tibetans don't usually like to talk about, but he was right.

Desire is obviously more complex – imagining that women are dirty and rotten may help the occasional straight monk shut down his desire, but not every monk is necessarily straight, and if we look at the number of monks who still break their vows of celibacy with women even with these methods, we can see that counter-acting or denying desire is not always enough.

When celibate religious practitioners don't know what to do with their sexual desire this can result in all sorts of problems and genuine sickness. The suppression of sexual desire can drive people crazy. Someone can talk about spirituality, restraint, meditation, compassion, or love endlessly, but if they are beset by desire and don't know what to do about it, nothing will help. If a person doesn't know how to work with their desire, to meditate with it, then celibacy can be a form of suppression. There are so many sexually abused kids who have suffered at the hands of pedophiles. One hears stories of serious torture. Cases of terrible abuse take place in all sorts of contexts. There has been quite a lot of discussion about the Vatican and child abuse in Christian contexts but not so much talk about similar occurrences that take place in Tibetan Buddhist monasteries. The abuse of children involves no choice for them, they are victims. We really need to discuss these things and make them public, wherever they happen. We need to protect these little monks and other children who are vulnerable to abuse.

Any kind of sexual abuse is horrible – it produces so much suffering and trauma. In my work as a doctor I come across many patients who have been sexually abused from a young age and they have enormous trauma. Sometimes pedophiles have themselves been abused. It's important to note that homosexuality and pedophilia are completely different things. Being gay or lesbian has to do with a person's personal life and orientations. I think that no one religion or culture should judge this too much. People should have a choice who they love – it's your love, your orientation, your life, your affection. People often ask me what I think about homosexuality. Your sex life and sexual orientation is your business, not mine. I respect everyone's right to conduct their private lives as they choose. Homosexuality is a completely valid way of living in society. Sexual abuse and pedophilia is something else entirely. I think that these individuals have a syndrome, a mental illness. I don't judge them because they too are suffering, but I am concerned with the causes of their terrible behavior.

The negative consequences of suppression and denial of desire are key here. Sex is such a culturally sensitive topic that just mentioning it tends to invoke a range of defensive and rather negative reactions from people. And when you talk about combining spiritual practice with sex, the most common initial reflex is to reject the idea out of hand. People's first reaction is shock and suspicion. This is interesting because privately, virtually everyone loves sex. I think that accounts of sexual scandals between gurus and students and sexual abuse in religious institutions are part of why it has become normal for people to say that when sexuality and spirituality mix it can only ever be something negative. Yet the more we think sexuality is negative, the more we try to repress it and the worse our situation becomes.

Those who experience strong sexual desire know the power of that desire. I once met a Buddhist nun in her late forties or early fifties in Southeast Asia who told me that she was possessed by a mara demon (these are called *düd* in Tibetan). She asked me if I could perform an exorcism. I said "Yes!" I was quite excited, I thought to myself, "Wow, I'll get to take a demon out of a Buddhist nun, won't that be something!" The nun told me that she needed to get her translator and went off. A little while later she returned. I asked her, "So, how is your demon?" And she said, "Oh, this monster, this mara, it is so powerful! It enters into my body and I feel so many sensations – in my breasts and you know, down there – there's all this energy moving!" She said that when this demon overcame her she would lose control and feel like she had to do something to protect herself. I asked her, "What do you do?" And she said, pitifully, "Oh! It's so bad but I have to do it!" "What is it you do?" I asked her again. "You have some sort of strategy for stopping this demon?" "Yes," she replied. Again I asked her, "Ok! What is it?!" And finally, she said, "I masturbate!" I asked her what happened next. "The demon disappears but the next week it comes back all over again." So, this demon was visiting her every week, basically. This nun tried so hard to prevent herself from succumbing to pressure from the demon, she told me that she even tried to tie her fingers together but even that did not work.

It turned out that it wasn't necessary for me to perform an elaborate and time-consuming ritual of exorcism after all. I said to her "This is not a demon – why do you think that? You are just talking about sexual desire, this is normal. I know you are a nun, but you have a human body, this is your natural human sexual desire." But she didn't listen, "No, no, no! This is mara. I have to masturbate because of the demon, but then after I do that

I feel so bad." This nun felt tremendous guilt, at least until the following week anyway. Then the demon returned and her guilt disappeared for a little while and she had to repeat the process. This woman was really suffering, she would try to meditate but she was so distracted by this problem. I tried to explain to her that according to Vajrayana what she was describing was not a problem. I told her that she could just do Karmamudra or *Tummo* inner heat meditation and process her desire and that then everything would be fine. I know some monastics who are familiar with how to move their sexual energy up and down with their breath and then pervade it throughout their whole body. Through doing this they are able to get great relief from their sexual frustrations. Even if they don't have a regular kind of orgasm it relieves the pressure of that feeling and then they are very happy for a great many days. I tried to tell the nun about these procedures but it didn't go through her ears, she was so focused on the Sutric approach. I asked her if she had talked with her teacher about the problem. She had. It turns out that her teacher was a monk and when she talked with him about her problem he said, "Yes! This is definitely mara!" And he likely said this because he knew the demon all too well himself. She begged her master to give her a solution. She really couldn't handle the situation anymore. What he told her was this: "There is no solution. Wait until you get old and then the mara will go away. In the meantime recite the Heart Sutra."

I think this nun's story of demonic oppression is very revealing. In the symbolic language of Tantra, our afflicting desires, emotions and mental states are often referred to or conceived of as 'inner demons' or 'poisons'. Whether you call them poisons or you call them demons, our desires are powerful and dangerous. Sexual desire can become a very negative force in our own and others' lives. It can cause us to lose control and to suffer and can cause suffering to others. In our society sex is sometimes a forbidden word, and honest and direct discussion about and acceptance of sex and its power is rejected by so many sectors of society and so many different people. But this sort of rejection helps turn sex into a dark force that gives rise to terrible things like rape, sex trafficking, and child abuse. There is a great need in general for more awareness and understanding around sex and sexuality.

When confronted with accusations of institutional sexual abuse religious leaders like to say, "Oh, this is an internal issue, we should not be held to the common law". But the damage done by religious figures who abuse people is terrible, especially when it involves defenseless children. I have one patient whose mind is completely destroyed as a result of the abuse he experienced at the hands of Catholic priests. Stupid men who didn't know how to handle their sexual energy and desires destroyed this young boy. He is seven or eight years old and his life has been completely destroyed, all because somebody wanted to get some sexual pleasure or let out his frustration and aggression a few times. And now one human life has been destroyed completely. This boy can hardly function at all anymore. He suffers from severe panic attacks and many other terrible symptoms. He has been in and out of psychiatric hospitals and everybody knows that the cause was rape at the hands of priests. So, when it comes to topics like rape and sex trafficking it is not just about protecting kids but also about education. Obviously I'm not saying that everyone everywhere should practice Karmamudra, but educating adolescents and adults, and men in particular, about healthy sexuality in some or other fashion is very important. This is one of men's weak points. We live in a world today where a culture of sexual abuse and violence is supported and tolerated at even the highest levels of society, so this topic is extremely important.

Almost everybody likes sex, including monks and nuns, and priests. Even the current Dalai Lama, when he was asked once in an interview about whether he likes women or has desire for women said, "Of course I have desire!" The Dalai Lama explained to the interviewer that he will sometimes dream of ordinary women and think that they are really nice and desirable, but he always remembers that he is a monk and doesn't penetrate these dream-women even though he has desire. The Dalai Lama is a great master and one of the greatest examples of monastic conduct in Tibetan Buddhism today – he knows how to handle his sexual impulses and desire and how to maintain his celibacy in a healthy way. He knows how to work with that kind of energy. Even the Buddha Shakyamuni had sexual desire when he was living a life of luxury as a prince, a husband and a father. But after leaving the palace life and wandering in the forest for six years practicing fasting and other asceticisms, he was able to completely alter his entire physiological and psychological functions and free himself from all desire and craving.

According to Tibetan Tantric tradition it is easy enough to liberate yourself from sexual desire, if you know a special form of sexual yoga practice known as Jnanamudra or 'Wisdom Seal'. This is a version of Karmamudra which Tibetan Buddhist monastics can practice without compromising their vows of celibacy. Using an imaginary partner or Jnanamudra consort provides monks and nuns who have Tantric meditative training with a perfect way to handle their sexual energy and desire. When a person practices with a mental Jnanamudra partner they work with their breath and visualization and intentionally increase and then expand this energy. It's almost like a softer version of having an orgasm through physical sex. When sexual energy is reduced and refocused in this way, monastics can deal with it more easily and use it in beneficial ways. Without Jnanamudra it can be very difficult for them to handle this energy however, and as discussed above, their desire can be channelled in harmful directions. If these methods or options don't exist for religious practitioners then they might think, "I have so much desire, but this desire is a sin!" They may feel hopeless and ashamed. They may pray for help, or even beg to be punished. But even if some higher power were to punish them, their desire would still be there.

'Crazy Wisdom': On Eating Meat, Drinking Alcohol, Having Sex and Acting 'Wrathfully' in Tantric Buddhism

In Vajrayana, as part of the idea of turning poison into medicine or a source of blessings, practitioners will sometimes consume small amounts of meat or alcohol which have been transformed through prayers and mantras into nectar. This consuming of what seem like quite worldly or impure 'substances' from the Sutric perspective, and the use of sex and wrathful behavior on the Tantric path is easy to misunderstand so I would like to clarify this a little. Some people think that using meat and alcohol and having sex is the core of Tantric vows, while other people speak very badly about these things. In the Tantric texts and in the commentaries of the great Tantric masters it is sometimes taught that one *must* rely on meat, alcohol and women while sometimes it is taught that one should completely abandon these things. So many people get the wrong idea about this, but if one investigates closely, one can come to a clear understanding.

Generally, it is taught that monastic vow-holders in the Sutric tradition have to abandon meat, alcohol, and women, but in the Tantric tradition there are vows to rely on these things. The most important thing is that non-celibate Tantric practitioners preserve their vows correctly – consuming small amounts of meat and alcohol or engaging in sex in more mindful ways at specific times and in particular contexts is part of these, but lusting after these things for their own sake is not what these vows are all about. Eating meat excessively in the name of Tantra is harmful to both animal life and our own health. Drinking alcohol or taking drugs excessively in the name of Tantra, using these substances in an undisciplined, gluttonous way with a mind filled with ordinary attachment and desire can lead to addiction for some people. And as we have seen, having sex in the name of Tantra when you are really motivated by selfish and harmful intentions is nothing other than sexual abuse. Most sexual abuse is perpetrated by men on women and children, but this can occur in any context, between men, by a woman to a man or child, between adult women, and between people who do not identify as either men or women.

These days whenever one hears about practitioners of Vajrayana behaving badly, sooner or later somebody mentions the idea of 'Crazy Wisdom'. This is a very popular explanation today – when teachers force themselves sexually on students, physically or verbally abuse them or act in crazy ways, people will say that the teacher only appears to be acting badly, but that in reality the teacher is a Buddha motivated by compassion and is helping us purify our karma and our perception through practicing Crazy Wisdom. The idea of Crazy Wisdom is connected with the unconventional and sometimes aggressive or shocking behavior of the Mahasiddhas or great Tantric saints. It is not only linked with lamas having sex with students but also with lamas beating or physically and mentally torturing them. Very recently, while visiting Bhutan, I heard stories about one local lama who was seriously beating his students. Some people were saying this was okay because the teacher was very realized and he was helping to purify the students karma and snap them into awakening by beating them and behaving in shocking ways, but many other people were unhappy. There was a lot of division and confusion.

Historical 'crazy lamas' have practiced *tulshook kyi chöpa*, the special taming 'discipline', an advanced Tantric yogic practice which makes use of conventionally polluting or harmful substances and behaviors to stabilize practitioners' realization of non-dual pure awareness or 'one taste,'[12] where every experience arises as bliss, beyond pure or impure. Historically lamas have undertaken this special discipline or practice during specific periods of their life and in specific places as a kind of intensive, wandering retreat. Unfortunately the term 'Crazy Wisdom' has now become so polularized that people will use it to explain any kind of bad behavior by gurus, as if 'Crazy Wisdom' is some special Tibetan cultural practice which allows a Vajrayana guru to ignore all laws and vows, all of the Buddha's teachings on ethical behavior, and any consequences for their actions!

Today when people explain the unconventional and aggressive behavior of famous Crazy Wisdom lamas like Karmamudra master Drukpa Kunley, they will often say that lamas like this have transcended dualistic perception, so they are beyond all ordinary categories and expectations. But as I pointed out in my preface, today most masters are not qualified enough to make use of Crazy Wisdom teaching methods and most disciples are not qualified either, they are not ready for that level and don't have the right kind of devotion or orientations for those methods to work and be beneficial. In Tibetan there is a phrase used to describe how a Buddha or teacher with enlightened, compassionate intention behaves: *gang la gang dul.* This expression means something like 'whatever tames beings,' that is, teaching or acting in whatever way is necessary or most effective for helping others to discipline their minds, to subdue their afflictive emotions and progress on the path. People often like to talk about this sort of 'skillful means' or 'doing whatever is necessary' when lamas are behaving badly but *gang la gang dul* is about working with prevailing circumstances and conditions to have the most beneficial impact. 'Doing whatever needs to be done' doesn't just mean Crazy Wisdom at every opportunity. In many, if not most cases, it means respecting the ordinary laws of the society that one is in and operating in line with normal or conventional social views and morality. Being a skillful teacher often means adapting and working creatively with people's mentalities and understanding. Rather than being about breaking morality or laws, it can be about teaching in a way that fits with society and social values.

---

[12] *Ro chik* in Tibetan. This refers to the abiding state of non-dualistic perception enjoyed by realized practitioners of Tantric Buddhism and Mahamudra in particular. A person with 'one taste' experiences or savors everything that occurs with equal appreciation, as an unfolding of Buddha-nature. For such a person there is therefore no good or bad, pleasant or unpleasant – everything is perceived as impermanent and empty of inherent existence and 'tastes' equally of bliss.

The true path of Vajrayana is transformation. This means that anything can be transformed, all circumstances are serviceable. If a teacher is skillful they should be able to guide and help beings effectively at their level, they should be able to work within constraints and restrictions rather than having to constantly push against them. They should be able to accomplish transformation while respecting prevailing laws. Ultimately, even when we have to break with logic and conventional rules as part of Vajrayana, the most important thing is that we break with or transcend rules and norms on an inner level, internally at the level of our mind or perception. This is much more important than simply breaking the outer rules of society. Anyone can transgress external rules and norms but liberating oneself from the restriction of these on an inner level is much more difficult and crucial. Even if you are constrained by society, even if you are literally in prison, you can still be free inwardly, mentally. Guru Rinpoche used many wrathful methods to subdue his own and others minds but he stated that his appreciation of cause-and-effect, his commitment to ethical conduct based on the understanding of karma (how negative actions have negative results) was as 'fine' or exacting 'as flour'. What this means is that the true yogi or yogini understands, accepts and respects the laws that exist at every level.

Some yogis are hidden or secret yogis – they do not reveal or show off their Tantric commitments and practices through their appearance or behavior in a very public way. On the outside and from day to day they look and act in very typical or unremarkable ways. As discussed earlier in this chapter, many yogis also regularly wear Tantric robes and items to mark their status and social roles. Both of these are valid styles. But the main point is that being a yogi in the Tibetan context doesn't just mean you are always doing Crazy Wisdom, it isn't synonymous with bad behavior. Just saying 'yogi' doesn't mean everything is always against all laws and rules. Ultimately, whenever a guru makes a demand or behaves in a certain way we have to think carefully about this in the context of our relationship with the teacher, our practice, our vows and our devotion. There have been so many accusations of abuse against lamas over the last few years. Of course, whenever accusations arise we have to look at all sides of the situation since it is always possible that some accusations may be the result of misunderstanding or that some stories might be fake or manipulated. Yet it is also true that many teachers have in fact abused their students without any consequences. That is why I think that the time for the misuse of Crazy Wisdom is over. Crazy Wisdom is not an excuse for breaking vows or for bad behavior.

A Tantric Yogi Among Monks: The Story of my Teacher Akhu Lhamo Jab and the Meaning of Renunciation Today

The difference between the Sutric and Tantric orientation can be seen in the life-story of one of my own teachers in Tibet, Akhu Lhamo Jab[13]. Akhu Lhamo Jab was a true nomad, he never wore shoes but went barefoot even in town on the street. He was so renowned for his knowledge that the local college in my home region invited him to teach there, but although he agreed to come he always followed his nomadic customs. The school gave him a house but because he grew up in nomadic areas and had never lived in a permanent dwelling he preferred to sleep outside. School officials gave him a sofa, but because he was raised in a tent he just put all his cups, cooking pans and other belongings on it and sat on the floor. He was a truly great master. I started learning from him at a young age and I really enjoyed his teachings because when you attended his classes you never had to open a book. All of his teachings utilized imagination and fantasy in addition to real life examples, he was very skillful at transmitting knowledge. He was also a non-celibate *ngakpa* and expert in Karmamudra practice.

He wasn't always so sure of his non-monastic yogi path, however. When he was young, he studied under a very famous monk teacher. One day this monk master requested that all of his disciples become monks but Lhamo Jab refused. In the Tibetan tradition it is considered very bad to refuse a request from one's teacher. "Why don't you want to become a monk?" his teacher asked him. "Nobody else objected – it's important for you to do this!" My teacher told him the truth: "Master, I have to be honest with you, I don't want to deceive you. If you really want me to become a monk, I'll do it, but I know myself and within a week or a month I will be a layperson again. I have too much sexual desire, I can't control this desire, I cannot live a celibate life." At the time my teacher was a very young man and the monk

---

[13] Akhu Lhamo Jab's Dharma name was Tseshung Lhanyön Rölpatsel ('He of Tseshung, the Creative Expression of the Playful Display of the Crazy Deity'), and his teacher's name was Chisa Lodrö Gyatso.

master was quite taken aback to hear this. "If you can't become a monk then you're not allowed to come to the teachings anymore" and the monk kicked my teacher out. Lhamo Jab really wanted to study with this lama though, so every day he sat outside the window of the room where classes were taking place. He did this for a long time. He was very smart and a very good student but he just didn't want to become a monk. This monk teacher was very well-known for his knowledge of Tibetan language, grammar and literature, and if my teacher didn't study with him there would be no chance of him receiving a better education. Master Lhamo Jab told me that he was really crestfallen, but he truly thought at that time that his sexual desire was just too powerful and strong. He said he knew it would be bad if he became a monk because he was sure he would have to hide his desires and have sex in secret or would have to give up his vows.

Still, as powerful as his sexual desire was, his desire for knowledge was as strong if not stronger. Eventually the monk-lama, who knew of course that my teacher had been camping out outside auditing his class in secret, called him to come inside. He again asked my teacher if he would become a monk, and when my teacher once more declined, he thought for a while and then said, "Okay, okay, fine – don't become a monk then. But you should at least become a *ngakpa* or yogi." And so he gave my teacher a yogi name and the rest is history. Akhu Lhamo Jab went on to become a consummate yogi and Karmamudra practitioner and even in his seventies he still had so much vitality and energy as a result of his Karmamudra practice. Because of his orientations he also ended up going with what's known as the Nyingma school, even though his teacher was from the Gelukpa school, since the Nyingma school talks much more about non-celibate practices. In this way he was a little like Master Lelung.

Lelung Zhepai Dorje was heavily criticized by others. People said that he was bad, that he was crazy, that he misunderstood and was deteriorating the teachings, and so on. If you read the Dungkar Tibetan language dictionary you'll see that the compilers included a very bad entry on Lelung[14]. I, however, really like Master Lelung's story because he is the one figure who really made Karmamudra public in Tibet. Neither Ju Mipham nor Gendün Chöphel did this. Both of them published works about Kamasutra and they were also both somewhat controversial but Lelung was the one who really opened up the topic of Karmamudra. Actually, more accurately, it was the

Dakini Nyima Zhönnu herself who did this. What she told Lelung was: "If you think about humans' desire and humans in general, they have so many desires and they don't know what to do with them." At one point in his book Lelung expands on the Dakini's teachings on desire with great clarity and insight. Nyima Zhönnu called us humans 'desire animals'. Dogs desire food but they don't lust after nice dresses or yearn to become famous. This is what Nyima Zhönnu meant when she said that humans are full of so much desire, desire they don't know how to handle. She acknowledged that humans experience many different desires but pointed out that sexual desire is one of the strongest. Because of this, she instructed Lelung to "go out and help people, teach them how to work with their desires, teach them Karmamudra!" And he did it. Of course he knew that it wouldn't be easy as Tibet was a predominantly monastic society. Still, despite the pre-eminence of its monastic doctrines and systems, there were also other non-celibate traditions. That's why when he had that dream, Master Lelung said 'basta!' to being a monk – he exchanged his red and yellow robes for white ones, he stopped shaving his hair and grew it out long, and became a *ngakpa*. What Lelung taught were true teachings but he was nonetheless criticized by some of the highest monastic Gelukpa authorities, which is understandable because for them monasticism is very important.

When we talk about ourselves and our problems today, the unique teachings and approach of a master who was unconventional in his time like Lelung are perfect for us. Buddhist teachings are like the medication and our desire is the sickness. With Karmamudra, our sickness of desire receives the perfect medicine. Of course there are other, genuine medicines but they work for different, specific problems – they are the wrong medicines for the problem of desire. Medically speaking, if you have heart problems you have to take medicine for the heart and not the stomach. This is just common sense. But when it comes to spirituality, for some reason things are often

---

[14] Part of this entry states specifically that "Although he took *getshul* and *gelong* monastic vows he later relied on a number of women [i.e. Karmamudra consorts]. He is said to have had unobstructed clairvoyance and to have been a Tantric adept or *siddha*." The compilers go on to accuse Lelung Rinpoche of composing several volumes worth of texts which "mixed together Nyingma and Gelukpa teachings that don't belong together at all" and which described "practices and medical treatments [to be performed] while using a consort" *(rnying ma dang dge lugs gang la yang mi gtogs pa'i chos phar bsre tshur bsre mang po zhig dang bud med bsten skabs kyi lag len sman bcos bris ma sogs kyi dpe cha brtsams pas), 2002."*

taught in a completely opposite kind of way: you have 'heart' problems but you're told to take stomach medicine! You are filled with sexual desire but you're told open discussion about sexuality is inappropriate and you should take spiritual medicine that has nothing to do with your problem. Sometimes teachers will justify this, by saying "You have to do it this way, it's tradition!" But if you think about it, that's a ridiculous approach. I for one appreciate Lelung and Nyima Zhönnu's teachings and I think that now is the time for Lelung's more open, practical and gender-equal tradition to come back.

Both monks and non-celibate Tantric yogis or *ngakpa* are people who commit themselves to the Buddhist path of renunciation. Even though it may look like some yogis are still involved with worldly life, their renunciation can still be authentic because true renunciation is about re-orienting oneself differently in relation to the world and one's own experience. It is about living and reacting differently based on a clearer understanding of the world, of the ultimate nature of things. That is why it is important for us to understand the nature of mind as Bliss-Emptiness if we want to practice Buddhism. When we understand the blissful and empty nature of mind, it is impossible for us to be taken in by all the poisons of our ordinary mind. All of us need to renounce ordinary life and mind, but today this doesn't necessarily mean we have to give up ours jobs, our families or our worldly lives. After all, if you opt to live the full wandering yogi style today you will most likely be classified as homeless or crazy and locked up. This free, 'hippy' style doesn't work today. That's why I tell students to not think too much about these things. I tell them not to worry about whether their renunciation is good enough and to not compare themselves anxiously to great yogis of the past like Milarepa.

What does renouncing ordinary life really mean? It means that you no longer believe or invest in ordinary life and its problems. It means that you renounce depression, for example. For a lot of us today that might seem impossible. But Buddhism provides a path through which we can renounce our stress and our anxiety. That's samsara – samsara is the source of our stress and anxiety, samsara gives you panic attacks! There are ways to renounce samsara without being like Milarepa though. Sometimes people think you have to renounce everything – 'Oh I have to give up my home, my family,' but our mental dispositions, how our minds work today is different from how they did in the past. Previous practitioners hundreds of years ago like Milarepa had extremely strong minds – they could actualize that kind of renunciation and make it work, but our minds are not strong like that. Maybe previous practitioners didn't have the kinds of stress and depression we have today, perhaps our samsara is a little bit different or has a different flavor. One hears teachings on renunciation often enough but how much can we realistically renounce? And which things are really essential to renounce? Do you need to renounce your family? Or is it better for you to renounce your stress and depression? I think it's better if we think about renunciation in a new, more modern way – a twenty first century way. I love that concept. His Holiness the Dalai Lama often uses it to describe how we should practice Buddhism today. He says we should be 'twenty first century Buddhists,' practitioners who understand the rationale and meaning of the teachings, and who know how to apply them to our current circumstances without just blindly following tradition. I love that. The Dalai Lama's idea encourages us to practice with understanding. It means we should reflect on how we interpret renunciation today. We are a new generation of practitioners living in a new century. We are new people with new mentalities and new problems.

Poison as Medicine: Tantra and the Transforming of Desire

As mentioned above, according to Buddhist philosophy, the origin of all suffering is generated in our own minds. Put simply, Buddhism teaches that all beings suffer and are deluded as a result of three main mental 'poisons'. These poisons are ignorance or confusion; attachment or desire; and anger or hatred. If we look carefully, we can see that these three poisons of ignorance, desire and anger are at the root of all our psychological diseases and pain. The Buddha's use of the term 'poison' to describe this reality is very apt. To describe our mental suffering as 'poison' is not to say that poison is some sort of 'dark energy' or that poison is something irredeemably negative or that everything to do with poison is dark and evil. A poison is something dangerous, even deadly, but it is also something that can be incredibly useful. Poisons can generate all kinds of good effects and have all kinds of beneficial aspects if you know how to use them. Poisonous substances are one of the primary sources of medicine. On the other hand, medicines used incorrectly can become poisons. The wrong medicine for the wrong problem is poison. Antibiotics are a kind of poison, but if you take the right antibiotic at the right time for the right problem, they are good medicines and can cure all kinds of diseases. In Tantra, we apply special skillful methods to transform our inner poisons into wisdom. We take what is impure and make it pure. Through engaging honestly with the realities of our body, speech and mind as they are now we uncover their basic Buddha-nature and even negative or demonic appearances arise as pure and helpful expressions of our own realized potential.

One of the most common words used today is 'stress'. Why are people stressed? One main cause of stress is desire and attachment. I often say that in today's world the typical person wants to accomplish a hundred things in a single day. Why? Because of desire. And yet due to ignorance the typical person cannot see that they are unable to do all that. And what is the result when this person's desires are frustrated? Anger. That anger and frustration then makes some people depressed or turns into resentment and aggression. Seen from this perspective, it is obvious that one of our main problems today, stress, is deeply connected with the three mental poisons. As such, were we to find a remedy for the three mental poisons, then this would be the best solution for all of our mental disorders. It should be obvious now why Buddhism encourages us to start assessing our suffering and problems from the level of the mind, from an inner, psychological stand-point. While outer conditions, people and events most certainly cause us to suffer these things and the harm they can cause are nonetheless linked with our state of mind. In medicine, it is far better to work on the root cause of a disease before we get sick, rather than just treat the symptoms once we are already ill. In the same way, we need to act directly on the root of the three poisons.

If you have the proper training, then even strong afflictive emotions, strong poisons, can be used as medicine. If you feel a giant rush of anger – "I want to kill you! I'm so angry! Rrrrrraaarrr!!" – if you analyze, you realize that the essence of this anger is a kind of vital heat. When I feel angry I focus on that heat and energy and breathe it down into my red *thiglé* and then up into the crown (we will learn about this Karmamudra style of breathing in Chapter Four). If you are a master of Karmamudra then whenever you feel rage you can transform it into bliss. You feel so angry and then you turn that heat and energy into an amazing orgasm instead! It sounds funny but it's true. With this approach we don't have to go inside our minds to analyze this or that, it is not about saying "Oh, this is good, this is bad." No, we accept and make use of whatever arises. Whatever arises is workable energy. Once I was in the airport in Rome and I missed my flight to Amsterdam. Often I tell people I don't really know what stress is because I never have it. But when I missed my flight that day I felt something rising up in me, like heat, hot and quick. After I accepted I'd missed my flight, I was sitting down and meditating on this sensation, and I realized that I liked it. It was good, almost like automatic *Tummo*, or inner heat yoga. And for Karmamudra it was even better. You see, if I had stuck with that 'stress-heat', then I would have been torturing myself and my mind wouldn't have functioned clearly, but when I took the Karmamudra bliss-heat approach to the sensation, then I really liked it. Initially, I thought that maybe I should run here and there to try to do something about my flight, but then I just sat on the chair and breathed and focused on the feeling and I ended up really enjoying it. And then when my panic passed away I said, "Stress, come back, I like you!" It didn't come back though.

These practices show us that everything is energy – anger, jealousy, pride – these emotions are all energy. You let them arise and even if you start with anger or other 'bad' emotions, you end up with a happy result. That's what Karmamudra is all about. You don't say "stop having anger, stop feeling this or that emotion." Instead, you become the master of your emotions, you realize you can work with their energy and use it. That's the essence of Vajrayana. Vajrayana is the *indestructible* vehicle. What is it that is indestructible? The non-dualistic mind is indestructible, the bliss of its nature, of pristine awareness is indestructible. Nothing can destroy that bliss – suffering, pain, anger, jealousy, pride, these and all other poisons are no match for it. Vajrayana or Tantric Buddhism thus offers very fine and precise teachings and methods that allow us to transform our emotions. This inner alchemy is what Vajrayana is all about. When you feel sad or depressed, when your mind and energy have sunk down low, when you are weighed down by hopelessness and negativity, these practices can lift you up. They can transform your emotions, return you to hope and joy and bliss. We have so many poisons but, like with mercury, we can purify and refine them and turn them into medicines. This is what is known in Tibetan as *lam khyer* or *lam la khyerwa*, bringing experiences onto the path of practice, or as I like to translate it, 24/7 'portable' meditation.

Nyingma and Sarma: The Old and New Schools

Understanding the differences between the various schools of Tibetan Buddhism is important for making sense of how Tantric teachings are organized, taught and practiced. The different transmissions of teachings in Tibetan Buddhism are categorized into two groups: the lineage-teachings of the 'Old' Translation and 'New' Translation schools (*Nyingma* and *Sarma* in Tibetan). This division is a historical one. The oldest school of Vajrayana in Tibet is called the Nyingma school, or the 'School of the Ancient Ones'. When Tantric teachings first came to Tibet, the way that they were translated from Sanskrit into Tibetan and how they were organized and categorized was slightly different to how this was done when a new wave of Indian teachers came to Tibet and spread Buddhist teachings centuries later. There are three primary new schools: the Kagyü School, the Sakya School and the Geluk School. These schools have many inner divisions too. For example, there are twelve internal divisions or sub-lineages within the Kagyü, two within the Sakya school, while Gelukpa practitioners just have one.

The teachings of Master Yuthok as found in the Yuthok Nyingthig – the ones we are concerned with in this book – cut across the different schools of Tibetan Buddhism in many ways, but they are organized according to the nine-fold Nyingma (Old Translation School) scheme. In this system, Karmamudra practice is called Anuyoga, which is the second highest vehicle. Anuyoga is second only to Atiyoga, which refers to the teachings of Dzogchen or the Great Perfection. Although these vehicles are mapped out as distinct, there are some Nyingma masters who say that Anuyoga practice can be integrated with Atiyoga. We can thus see that Karmamudra is held as an extremely important teaching in the Nyingma School.

The way that the Nyingma and Sarma schools classify the more advanced Tantric yoga practices are somewhat different. In the Nyingma system the three highest of the nine vehicles – Mahayoga, Anuyoga, and Atiyoga - are called the 'Inner Yogas'. By contrast, the Sarma School usually talks about four classes of Tantras. The first three of these – Kriya Tantra, Charya Tantra and Yoga Tantra are the 'Lower' Tantras and the last and fourth is Anuttarayoga Tantra or the 'Supreme,' 'Unparalleled' or 'Highest Yoga Tantra'. The practices of the Anuttarayoga Tantra or Highest Yoga

The Nyingma school organizes Sutric and Tantric teachings according to a special 'Nine Vehicles' system

The Nine Yanas

SUTRAYANA			TANTRAYANA					
The three outer yanas leading from the origin, i.e. the three yanas related to the outer vehicle of leading from the origin [of suffering] and the three pitakas of characteristics.			The three yanas of vedic asceticism, i.e. the three yanas related to the inner vehicle of Vedic asceticism and the three outer classes of Tantra.			The three yanas of powerful transformative methods, i.e. the three yanas related to the secret vehicle of powerful transformative methods and the three inner classes of Tantra		
BASIC VEHICLE		MAHAYANA	VAJRAYANA					
Path of Renunciation			Path of Purification			Path of Transformation		
1. The Shravaka Yana	2. The Pratyeka-buddha Yana	3. The Bodhisattva Yana	4. The Yana of Kriya Tantra	5. The Yana of Charya Tantra	6. The Yana of Yoga Tantra	7. The Yana of Mahayoga	8. The Yana of Anuyoga	9. The Yana of Atiyoga

Tantras are similar and parallel to the three Inner Yogas of the Nyingma School. Whatever way we might classify them however, these are all Tantric yoga techniques which work with our body, speech/ energy and mind, they are the highest form of transformation in Tantric Buddhism. Highest Yoga Tantra works directly on our mental issues and poisons in a very profound and sophisticated way. While the three lower Tantras address the poisons in a more indirect way, Highest Yoga Tantra engages with them head on. It is like an arrow hitting a target, it goes directly to its mark. That is why these Tantric teachings and texts are described as 'highest' or 'unsurpassed'.

If you look at the chart on the previous page you will see a list of what are called the Outer and Inner Tantras in the Old School and the Lower and Higher Tantras in the New Schools. The Lower or Outer 'Vedic-like' Tantras of Kriya, Charya and Yoga exist in the Hindu tradition as well. Simply put, the Kriya and Charya Tantras say that external space is very important – you make your shrine very nice and your temple nice and clean, you wash yourself and keep yourself physically and ritually clean. With the first of the three outer Tantras everything is external. The idea is that if everything is good and orderly on the outside then that helps with your inner cleanliness, calmness and so on. The first class of outer Tantras is all about the external aspect so these texts talk about how to construct the perfect mandala, how to make your shrine and all sorts of outer, technical details. The second of the outer Tantras says external factors are not so important, your mind is important too. Perhaps your altar is not so perfect or your temple not so clean but your mind and behavior is pure. Then, with the third category of Yoga Tantra, things are half-half, your house or altar and your mind and inner condition are both relatively clean.

With Anuttarayoga Tantra things are a little different. Anuttarayoga Tantra has two main practices or components. The first one is *Kyerim* or the Creation Stage, and this relates to how we recreate ourselves in the image of the *yidam* or special Tantric deity which we meditate on. The second component is *Dzogrim* or the Completion Stage. The Six Yogas of Naropa are Completion Stage practices – all of these involve manipulations of the subtle winds, channels, energetic drops and chakras, a key feature of Completion Stage methods. Then there is Karmamudra: in the Nyingma School, Karmamudra is called Anuyoga, and is one the three Inner Yogas, as explained. But in the scheme of the New Schools, Karmamudra is found solely within Anuttarayoga

Tantra, so when adherents of the New Schools talk about the Completion Stage, Karmamudra is one of the highest forms of practice, a very advanced practice. That is part of why the New Schools insist that Karmamudra is a highly secret teaching and why it is very rare that people can receive this teaching. The New Schools consider Karmamudra to be an extremely advanced practice, so lengthy training in preliminary practices is required. The Nyingma school also requires lengthy training in preliminary practices as part of Karmamudra, but because many practitioners in this school are non-celibate and married with families slightly different kinds of Karmamudra techniques have developed in the Nyingma school. While the Nyingma School also recognizes that Karmamudra is one of the highest practices, one that leads to full Buddhahood in this lifetime, it has also preserved a range of Karmamudra practices for practitioners of varying capacities, as we can see in the teachings of the Yuthok Nyingthig, for example.

These highest Tantric teachings say we have to know what our problem is, and we have to know what our potential is. Anuttarayoga Tantra asks us to identify our problems. Maybe we have too much desire, too much jealousy, confusion, anger, pride and so on. Maybe we sleep too much or think too much. But with Anuttarayoga Tantra the things that we normally think are our problems are actually not problems at all, they are our talents or opportunities. If you have lots of sexual desire then that is good, that is your talent. But with Anuttarayoga Tantra you don't misuse that energy or desire, instead, you use it skillfully and then that brings you swift results in your spiritual practices. Anuttarayoga Tantra is like a highly skilled physician – it analyzes everyone to determine their unique talent and then diagnoses them and then they just work on that. The cleanliness of either internal or external space or conditions does not matter as much – you just focus on your particular talent and you work on that.

This is why I always say that if you really know and understand Anuttarayoga Tantra then there is always good news for you! You may have always felt that you were bad, that you were weak, negative and so on. But Anuttarayoga Tantra really empowers those weak points – it shows you that you are not weak, that those parts of yourself are not bad, but can be useful and good if properly understood. It is called the supreme or Highest Tantra, because nothing is excluded in it, all human emotions and all human experiences are included. If you talk about sexuality with Kriya or Charya

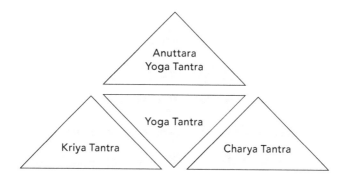

The Four Classes of Tantra according to the Sarma School

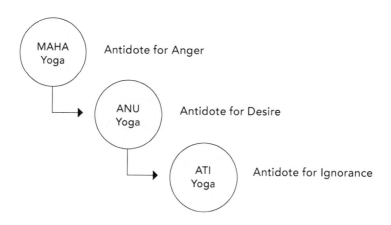

*The three Inner Yogas of the Nyingma School as antidotes
for the three mental poisons*

Tantras these teachings say "No, no, no! That's something very bad!" The first outer Tantras say "No, no!" and Yoga Tantra says "Maaaaaybe, but it's better not to," but Highest Yoga Tantra says if you have desire, then why not? This is what makes Anuttarayoga Tantra unique.

Maha, Anu, and Ati: Three Inner Yogas

The three inner yogas of the Nyingma school each correlate with one of the three inner poisons. The first inner yoga, Mahayoga, is the precise antidote for anger, it teaches us how to work with anger. The second one, Anuyoga, is the precise antidote for desire and attachment. The third one, Atiyoga is the antidote or remedy for ignorance. We have all regularly experienced and do experience the three poisons but one usually predominates over the other in particular individuals. It is thus possible to classify people into one of three groups: those individuals with more anger, those with more desire and those with more confusion. This is the power of Highest Yoga Tantra practice. It's about how to really target and work with the mental poisons as they apply to your specific life and situation.

When we talk about Anuyoga, we are dealing with desire. We can identify many different kinds of desire: the desire for nice clothes, the desire for good food, for wine, a fancy car or house, for money, fame, and for power, be it political power or spiritual power. All of this is desire, desire and more desire. There are just so many different kinds of desires: desire for chocolate, desire for tobacco, desire to travel, desire for love, desire for happiness and harmony, desire for contentment, health and well being. Of course not all desires are bad. We have many positive desires too, but it is impossible for all of our desires to be satisfied. The human mind is so huge and yet so unfulfilled because of this endless craving. I often give the example of Genghis Khan, who was historically perhaps the number one military leader and conqueror in the world. At the end of his life, he owned almost one third of this planet, but right before he died he instructed his generals to fight and conquer even more. Can you imagine? I don't mean to say that Genghis Khan was somehow the worst or most greedy person (my grandmother was actually Mongolian, so I have at least some Mongolian pride!), but what's important here is that however great or mighty Genghis Khan was, he was human and his predominant poison was desire. Desire snowballs from humble beginnings. If we don't have a house at all, then initially we desire to have just a little house, but after we get that little house, very soon it's not enough and we feel we absolutely must have a bigger, better one. Then when we get a bigger one, we suddenly need to have an entire villa. Then in the end, we are not happy with our villa because other villas are bigger and nicer than ours. Then we want to own a village, then a town, then a whole city. All of this want is driven by human desire. If we don't know how to work with our desire, this snowball effect can prove disastrous for us. It can bring us deeper and deeper into problems.

If there are so many desires, then sexual desire has to be the foremost of all of them. A great king could lose his entire kingdom just because of sexual desire. A king might have the power to control an entire empire but as a result of his sexual desire and the overwhelming power of the object of his desire, he might very well end up doing something stupid and lose everything. Someone as powerful as Genghis Khan could lose all his power, could lose one third of the whole world just because of sexual desire. If you don't believe me that it is true, then that simply means that you don't fall into the 'desire' category and are probably in the anger or confusion group instead! Of course, sexual desire is not that powerful in everyone. Many women have not even experienced orgasm and some studies state that a large percentage of women feel very low sexual desire. Many women and men may find that their main desires lie elsewhere, in food, entertainment, clothing and so on.

Finding Your Talent: Tantra's Multiple, Individualized Methods

Meditation styles linked with the Sutric Tradition, like Shamata (calm abiding) and Vipashyana (insight) meditations are great practices, but in some cases they are too general. Some people, if you tell them to calm down, will never calm down. They try so hard to do Shamata but they just don't get it, whereas other people find Shamata easy and helpful and think it is totally strange that other people don't get it. Yet it is absolutely true for those other people that their efforts to calm themselves down simply don't work. And then those people get frustrated and say, "Okay, I'm not going to practice Shamata, I've tried it, I've done it too much and nothing has happened! Now I guess I have to take tranquilizers!" This is not just a joke – it really is like that in some cases. Meditation is like medication: not every medication works for everyone. Some medicines work and some don't and there are all sorts of different reasons for this. It is the same with Vipashyana. Some people really try to see the nature of their mind, to analyze and perceive their inner clarity, but they simply don't get it. The reason for this is that we are all different people, we all have different mentalities and personalities, so that is why Vajrayana or Tantra emerges. Tantra is more personalized, it provides more individualized and targeted meditation techniques. It goes without saying that Shamata and Vipashyana are really good for many people today but I think that maybe Vajrayana meditations are more effective in some cases because of this focus on the individual.

Tantra is traditionally described by Tibetans as something that has 'many methods' *(thab mang)*, is easy to do *(kawa meypa)*, and which requires you to be 'smart', to use your own intelligence *(wang po nö(n)po)*. When many people settle down to meditate they try to calm themselves with breathing but then it doesn't work, so then they try to calm themselves by focusing on external objects and then that doesn't work, so they try everything and none of it works and then they just say, "Ok, I don't want to get calmness anymore, I want to get crazy! I need madness!" So, these people make up their minds, make their decision, and then suddenly, ironically, they are calm! Sometimes it's like this. It's the same with sleep: sometimes you can't sleep, you want to sleep so badly and try so hard, until finally you give up and tell yourself "Okay, fine! I don't want to sleep, I want to meditate!" Then you start to meditate and you fall asleep! Our personal experiences with meditation techniques like Shamata are very individual which is why Vajrayana is so important and necessary. Vajrayana offers many different kinds of methods to suit all individuals. For example, Vajrayana talks a lot about chanting mantras and singing. Chanting is a typical Tantric type of meditation. Just sitting in silence and meditating, your mind is often too busy and you can't calm down but then if you start to sing, your mind focuses and calms down right away. This is what is called 'chanting contemplation'. In a similar fashion, with Vajrayana, instead of telling your mind, 'Relax, don't think about anything!" You tell your mind, "Think! Imagine! Fantasize!" Many meditation practices say, 'Don't think!" "Don't imagine!" "Don't dream!" "Don't, don't, don't!" But in a certain way Vajrayana says "Do! Do! Do!" If you like some activity, if you're partial to it, then you do it, in a full and skillful way. If your mind is thinking too much you have to know that that is the nature of your mind and so allow your mind think. The problem is not necessarily that you don't know how to calm your mind, the problem is maybe that you don't push it enough to think as much as it possibly can, as fully or as excessively as it can. The funny thing is is that if you really push your mind to think more and more, your mind eventually exhausts itself and its capacity.

Our mind is like a little baby – the problem really starts when you make the baby sit or try to shut him or her up. Beyond all our elaborations and justifications, our mind is really just like that baby, it goes along without any particular plans or programs. It goes this way and that way, but the real problem starts when we tell the baby "Don't run, don't touch, don't go, don't play! Don't don't!" And then of course they want to do more. If you let the child become very wild and go every which way, then he or she comes back tired and falls asleep. Our mind works in exactly the same way, so that's how Vajrayana skillfully teaches us to work with our mind. Working with our mind is not only a question of control, it is a question of mastery. You can let your mind indulge in thinking and still have mastery over it, or you can even let your mind get angry. You can train your mind with anger so that meditation is not about stopping or blocking your anger but about processing it and working with it in empowering ways.

The type of experience we talk about in Vajrayana is not just some kind of general experiences, it is about each of our personal experiences and realization. Each individual can experience things in different ways. For example, some people may be very talented in sleeping and may experience the power of meditation in sleep, that is why we have Dream and Sleep Yoga. Let's say we have two brothers, two twins. One brother might love to sleep and be very good at it, maybe he can sleep for hours and hours without waking and he has many dreams. Yet the other brother might hate sleeping because he sees it as a waste of time and wants to sleep as little as possible so that he can experience the waking world as fully as he can. This is the essence of Vajrayana: two brothers of almost identical age, with the same family, the same background and education, even the same appearance, but they have two different mentalities. Meditation approaches like Shamata say, "It doesn't matter whether you like to sleep or not, use this approach." Everyone uses the same method, there is equivalent and equal training. Monks and nuns' training, this more Sutric approach, is a little bit like army training

– you all have to receive that training and you all have do it equally to earn your titles and status, and that's it. You don't bring your personal conditions with you.

In the Tantric approach, these sorts of individual conditions are very important. If one brother loves to sleep and he remembers his dreams, he can do Dream Yoga, or if he doesn't remember them he can do Deep Sleep or 'Clear Light' Yoga. And for the one who likes to explore and experience the waking world, he can do the second daytime yoga, 'Illusory Body Yoga'. This yoga is all about how you experience your life, your waking self. When we are awake there is one waking 'I' here, then when we go to sleep and dream there is another 'I' in the dream. We always have this idea of self, but as our state of consciousness changes we identify with different persons as our 'I' or self. Sometimes our 'I' is here, seemingly in our body in waking life, but then there is another 'I' in our thoughts. When that 'I' is running around, having all kinds of troubles, then we completely forget about the other 'I' because the self in our head is getting into trouble! This 'I' is sitting so nicely in meditation posture but that other stupid self in our thoughts is having all sorts of problems. It is the same in dreams, sometimes we get into trouble in the dream-state as well. One 'I' is lying in bed sleeping and snoring and doing fine, but somebody else is saying "Me! Mine! Myself..." in the dream and getting into all sorts of stories! So, this is what we call Illusory Body Yoga. Our perception of self is shifting and mirage-like, our perception of our physical self is shifting and illusory, the self running around in our thoughts is illusory, the one in our dreams is also illusory. So, if you're someone who likes to explore and experience the waking world then Illusory Body Yoga can allow you to realize the nature of your illusory self or selves and teach you how to not get lost in these.

The point is we can't just train both brothers in one meditation. Both of them can and should find their own personalized path or approach. Vajrayana is known as the 'many methods, not difficult' approach. Today many people meditate and discover that meditation is very difficult. Why is this? If somebody has a sleeping problem, if they suffer from insomnia, then doing sleeping meditation is obviously very difficult. If you force yourself to go to sleep, you experience all kinds of resistance. That is what difficulty means, going against your tendencies. If one brother hates sleeping and then someone says to him, "You have to sleep, you have to do Sleep Yoga!" then of course it will be difficult for him, but for his brother it will be difficult to stop sleeping. So that is why Vajrayana says that if you sleep a lot then you should integrate your sleep into meditation, if you like exploring waking life, then you integrate that. The result will be exactly the same: one brother will wake up through sleeping and one will 'wake up' through exploring waking life. There are many, many people who say, "Oh, I know that meditation is good, but it's so difficult!" This is actually true, students learn that they have to sit still and in uncomfortable postures for long periods of time, of course it's difficult! It is a generalized training, whether it suits your tendencies doesn't really matter. But if you practice Vajrayana then you really have to find out what your nature is and what your preferences are. In a way, with Vajrayana, you meditate on what you love or prefer to do. You are not forced to meditate on something that disagrees with you. Many people have difficulties because they are forced to do this or that meditation and then they get meditation burn-out and spiritual exhaustion, or spiritual panic attacks! With some people you just have to say the word 'meditation' and they react terribly. "Oh, no meditation! I can't breathe!" It can happen and does happen for many people.

Vajrayana meditation methods are designed for our individual intelligence or talent, they are about recognizing that we are smart. In a certain sense, according to Vajrayana we are all smart, there are no stupid people. Maybe you are very smart in art and artistic activities but when it comes to doing mathematics you are stupid. You cannot judge your intelligence only in terms of your capacity to do mathematics, that's not your thing. Your thing is art – in art you are excellent, really good, you're a genius! So, in that way, everyone is super smart and intelligent, everyone is a genius. Some people are so talented at just thinking and thinking – they think of everything, they never stop thinking! Of course if they don't meditate, they get lost in all their thoughts and that becomes a problem, but if they can integrate their talent for thinking into their meditation practice, then that helps them to wake up and to be liberated.

Some people are super talented at anger. I once met an Italian man who was ninety-six years old, my oldest student, a very strong and fit man. He came to talk to me and told me that he had some health issues. So, I spoke with him and he explained, "My main problem is anger." I asked, "Who are you angry with?" And he said, "My wife!" I asked where his wife was and he said very angrily, "She's DEAD!!" His wife had died thirty years prior and he was still angry with her. He told me that because of all his anger towards his wife – "You are dead and I don't want to die! So, I'll eat good food, exercise!", something like that – he actually extended his life. I thought, "How cool!" This was his talent! At first I said to him, "It sounds like you have some kind of trauma connected with your wife? Just let it go," and he said, "NO! I can't let it go! Impossible!" And so I said, "Good then! I can give you some angry mantras that will increase your anger," and he said, "Oh! That's great!" I gave him a wrathful Hayagriva mantra which is meant to be chanted aggressively and he loved it. This mantra includes the repetition of the mantra syllables HULU HULU! which to him sounded like the word culo or 'asshole' in Italian which helped to refine his anger even more! Through using this approach I think he was able to gain some very special meditative experiences. If I had told him to deny or to block his anger things might have gone worse for him, he might have had a heart attack.

In the same way, some people are super talented in jealousy. Jealousy is a very disturbing feeling, but if you really use and integrate that feeling then one day you will thank your jealousy. You won't feel bad or guilty about the arising of your jealousy, you'll feel really grateful. "Wow, thank you jealousy! You really helped me to understand everything – how my mind works, how my emotions work!". None of us should think we are not smart enough to practice meditation. All you need to do is find out which of the poisons or afflictive emotions you are really good at. Interestingly, many Vajrayana meditations also work very well for kids. Somehow, children are able to practice some of these methods on their own, without formal instruction. For example, many young children have bad dreams but they are naturally able to wake themselves up in their dream and work with their nightmares. They become lucid so that they can transform their dreams, which is exactly what Dream Yoga teaches us to do. This suggests to me that when it comes to real spirituality and real intelligence, we have this as an innate part of our human nature. It is like a kind of instinctive wisdom or knowledge, a sort of intelligence that we are all born with. The problem often comes later when we go to school and get brainwashed by norms, formal education, and society. We really lose our inner spiritual power and ability, our intelligence, and then we get depressed.

The Antidote for Desire and the Antidote for Ignorance: Karmamudra, Mahamudra and Progress on the Path

As I mentioned previously, two different mudras or seals are taught in the Yuthok Nyingthig: Karmamudra, which is the path or technology of the 'Lower Gates of Great Bliss', and Mahamudra, which is the path of the 'Upper Gates of Great Liberation'. What this means is that if you don't like orgasm, if you have decreased sexual desire, cannot generate bliss, if you're asexual or a monk or nun, you shouldn't feel hopeless. Yuthok explains that there is another approach, that of the *trekchö* or 'Cutting through Hardness' Mahamudra practices, which is appropriate for the elderly or for people with diminished sexual desire or impotency. Mahamudra and Atiyoga (Dzogchen) practices also suit older people because you might say the elderly's special power is over-thinking or worrying about everybody! Just as you need a lot of desire as fuel for Karmamudra, with Mahamudra and Atiyoga you need lots of thoughts to work with. Mahamudra is precisely designed for cutting through this kind of excessive conceptuality, it is quite an elegant approach, really. If you have too many thoughts you do Mahamudra, if you have too many desires you do Karmamudra. If you have both, you do both. As esoteric as these things seem to be, it's really quite simple and practical because it works with the circumstances of our life as they are. You can do Mahamudra before work in the morning and Karmamudra in the bedroom in the evening! These two paths or 'seals' are two different ways to transform your mind: the one, Karmamudra, relies directly on the *thiglé*, chakras and other elements of the Vajra Body, and the other Mahamudra, which we can do even if the *thiglé* have dried up, is literally the 'Great Seal', sign or gesture, or what I like to call 'the Big Slap' which jolts you out of the confusion and duality of conceptual mind.

Mahamudra and Atiyoga are often explained using all kinds of complicated and technical descriptions. You will hear all sorts of talk about 'formlessness', 'non-conceptuality' and so on, which can get quite confusing. But simply, in its most naked form, Mahamudra is a kind of meditation that uses and works with thoughts. Many of us have too many thoughts, we think too much and this meditation teaches us how to work with these thoughts. Mahamudra doesn't say, "Don't think too much!" It says "Go ahead! Think! Imagine!" With Mahamudra you stop trying to control things – you let your mind be active and then through thinking you realize non-conceptuality.

If you suffer from over-thinking – from excessive worrying, thinking about your traumas, fantasizing, and so on – then you practice Mahamudra, and as a result your thoughts and thinking stop being a problem and become an opportunity. They become something that offers the potential for liberation. With Mahamudra you use your thoughts to liberate yourself from thoughts. Then when you really understand the practice, even if you want to produce more thoughts, you will find that you are free from them – that is why the final stage of Mahamudra is called *gom mey*, 'without meditation'.

In Vajrayana it is really important to know the key or essential points about different practices. When it comes to Mahamudra and Atiyoga, you can read so many books, hundreds and hundreds of pages about what Mahamudra is, how it is classified and so on, but what can end up happening is that you get lost in these pages, you become an expert in 'book Mahamudra' and little else. Mahamudra can get very theoretical, but in essence what it is talking about is thought – it is all about thoughts: thoughts of the past, of the present, of the future. By thinking too much and getting caught up in all of these we normally get lost and it becomes a problem. But Mahamudra says that our thinking is like a super-power, it says that we need to let our minds think and be mindful, that we need to have awareness. It says that even if our mind doesn't want to think we should push it to do so – to experience anger, fear, anxiety, to have all emotional expressions. Once the mind has experienced everything it is finally relaxed. It is a bit like a person who spends ten years indulging in everything – alcohol, drugs, partying, anything they can get their hands on, happiness, despair, everything – then after ten years they say, "Ok, basta! enough!" Of course, Mahamudra is not saying that you should go smoke and drink and swallow pills with abandon. Still, our addictive and indulgent behaviors go with our thoughts and feelings. Mahamudra is the 'Great Seal', the all-encompassing basic awareness that includes everything, every aspect of our conceptual life. As a method it can liberate us from all the ways in which our thoughts, feelings and concepts can keep us in bondage.

People often ask about the difference between Atiyoga or Dzogchen and Mahamudra. Many explanations of the differences between these two focus on sectarian differences, on the different schools of Tibetan Buddhism and their different histories. Simply put, however, the first 'formless' stage of Atiyoga which is called *trekchö* or 'cutting through the hardness (of thoughts)' is almost one hundred percent the same as Mahamudra. Where Atiyoga *trekchö* and Mahamudra differ is mostly in their methods and vocabularies. Mahamudra has four yogas: 1) single-pointedness, 2) non-elaboration, 3) one taste and 4) non-meditation, while Atiyoga has four steps or stages: 1) the non-existence or emptiness of thoughts and mind, 2) uniqueness, 3) all-pervading, and 4) all-spontaneous, completely and naturally accomplished. Where Atiyoga diverges from Mahamudra is in its later stage which is called *thögal*. This 'form' stage of Atiyoga deals with meditations using light and darkness, and includes intensive dark retreat. These practices are not found in Mahamudra and are unique to Atiyoga. So, while the base of Atiyoga and Mahamudra is the same, when it comes to the techniques, Atiyoga has something extra. *Thögal* means 'crossing the skull' and these practices are especially linked with the attainment of the rainbow body. With *thögal* everything we have inside our head chakra, everything in our Vajra Body manifests before us in our vision. With Atiyoga what your third or 'wisdom' eye of inner vision sees can be seen by your two physical eyes too. Everything manifests in space, you can see inwardly and also project it outwards. All of this is connected to the nature of light, which is why the final stage of Atiyoga is the rainbow or light body in which the human physical body or form is transformed into pure light or rainbow. In sum then, if you practice Atiyoga or Mahamudra and you are very good at either one, then if you practice the other system you'll be very good at that as well.

Karmamudra is the appropriate medicine for those of us with great sensual desires. That said, these practices are not wholly separate, and there are ways to segue into Atiyoga from Anuyoga. Rebkong Karmamudra masters have done and still do this – they practice Atiyoga style sadhanas where the two paths are not entirely separate[15]. This underlying compatibility or integration between different kinds of yogas is a key point. When you master Dream Yoga, for example, and truly understand what this practice is about, then the illusory body that is part of advanced Karmamudra practice is already there, you already understand it. The different yogas complement each other. In the same way, if you're really good with *Tummo*, then Dream Yoga comes automatically. So on one level while the Six Yogas, Karmamudra, Mahamudra and so on may seem like highly systematic, sequential, orderly and distinct practices, they are necessarily unified. They are all about your own mind – all of these yogas are the same in that they are all methods for realizing and sustaining the Clear Light mind, they are all united by the common basis of awareness. How then can we parcel out or separate our mind?

Still, these yogas can differ in their approaches or orientations in ways that can confuse some practitioners. Mahamudra and Atiyoga teachings sometimes say that you do not need to worry about practices for purifying the body, speech and mind or the channels, wind, drops (*tsa, loong, thiglé*). Because these are ultimate teachings that go beyond all else, you will sometimes hear that Mahamudra and Atiyoga dispense with or make all other methods null and void. These teachings are very simple but for that reason they are very hard to get. One of my favorite sayings that relates to Atiyoga and Mahamudra is "simplicity is the ultimate complexity or sophistication." This is very true, but when people miss that simplicity, if they fail to grasp the essential point of Mahamudra and Atiyoga it is very dangerous. These days a lot of people misunderstand Mahamudra and Atiyoga. They think that because they do some Mahamudra or Dzogchen practices they are now beyond all categories, that good or bad or everyday morality doesn't apply to them, that they are completely free of karma just because they have a vague intellectual understanding of what the Great Seal or the Great Perfection teaches. I come across this a lot all over the world. "I practice Dzogchen! I know Mahamudra! I don't need anything else!" This is a very scary situation, and many of the great Mahamudra and Atiyoga masters of the past warned about it. They said, "Don't separate the view of Atiyoga from your behavior, from your compassion." You encounter a lot of people who think that talking about Mahamudra and Atiyoga means that they can commit any act, that they can kill animals, or who knows, even people! "I know Mahamudra, so I can shoot you!" It's scary, and makes me think that sometimes it's better not to teach Mahamudra to people when they are not ready. There is the danger that people can receive a few Mahamudra instructions, miss the subtlety or ultimate point of them, and then jump to all sorts of wild conclusions and delude themselves.

Considering these dangers, it is interesting that today giving teachings on Mahamudra and Atiyoga is more common and less controversial than

---

[15] See the Appendices for a translation of one such Ati-Anuyoga combined sadhana from the great master Tokden Shakya Shri.

talking publicly about Karmamudra. Just like Yuthok says, I think it is better to focus when you are younger on Karmamudra and then to turn to Mahamudra later. The reason for this is not just that younger people tend to have stronger sexual desire, but also because the Karmamudra approach is very experiential – even though it is a fast path it is a lot more gradual and tangible than Mahamudra, which I think actually makes it a lot safer. The Karmamudra meditations in this book contrast with more familiar, very mind-focused Buddhist meditation methods like Shamata meditation in one key way. With Shamatha, it can actually be very difficult to determine where you are at in your practice, it is not always so easy to assess how you are progressing. It may be difficult to express your experiences, to articulate the level or quality of your mental focus and so on to your teacher, and your teacher cannot necessarily rely on telepathy to read your mind and see for sure where you're at in your practice. It is very important with meditation to know your level and to not delude or set unreasonable expectations for yourself. Just like with sport or any form of physical exercise, you have to be able to assess your capacity and measure where you are at in your practice. Many masters might say this is a ridiculous idea, that you shouldn't try to measure or judge your meditation – you should just practice without fixation on results or your progress. This is very good advice. Nevertheless, Vajrayana methods are unique in that they allow us to measure our progress quite precisely, in ways that leave little to no room for confusion, delusion or ambiguity. This is why the Tantric path is described as the 'Swift Path.' In general, the Sutric approach is much slower and does not focus as much on meditative experiences of bliss and clarity and it is also not as thorough at explaining the mechanisms of these experiences.

Earlier I mentioned 'portable' '24/7' meditation, that is, bringing your meditation experience into your everyday life. These sorts of Vajrayana practices are a quick and convenient kind of alchemy. When you wake up in the middle of the night and feel sad, say, this is the best time to practice. You catch that sad feeling then transform the energy of it into bliss and joy. You transform your mind into the turquoise light of Yuthok's seed-syllable HUNG, you think to yourself, "My mind is the turquoise HUNG, my mind is happiness – the underlying nature of my mind is not sadness, it is joy, it is bliss". If you can take the essence of disturbing emotions and transmute their energy into bliss and selfless emptiness, that is a sign that your meditation is somewhat grounded or stable. Without these signs, one can easily become an old 'experienced' but nevertheless misguided practitioner, full of ego. The problem here is that we don't have a clear sign showing whether our meditation is working or not. It is much better to work from pure experience, thousands of empty words don't work. If you can transform your sadness, this is a sign that your meditation is working.

Scientists don't yet fully understand the interplay of hormones and consciousness, nor do they fully understand orgasm, and especially not subtle orgasmic states like in Karmamudra. Some practitioners are content with the blissful experiences that they experience from solitary meditation and feel no need to engage with partners. The Sutric system describes the possibility of experiencing highly refined states of mind-and-body bliss from practicing Shamata and Vipashyana, but the nature and components of these experiences are not explained in any kind of detail. In contrast, Vajrayana provides a wealth of technical details and instruction on these things. We can liken these two approaches to two different ways to warm up an object. The Sutric approach is like rubbing our hands together and then holding the object to heat it up. It is a slow and stable way to warm it. The Tantric approach, in contrast, is like bringing the object directly to a fire that you know is blazing right in front of you, as close as you need to warm the object up to the necessary temperature.

As I mentioned in the previous section, ultimately, the real key point is this: which method is truly practical for you? Are you really serious about practicing Atiyoga? Do you actually do Atiyoga every day or not? Are you really serious about Mahamudra, about one yoga, are you really doing the practice every day and are you really connected with it or not? Many people say they practice or want to practice Mahamudra or this or that yoga but they are not really connected. One of the advantages with Karmamudra is that there is a strong focus on embodied feeling and bliss. This is something almost everyone can appreciate. You don't get lazy with these things – very often your body itself reminds and encourages you to practice. This is another reason why Karmamudra is described as an 'easy' path. You have a good, strong motivation to practice. One problem common to most other practices is that when our body and mind is tired, then we don't do the practice. But if your body is awake, aroused, if your body has a need, then when you practice it works better, you see results faster.

This sort of tangible, demonstrable progress is an important aspect of Tantric Buddhism. Tibetan masters like Yuthok, who achieved the rainbow body of the Greater Transference, in which one's body dissolves into rainbow-colored light when one passes away, demonstrated this sort of spiritual accomplishment publicly. Master Yuthok deliberately called together his students and whole crowds of people before he died and demonstrated this attainment right in front of them. He sang his final teaching song and then dissolved into light. If there had been a camera there we could have documented this event. It's a pity cameras didn't exist back then – it would have been better than a Hollywood movie! Rainbow body live-streaming! Some people might frown at this idea. Normally, of course, the rainbow body process is somewhat secret – a master practitioner's body is left covered in a tent, and is not to be disturbed for fear of disrupting the process[16], and only a select few people watch the changes unfolding directly. With most rainbow body stories, rainbow body attainments are secret, but Yuthok had the confidence to make his transformation public, and did so. No one attacked him then for making his rainbow body public, but then again, there weren't any journalists at that time!

Traditionally, there are certain external signs that occur during retreat – the butter for the lamp lasts for twelve days miraculously instead of four, you smell a good smell of incense in your retreat room, and so on. When I was doing a *chudlen* or elixir extraction retreat practice many years ago in Tibet I stayed in a cave about 5000 meters above sea level, and during that time I had many olfactory and auditory external signs. I smelled delicious smells and heard music coming from the rocks. Of course, I was happy, but these things are not really important, what's important are the more internal signs, what really counts is mental transformation. The sign that matters is that in your mind you feel youthful and happy all the time. You experience mental rejuvenation, your mind isn't old and full of problems. Today we should not search too much for outer signs – "Oh, I did that meditation, there was a special sign, I saw one particular animal omen" and so on. The best meditation involves inner signs. You are able to perceive directly that through your meditation practice you are able to do some little tricks with your mind, that you are able to transform your mind and your emotions.

All this is to say that being able to track your progress, being able to tangibly feel and demonstrate the extent of your meditation is really important. It is really important to be able to gauge the grounded-ness and efficacy of your practice. Just accumulating endless amounts of recitations, prostrations, or even experiencing miraculous outer signs doesn't really reveal anything. This is why the methods and practices found in Vajrayana are so special. With Shamatha, you can easily convince yourself that you have achieved mental stability and 'peaceful abiding', even though your mind is just dull, sleepy or dissociative. When it comes to Tantric methods like Karmamudra, however, things are much more tangible, observable. You either have sexual desire and arousal, or you don't. You either feel heat in your body, or you don't. You can tell unambiguously whether you have made progress, whether you've developed control over your body, your muscles, your energy – whether you have obtained mastery over your mind and bliss.

---

[16] There are three main types of rainbow body attainment. The rainbow body of Greater Transference is when a practitioner dissolves completely into light, leaving absolutely no trace of their physical body behind. As in the case of Yuthok, this can be a fairly quick process. Alternatively, practitioners may dissolve into light but leave minimal physical remains: finger nails, hair or their shoes, and so on. The third option is when practitioners' bodies shrink dramatically after death – usually over the course of about a week – until their entire body is about the size of that of a toddler or large cat. When this occurs the practitioner's head remains its original size. Interfering with a practitioner's body or space while they are meditating in preparation for 'transference' or during the extended dying process that takes place after the body has become lifeless by biomedical standards, even in subtle ways, can block dissolution entirely or lessen the extent of attainment, which is why access to practitioners' corpses is traditionally restricted, at least initially. Cases of the rainbow body have been documented in Tibet up until as recently as a few decades ago – see Tiso (2016) for more information.

Worldly versus Wisdom Sex

The Goals and Benefits of Kamasutra and Karmamudra

The discussion of renunciation and yogic training brings us back to the subject of worldly versus spiritual sex. In Chapter One, I mentioned that many people today confuse Karmamudra with Kamasutra, which is a set of teachings about 'secular' and not spiritual or 'Tantric' sex like many people believe. While the teachings of the Kamasutra are most probably very old, they were organized into their best known form in Sanskrit by the scholar and poet Vatsyayana in the second century C.E. There are eight main practices in Kamasutra that are expanded out into sixty four practices in total. By contrast, Indian Tantric master Padmasambhava introduced Karmamudra practices to Tibet in the eight century C.E. Prior to Padmasambhava's arrival in Tibet, Karmamudra had been incorporated into the monastic traditions of the great Buddhist university Nalanda in Bihar, India, and Karmamudra practices were a key part of some of the most important Tantric scriptures studied there. Yet, at the same time we know that Kamasutra style instructions have had a long history in Tibet as well, and the study and practice of Kamasutra teachings has been an important part of Karmamudra in Tibet.[17]

---

[17] For more on this question, see Tibetan Studies scholar Sarah Jacoby's recent article which discusses the significance of Ju Mipham's Kamasutra text and the existence of Kamasutra material in the Tibetan *tengyur*, or collection of translated canonical commentaries. (Jacoby, 2017)

The following chart summarizes some of the key differences between Kamasutra and Karmamudra:

KAMASUTRA goals and benefits	KARMAMUDRA goals and benefits
Worldly enjoyment and pleasure	Rebalanced energy (through the transformation of karmic winds into wisdom winds)
Psychological balance	Experiencing clear light (through the increase of *thiglé*)
Improved relationship with partner	Transformed negative or afflictive emotions
Physical health	Spiritual enlightenment
Improved social standing and stability	Recognition of the true nature of mind and achievement of the Rainbow Body

In ancient India Kamasutra or Kamashastra was the ordinary or worldly approach to engaging in sex. In the Tibetan language Kamasutra is directly translated as *Döbay Tenchö* or the 'Treastises on Desire' and it is said to have originally come from the God of Desire, Shiva. As mentioned, the main subject of the Kamasutra is the 'sixty-four arts of desire'. These are divided into eight sections: embracing; kissing; scratching; biting; uniting (penetrating); moaning; games or stimulation for women's genitals; and equivalent ones for women to do with men, each with eight divisions, making sixty four. These are the root of the Indian Kamasutra. Today many people think Kamasutra is just about uncomfortable sex positions and that it is boring. Of course, the paintings that accompany these teachings do show various positions, but the ultimate point of these, the real meaning of Kamasutra, is to understand sexuality. Sexuality is an art. Kamasutra is not just about sex positions, it is about understanding relationships, about understanding attraction, the senses, human interaction and ways of thinking and feeling. Kamasutra deals with psychology, medical traditions, and with cultivating relationships and resolving problems between men and women in actual, everyday life. Although the heart of the core scriptures of the Kamasutra probably appeared about 2500 years ago, today the Kamasutra has spread and continues to spread all over the world and across international borders.

The influence of Kamasutra can be felt all over the world. While there are still a few practitioners of these specifically Indian forms of Tantric methods today, for the most part the traditional teachings of non-Buddhist Tantra have greatly diversified and have become somewhat mixed up with other religious systems. As a result of the deterioration and adulteration of these lineages it is very hard to find sources that offer clear explanations on the practice. Some renowned Indian Buddhist *ngakpa* did receive direct oral instructions, however, which have continued to be passed down continually from teacher to student until today. In China, the Han dynasties recognized sexual intercourse as a religious practice and there are clear practices involving penetrative intercourse in Taoism in particular. The so-called 'bedroom arts' or *fángzhōngshù* explain the bliss of uniting the two sexual organs and how elderly male practitioners in particular can obtain things like siddhis or spiritual powers of longevity and immortality by having sex with young women. The main practices involve balancing the vital winds of one's body and relaxing or loosening the mind. More specifically, during sex, the man draws up the woman's constitutive essence or else does practices similar to drawing up the *thiglé*. There are multiple practical instructions on how to retain the white male sexual energy without ejaculating by relying on techniques like pressing on the lower channels (near the perineum, for example) while one is having sex. In any case it is extremely clear that the primary origin of all these methods is Chinese Taoism. Unfortunately, with the spread of Confucianism Taoist sexual practices deteriorated and many inferior practitioners appeared. The main reason for this was because sexual intercourse was regarded as something impure by Confucianism and as a result these practices were put to an end and prohibited.

Similar traditions of sensual refinement and sexual cultivation have also spread throughout Japan. There we find ancient depictions of sexual intercourse with special characteristics and of young women skilled in the art of the *geisha*, who in general are not prostitutes but are girls or young women who work as highly trained hostesses. Over the centuries, some of these women who were experts in beguiling men through exceptional forms of song, dance, and conduct were also trained in the art of sexual intercourse, although this was not their original purpose. Given that the work of female sex workers is by far one of the oldest businesses there is, if one is highly skilled or qualified in it, then if nothing else it is 'traditional' work and should be respected rather than seen as something dirty. If female sex workers are impure then the male clients who have sex with them would surely have to be too, and in that case the number of men in the world today who could be called 'pure' would be very low! Legal business and activities relating to sex work in which precautions against disease are taken are completely legitimate. There's no reason to have a low opinion of sex workers and their trade or to belittle them or treat them with contempt. Just like in the Tantric tradition, there may well be a number of Dakinis hidden within the ranks of professional sex workers. No one should insult women – whether sex workers or not, they are all *rigma*, or embodiments of Pristine Awareness or Wisdom.

Among Wetstern nations, France was a key context for sexual revolution and many revolutionary activities relating to sex and desire emerged there. Western countries underwent political and cultural revolution in multiple ways. In Austria, through the influence of the psychological book written by founder of psychology Sigmund Freud (1856-1939) called 'Psychology and Sexual Freedom,' the so-called 'sexual revolution' took place until 1910, and this revolution or 'sexual liberation' became particularly widespread between the years of 1960 and 1980. The primary objectives of this revolution involved moving sexual mores beyond the restrictions of cultural and religious traditions to support and destigmatize such things as sexual relationships before marriage, contraception and sterilization, public nudity, masturbation, the use of dildos, sex toys and so on, oral and anal penetration, formal sex work, homosexuality, and increased public discussion about sex. Since that time, films, books and other things relating to sex and sexuality have sprung up like mushrooms and spread everywhere. Today, books and movies about sex have clearly become commodities. The main purpose or incentive for their production is economic. Nonetheless, following the sexual revolution, sexual practices in Western countries became very open-minded and relaxed, and no matter how much Christian authorities forbid or refuted these things, they found no way to put a stop to such sexual freedoms.

Today, many people in the West's exposure to Tantric sex comes from New Age or neo-Tantric sources. Many of these sources draw on ideas and practices from traditional Indian, Tibetan and Chinese religions but they have their own complicated histories and lineages. Individuals who teach this kind of New Age Tantra often claim that their practices are ancient or come from non-Western sources but often what these individuals are practicing is influenced as much by Western sex magic traditions (developments in Western esotericism mostly consolidated in the Victorian period that focus on the harnessing of sexual energy and orgasm to manipulate reality) as by traditional Hindu and Buddhist Tantra (which is part of much bigger religious and cultural contexts across Asia). Neo-Tantric practices are often more about what can be called 'sacred sexuality' and sexual self-help. Some New Age Tantra teachings include chakras and subtle energy more than others. In most cases these teachings are a mixture of different things. These teachings are not necessarily bad and many good people practice them and benefit a lot. My usual advice to students, however, is to make an effort to understand the different features, histories and intentions of different so-called Tantric or sacred spirituality traditions, and to avoid mixing these together. It is fine if you have received teachings or empowerments for different practices or lineages, but it is better to practice these separately. Keep these separate – taking this piece from one tradition and that piece from another one leads to confusion and can cause problems. Even within one lineage of teachings it is not a good idea to go on retreat and mix together elements of two or more sadhanas together. Meditations and rituals should be kept distinct for the best results.

It is important to note that Kamasutra is not a Tantric teaching. It does not include any of the methods for pulling up the *thiglé* or stimulating the chakras, or any of the traditional practices for generating the primordial wisdom of bliss-emptiness that are key to Tibetan Karmamudra and are also found in both the outer and inner Tantras of the Indian tradition. When I say the teachings of the Kamasutra are 'worldly' and not spiritual, I mean that they focus on the cultivation and refinement of worldly desire, and offer everyday advice on love, marriage and sensory pleasure for householders or non-monastics. According to ancient Indian thought there are four main pursuits in human life, which individuals ought to pursue as best they can in order to live a fulfilled existence and contribute to a harmonious society. In the Indian system, these four pursuits are: Dharma, Artha, Kama, and Moksha. Here, Dharma does not refer to the teachings of the Buddha, but signifies moral conduct, duty or ethics. Artha is commerce, business, power and material success, and Kama, as mentioned above, is 'desire'. Moksha, the last of the four, means 'Liberation' and refers to the ultimate goal of human existence: spiritual liberation or freedom from worldly attachments, illusions, and suffering.

What is important to note here is that even though mastery and refinement of worldly life – success in business, marriage and relationships and so on are superseded by spiritual liberation, these things can also set the stage for spiritual accomplishment down the line. Though the teachings of the Kamasutra are thus more secular in focus and are not Buddhist teachings about how to pass beyond worldly concerns and suffering and realize Buddha-nature, they nevertheless have become an important part of Karmamudra in the Tibetan tradition. As mentioned in Chapter One, the great Tibetan scholar Ju Mipham Namgyal Gyatso (1846-1912) compiled his own Kamasutra instruction text called *The Treasure Loved by Everyone in the World: A Treatise on Desire*[18] in the 19th century. This text is significant because in this text Mipham integrates Kamasutra and Karmamudra principles and practices. At one point in his text after describing different positions for penetrative sex, Mipham explains:

"Through making thorough use of these many methods which cause desire or arousal, your physical body will become supple and you will be able to experience unparalleled bliss. You will subdue your channels and conquer the winds or loong and will discover the primordial wisdom of bliss. Equipped with these practical, esoteric instructions on Karmamudra, you will be able to release your individual channel-knots. However, if you engage in sexual union without knowing how to do these things, your three humors of loong, treepa and beken will become imbalanced and this will stir up humoral diseases, so for this reason make use of the 'wisdom method of union' [Karmamudra] after you have become skilled in the 'worldly method of union' [Kamasutra]."
(Mipham 1984)

When I first encountered Master Mipham's teaching I was very young. I thought to myself, 'How could this be?!' I didn't agree with him. I didn't understand how samsaric and nirvanic sex could be combined in this way. But later, as I studied and practiced and learned more, I realized that what he was saying was so true. To be able to practice Karmamudra you need

---

[18] *död pay tsen chö jigten kuntu gawey ter* in Tibetan.

to be sexually experienced and have a deeper understanding of desire and relationships. In our normal sexuality, there are always misunderstandings which is why I think Kamasutra is so important. Kamasutra was originally pitched at lay people and its aim was to enhance sexual pleasure and understanding. Kamasutra recognizes that whether we like it or not, sexuality is a part of our lives, so why don't we enjoy and refine it? Why don't we make it an open subject, talk about and share ideas about it?

Lelung, Ju Mipham and Gendün Chöphel all worked in their own ways to develop approaches that brought together worldly and spiritual sex. Gendün Chöphel's Kamasutra was written using the sixty four arts of desire which explain sex from a primarily worldly perspective as its foundation, but his text drew on his own experiences and opinions as well. It is very clear that the basis of his book is the India Kamasutra(s) and he says clearly that his treatise is about the worldly approach to sex. Nonetheless, several views or perspectives from the Secret Mantra are cited in Gendün Chöphel's book (he quotes from the *sadhana* section of the Kalachakra Tantra in one place, for example). Still, even though he quotes things that lean a little towards the Secret Mantra, he does not disclose the Secret Mantra publicly in his book or reveal the basic facts of the Tantric scriptures or any details about Tantric methods of meditation.

This situation is a little funny. Ju Mipham's text was technically the first ever truly Tibetan Kamasutra text, yet *ngakpas'* virtually secret practice of integrating Kamasutra and Karmamudra only became more widespread after Gendün Chöphel's later text appeared. This is a bit ironic since it was Ju Mipham rather than Gendün Chöphel who truly spoke about how Kamasutra and Tantric Karmamudra methods were connected and explains clearly how they can be combined together without contradiction. In his text, Mipham outlines the sixty four arts connected with ordinary lay people, he includes formulas for aphrodisiacs drawn from Tibetan medical tradition, and describes techniques such as how to use the *la* energy massage to increase pleasure. This kind of massage can increase your so called *la* energy which refers to a certain subtle aspect of our consciousness or vital energy which circulates through the body according to the lunar calendar. Sometimes if there is an absence of sexual desire, it can be due to a blockage of *la* energy. *La* massage stimulates this energy and releases blockages through very soft touch and repetition of seed syllables, and Mipham recommends its use as an important aid to generating bliss and arousal.

Karmamudra is a traditional, Tantric Buddhist teaching and it is important to understand what this means. At the same time, this does not mean that Karmamudra has nothing to do with our ordinary worldly lives or relationships. Some students of Tibetan Buddhism I meet protest, saying that with true Karmamudra there can be no samsaric desire, no ordinary desire at all, so how can Karmamudra have any connection to worldly sex or worldly interests? Of course, on one level these students are correct, and it is the same situation with other kinds of Tibetan yoga: if it's true Dzogchen, Mahamudra, if it's true *Kyerim*, Six yogas, what have you – you absolutely have to be free from samsara, from samsaric attachments and thinking, you cannot mix that kind of meditation experience with samsara, it is the same issue.

But we have to be careful here. You might say, 'But if you have to be free from samsara and samsaric desire to do these yogas – if you can't do Karmamudra until you have no ordinary desire, until you experience all phenomena as 'one taste', beyond duality – then why do you have to practice? If you're on that level of realization then why do you even need the practice?' It is like this: of course, if you have gained and stabilized realization then technically you can do the practice or not do the practice and it is all the same. But the important thing to remember is that Karmamudra is not only about sexual desire, it deals with all kinds of desire. Look at some monks, they might be so good at meditation, but then they want to eat only the best food and are filled with desire for the best clothes and other material things and experiences. There are so many levels of desire, but sexual desire is one of the root desires, so if we are able to transform that, it is like we are removing the basis or root-cause of all other desires. When we are eating, when we are drinking, when we sleep, when we are living our normal ordinary life, we are living with desire. How do you live without desire? Let's say somebody says "Oh I'm practicing Mahamudra, I'm practicing Dzogchen. I'm not ready for Karmamudra." This is simply a misunderstanding of Karmamudra and Mahamudra or Dzogchen. Let's say you are a layperson who supposedly practices Dzogchen and you are having sex with your partner. What do you do? Do you still keep your *rigpa*, your pure awareness of the nature of mind, your Buddha-mind? You can't just say, "Oh, this is samsara, this is ordinary sex, I forgot my *rigpa*, sorry!" The Atiyoga or Dzogchen view incorporates everything. If you have sex with *rigpa* then the Great Bliss generated through sex and desire is a part of *rigpa*. When people practice Dream Yoga they do not get stuck on the possibility that they might have an 'ordinary' dream instead of a lucid, non-dual one, or that they might experience a little bit of both during their training. But when it comes to Karmamudra, people freak out. This is because Karmamudra involves sex and partners and these are sensitive issues for people. But if you look inside the practice, that's how it is – do you have pure awareness or do you not?

These days everyone talks about 'mindful eating', walking, sleeping, but what about mindful sex? "Oh no no no! Sex is not mindful! Oh no no! It's samsara!" That's one possible reaction. But in reality, according to that logic, walking is also samsara, eating is samsara. What part of your life is beyond samsara as a practitioner? So why should sex and sexual yoga practices be any different? I think the basis of these objections and discomforts, the root cause of all this paranoia, is the simple fact that Karmamudra is connected with sex and there is so much cultural sensitivity and awkwardness around talking about sex, and that leads to double standards and repression. But as I've already discussed, the problem is that when you try to repress and deny these things, it just doesn't work. Some people have expressed concern to me that if I publish teachings on Karmamudra for 'ordinary people', those people will look at the stories about Guru Rinpoche and Yeshe Tsogyal and think to themselves, 'Oh! Karmamudra grants full realization, immortality, and enlightenment! Now I have access to Karmamudra, so now I'm a Buddha, now I'm immortal, now I have special powers, I have transcended worldly things!' The thing though is that people can make these same sorts of claims with any other Tantric yoga practice. They can say, 'Oh, I'm practicing Mahamudra – I'm beyond everything and above everyone!' Normally, if any practice is working, people become simpler, more humble, happier. People who say things like this refute their own progress.

It is important that we look carefully and clearly at the goals and results of the practices we do. We need to keep both the everyday, more immediate results of the practice and the ultimate goals of the practice in mind. We have to see these things as having two parts: there are the ordinary goals, the conventional, temporary or temporal goals and results, and then there is the ultimate goal, which is fully realizing Buddha-nature. When it comes to Karmamudra, the ordinary goals and results are that you are healthier, you are happier and you live longer because the practice induces many *thiglé* transformations – our body substances change and transform, and many of the spiritual experiences we have are in and through the body. You have better sex and better connections with the people in your life. On the other hand, stress and anxiety disappear – Karmamudra practice is very healing for the mind. With Karmamudra, you're more relaxed, the mind is clear, and you feel happier. These are all general, more everyday results of Karmamudra practice, all good, beneficial things. But the higher goal of the practice is that you achieve *rigpa*, you directly perceive Buddha-nature. The goal is exactly the same as with Mahamudra. Mahamudra is the Path of Complete Liberation of the Upper Gates and Karmamudra is the Path of Bliss of the Lower Gates but the result is the same. The final goal is to become a Buddha, to recognize and rest in *rigpa*, it is exactly the same. Likewise, if you practice according to Atiyoga, still the goal is the same.

Gedün Chöphel stated that one of the main reasons he wrote his book about sex and sexuality was to make clear that Kamasutra and Karmamudra were distinct. I think one of his main goals was to write about Kamasutra in a way that was fun, that was aimed at the public and would be more accessible. There aren't any empowerments or special transmissions for Kamasutra like with Tantric practices as these are general and secular teachings. Unlike Ju Mipham's text, Gedün Chöphel's book does not include instructions on Karmamudra. Gendün Chöphel's book has become one of the best-selling books in Tibet, but it is forbidden in monasteries. When you say Gendün Chöphel's name monks hate it because he made sex-manuals even more public in Tibet than Master Mipham, and now monks are afraid that if they are caught reading his work they will get kicked out of their monasteries!

Jokes aside, talking candidly about sexual intercourse and sexual desire can sometimes be difficult. When I was younger I had my own struggles, many struggles in fact, with what I sometimes call 'my little Tibetan brain'. Sometimes clinging to cultural conventions without deep understanding, historical context or personal perspective can imprison you. Now that I'm older and have come to terms with things, I feel very free, like an ex-prisoner. Talking honestly about sex can benefit people and is a very important part of Karmamudra. So that's why today I feel more free to talk about these things.

CHAPTER 3

Tantric Subtle Anatomy

Sometimes just working with our mind alone is not enough – we have to make use of our body as well as our channels to ensure our transformation. Yoga, prostration, circumambulation – all these work with our body and the channels.

The Real You: Yoga and the Vajra Body

In Tantric Buddhism or Vajrayana, yoga is of vital importance. It is one of the main methods for working directly on the root of the three poisons and for working with and transforming our mind. The translation for the Sanskrit word yoga in Tibetan is *naljorwa* and this term conveys this idea of human transformation and potential very well. Yoga is about uniting with (*jorwa*) the most ultimate, natural or basic state of being (*nal*). Through the practice of yoga we transform the ordinary mind and body into its ultimate version. We actualize its true potential.

According to Tantric teachings, beneath the ordinary body is the Vajra Body, the body of the subtle channels and winds, or what we might call the 'energy body'. In Tantra we use the ordinary body as a means through which to somehow discover the Vajra Body – that's why we do physical yoga. We use every single component of our ordinary, physical bodies to uncover the Vajra Body, which is our ultimate and true form. Inside or beneath our ordinary mind there is a kind of ultimate mind as well. When we meditate, we can realize that primordial or ultimate nature, whatever you want to call it. Conversely, when we get stuck in ordinary mind we become afflicted with things like stress, depression, panic attacks – all these big inner 'demons'. If I used some sort of traditional Tibetan names for these big demons many readers would no doubt not recognize them, but when we talk about inner demons like this, in the language of psychology, they become much more familiar. So these are ordinary human problems which come from fixating on ordinary mind. But just like how we can use the ordinary body as a means to realize the Vajra Body, we can use our ordinary thoughts and desires as material for discovering our ultimate nature.

Physical yogic practices are often referred to as *trul khor* in Tibetan, which can be translated as something like 'magic wheel'. This sounds a little strange to English ears, but it makes sense when we understand that our own body is the wheel, the moving machine that is being described, and our body possesses the potential to become something magical. Right now, however, we are using it in ordinary and not very magical or extraordinary ways. It's a bit like Absolut vodka with their catch-phrase about extreme distillation: our everyday body-and-mind are the potatoes that we transform into clear, super refined vodka. In classic Completion Stage yogic practices, *leyki loong,* our 'karmic' or 'worldly' subtle winds or energies are transformed into *yeshe loong* or 'wisdom' winds through controlling the breathing and visualization. Transforming our ordinary body into the Vajra Body, by transforming karmic winds into wisdom ones is yoga, and it is for this reason that Vajrayana says *tsa loong* or channels-winds practice is very important.

The cultivation involved in Karmamudra makes use of our body, mind and subtle energy in a special way. When you practice Mahamudra and Dzogchen *trekchö* the focus is more exclusively on your mind, on the mental aspect. As discussed in the previous chapter, the goal of Karmamudra and Mahamudra is the same, but with Karmamudra we do not ignore the body. Vajrayana in general, and Karmamudra in particular, make use of the body, physical sensations and subtle energies. They make use of sex, but they are not just about sexual intercourse, they are about one simple and empirically verifiable question: what is the ultimate nature of this body of yours? Is it pain or is it bliss? What is the nature of your mind? Who are you? Vajrayana teaches that the nature of both body and mind is bliss. We can see this with very little children. All their experiences are so open, so happy and joyous. Even when they experience pain for the first time, their experience is fresh and direct. It is not so boxed in. Chronic pain and discomfort come later, they take time to build up in our bodies and in the patterns of our minds. The hidden, profound explanation of the Vajra Body teaches us something different. And that truth is this: we are born with bliss, we live with bliss, and we die with bliss.

Tsa, Loong, Thiglé

Working With Energy: Channels and Winds

We can think of the conventional, untrained mind as a crazy or bad king – this king doesn't want to be a slave like the body or the breath, but ends up enslaving itself. Through yogic practice we can learn to train, purify and transform our body, speech (energy), and mind. In Tantric Buddhist yoga we work first with the channels or *tsa* which correspond to the body. These are easiest to control and respond well to more physical methods. The chakras, (*khorlo* in Tibetan) or 'wheels' are concentrations of these channels (*tsa khor*, literally 'channel wheels'. There are five primary chakras in Tibetan Buddhist Tantric yoga. These are visualized in the crown of the head, throat, heart center (between the nipples), navel and at the root, in the genitals. *Tummo* or inner heat yoga is one of the main or best practices for unblocking the channels and what are referred to as *tsa dü*, or 'knots' in the channels. *Tsa loong* practices usually involve seven major exercises: two preliminary practices and five main channel opening exercises. *Tsa loong* practices are divided into three main processes: releasing the knots or blockages in the channels, making the *loong* flow more effectively, and transforming the *loong*.

Even though *Tummo* practice is seen as one of the best ways to release knots in the channels so as to clear the way for further practice, other more physical practices like prostrations can also unblock the channels in a similar if less focused way. I often advise both my students and patients to do prostrations regularly. Doing 108 prostrations after you get up in the morning is one of the best yogas you can do, and it is an excellent form of exercise. Prostrations have physical and energetic benefits due to the fact that they open the channels, and they have spiritual benefits too since they are a form of purification, concentration training and devotional practice.

There are roughly 24,000 channels associated with the poison of anger and hatred (connected with the right, solar channel), 24,000 associated with ignorance and confusion (connected with the left, lunar channel) and 24,000 associated with attachment and desire (connected with the central channel). When we ripen our channels and release or untie the knots or blockages in them we resolve the causes and conditions for these three

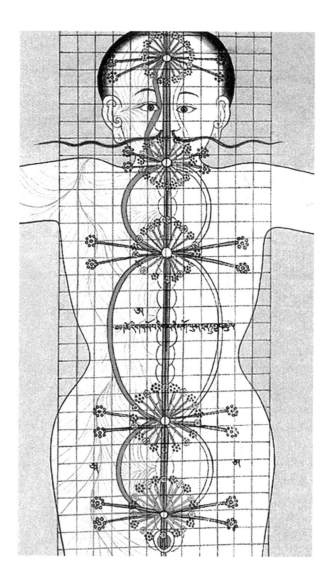

The three main channels and their junction points at the five chakras of head, throat, heart, navel, and root. According to the teachings of subtle anatomy, each of these three main channels has 24,000 branch channels, making 72,000 channels total in the body.

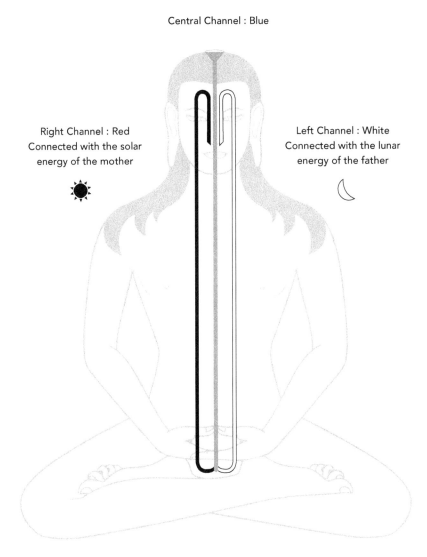

Central Channel : Blue

Right Channel : Red
Connected with the solar
energy of the mother

Left Channel : White
Connected with the lunar
energy of the father

In meditation practice it is appropriate to visualize the channels as straight, rather than crossed at the chakra points as shown in the previous image. Most traditional Tantric texts depict the red channel (roma) on the right side and the white channel (kyangma) on the left, as above. In some texts, however, the red and white channels are reversed for women.

poisons. According to Sowa Rigpa, Traditional Tibetan Medicine, the three mental poisons of desire, anger, and confusion manifest in the physical body as the three humors (*nyepa*) or dynamic energies of wind, bile, and phlegm (*loong, treepa,* and *beken*) which, when out of balance, can manifest as various physical illnesses. Thus by working with the channels through physical yoga exercises, we can help to prevent disease as well as address the deeper cause of all illness which are these three mental poisons, rooted in fundamental ignorance or non-awareness, known in Tibetan as *ma rigpa.*

Sometimes just working with our mind alone is not enough – we have to make use of our body as well as our channels to ensure our transformation. Trying to transform the mind through the power of the mind alone, is very difficult. Yoga, prostrations, circumambulation – all these work with our body and the channels. Doing breathing exercises and chanting mantras is how we work with our speech, our subtle energy known as *loong* or 'winds'. Dream Yoga can also be very effective for releasing blockages in our *loong*, since it works with our mind and energy in its less gross state. *Loong* can affect *loong*, so this is in part why these practices are effective. That said, many *loong* problems are caused by blocked and knotted channels (*tsa*). Our winds are like cars and the channels are the roads they travel on, so working on the road or the channels rather than the *loong* directly is a very powerful way to affect our energy, allowing the traffic to flow freely.

There are countless different categories of channels and winds. This is too vast and profound a subject to cover in this book. One of the best Tibetan works on the Vajra Body was written by Rangjung Dorje, the Third Karmapa. This book is available in English translation as a restricted publication from Shambhala Press, entitled *The Profound Inner Principles* (Dorje, 2014). I received teachings on this text from Dr. Troru Tsenam, the great yogi and doctor who was my teacher in Lhasa. I was strongly inspired by Dr. Troru Tsenam and I ended up writing my final dissertation in medical school on the today somewhat controversial topic (given Communist Chinese authorities' official policies on religion and public education) of how the subtle body connects with medical science and treatment. In addition to the Third Karmapa's text, students who would like to learn more about Vajra anatomy and its relationship to yoga and medicine can attend introductory classes on these topics offered through Sorig Khang International. I am also currently developing a book on Vajra anatomy which will be published soon.

The meditation techniques outlined in the following chapter do not delve too deeply into the first two components of subtle anatomy - the channels (*tsa*) and winds (*loong*) - they do however, make use of the third major component, the so-called 'energy drops' or *thiglé*.

Feeling the Butterflies: Bliss, Hormones and Energy Drops

If the channels are associated with the body and the winds with the speech or energy, then *thiglé* or the essential energy 'drops' of the subtle body are associated with the mind. It is impossible to truly understand Vajrayana and its perfect inner alchemy without understanding *thiglé*. Through *Tummo* Yoga we transform our ordinary body into the body of the meditational deity, through mantra recitation we transform our speech into Buddha speech and through working with *thiglé* we transform our minds into non-dual bliss. Karmamudra is connected even more with *thiglé* than with the *tsa* or *loong* – it is the best, most powerful practice for working with and transforming these essential energy drops. *Tummo* Yoga is the primary yoga for transforming the channels, the other five yogas transform the winds at various levels, and Karmamudra is the ultimate yoga for transforming the *thiglé*, through which we generate more and more refined levels of bliss. *Thiglé*, or bindu in Sanskrit, can be a difficult concept for people to grasp. The literal meaning of *thiglé* is a circle or sphere. In Amdo dialect, my native dialect of Tibetan, *thiglé* also means 'zero'. Sometimes *thiglé* is also used to refer to semen. So what is it then? Simply put, *thiglé* is wherever mind is. We Tibetans say that *rolang* or zombies, reanimated corpses whose human consciousness has been replaced by that of a demon, don't have *thiglé*. This is also why zombies never ask you for sex!

Thiglé is a special kind of energy, which at times operates like a kind of fluid. It is also called *jangsem* in Tibetan or the 'purified mind' of a Buddha. *Thiglé* is thus the essential quality and substance of the enlightened mind. It is the nature of our mind, soft, gentle, and joyful. In terms of our subtle anatomy this quality is the ultimate base of our mind, just as our brain is the base of our grosser consciousness. *Thiglé* pervade our body and move with our emotions and transform our feelings. We have channels in our body and these channels contain *loong* or vital energy. *Thiglé* derives from *loong*, it is the essence of this circulating vital energy. *Thiglé* thus depends

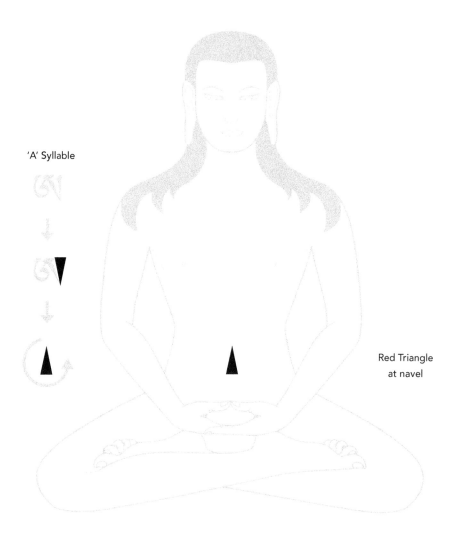

'A' Syllable

Red Triangle
at navel

Embryology and the Subtle Body

When the consciousness enters the sperm (before or at the moment of conception), it joins the white thiglé (energy of the father) and takes the form of an A syllable. This A syllable then joins with the red thiglé (energy of the mother) and transforms into a red triangle which forms the navel chakra. It is from the navel chakra that our fetus is developed and our subtle energy body created. At the moment of birth when the umbilical cord is cut, the red and white thiglé are separated for the first time, the white one going up and the red one down.

on *loong* which depends on *tsa* which in turn depend on the body. This is how mind, body and energy are interconnected. That is why it is so useful and effective to straighten your back when you meditate – when the physical spine is straightened so are the channels which in turn allows the *loong* to move and flow in a more balanced way. As a result of this, *thiglé* is balanced and amplified and our mind relaxes. This interdependent functioning also works the other way around: the body depends on the mind and mind depends on body.

One traditional metaphor for this describes our channels as a house. In this analogy, *Loong* is the person living in the house and the precious jewels that this person possesses are the *thiglé*, the *jangsem* or pure mind. If the house is in a good condition, the person inside can have a good life and enjoy their riches – if the body and its channels are taken care of, the mind will naturally be in a good state as well. *Loong* is connected with the mind, but there is something very fine and precise that exists between *loong* and mind and that something is *thiglé*, thus *thiglé* is the energy most closely associated with the mind. This can be described through a second metaphor in which the mind is likened to a legless man riding a blind horse: *loong* is the horse's movement, awareness is the legless rider and *thiglé* is the saddle. *Thiglé* is the connection between awareness and movement, which together we experience as our mind.

Another very easy to understand way I like to think of *thiglé* is as the 'butterflies of love'. Since *thiglé* is the base of our consciousness, they are connected with the innate nature of mind, which is bliss. When *thiglé* are stimulated and proliferate, they vibrate and produce pure unconditional bliss which is a lot like the 'butterflies' we feel when we first fall in love. On the other hand, when these butterflies die, when the amount or strength of *thiglé* in our energy body deteriorates or decreases this can lead to neuro-degenerative diseases. I believe there may be a correlation between the physical manifestation of conditions like Alzheimers and the depletion of *thiglé*. For most of us, a lifetime of suffering severely depletes us of our *thiglé* and weakens our capacity for bliss, and this can sometimes manifest on a physical level as neurological degeneration. It has often been speculated that there is some correlation between the chakras and the endocrinal system and I think that there is probably validity to this. My guess is that there is a strong connection between 'happy hormones' like oxytocin and serotonin, and *thiglé*. Once you have enough happy hormones or *thiglé* it becomes difficult to be unhappy even if you try!

The primary sorts of *thiglé* referred to in Vajrayana are the *thiglé karpo* and the *thiglé marpo*, the white and red energy drops. These *thiglé* are connected with the reproductive substances of the father and the mother, respectively. When our consciousness enters the sperm (either during or before the moment of conception, depending on which scholar you ask) it joins with the *thiglé karpo*, and takes the form of an A (ཨ) syllable. When the sperm, which carries the consciousness in the form of the A joins with the egg, this A combines with the *thiglé marpo* to become a red triangle. This red triangle then forms the navel chakra. From here the fetus develops and our channels and subtle energies are created and completed. Then, when the baby is born and the umbilical cord is cut, the energy of the navel chakra starts to move. This is the first point at which the red and the white energy drops split, the white *thiglé* goes up and the red one goes down. This is also when the earliest attachments to the mother and father develop. Traditionally, boys are said to have more attachment to the mother and girls more to the father.

Traditional explanations describe how the white *thiglé* takes the form of a HANG (ཧཾ) syllable and the red *thiglé* goes under the navel and takes the form of an A syllable. The white energy is held by the left channel and contains the lunar power from the father. In a parallel fashion, the right channel holds the A which contains the solar power or maternal energy. Our consciousness resides in the central channel with this energy from our parents supporting it. This composition remains until we die, with the core energy of our consciousness staying in the heart chakra in the form of a HUNG syllable (ཧཱུྃ). The white and red *thiglé* also move internally in the chakras in 24 hour cycles according to solar and lunar energy. This movement is affected by the interaction between internal and external sun and moon energies and yogic practitioners can plan their practice schedules based around when certain kinds of energy and certain channels are more or less active or strong.

When I mention my theories about the connection between hormones, *thiglé*, and the nervous and endocrine systems, some people have objection: "How can you say *thiglé* is something measurable? How can a person have a lot or a little of it, how can it be depleted, how can you compare it to hormones? If *thiglé* are connected with the mind, I thought in Vajrayana the mind was indestructible, immeasurable, transcendent, beyond physical quantification? What are you talking about?!"

Biomedical doctors and materialist scientists are not completely wrong – the brain is extremely important for consciousness. Traditional Chinese Medicine mostly ignores the brain, it talks very little about it. In Tibetan Tantric yoga, however, we have the crown or head chakra, the Mahasukkha chakra of Great Bliss, and with this we seem to have a link between more gross material and subtle dimensions of being. To people with these objections I say that we should not separate the energy system completely from the ordinary physical body and we should not completely separate Buddhist views from scientific views. The issue is more that many scientists are just too narrow-minded in their views and choose to only focus on the most gross or outer levels of certain phenomena. It is important to understand that *thiglé* has many layers or levels, just like the channels and the winds. We can think of *thiglé* initially as certain kinds of internal physical substances comparable to 'happy hormones' but it is important to realize that *thiglé* can be outside as well. As our mind expands outwards, its radiating influence or corresponding resonance is felt outside the apparent boundaries of our individual bodies. These are subtle realities and ontological questions which can be answered only by your own practice.

The main thing to keep in mind is that *thiglé* has many layers: some Vajrayana sources talk about ten distinct levels or layers of *thiglé*. When people talk about 'the aura', this is also an aspect of *thiglé* and its expression. Having a good, radiant complexion is a physical sign of good or strong *thiglé*. *Thiglé* moves and is present in many different ways, some *thiglé* become part of our skin complexion, some become our aura, some move in our body, some accumulate and remain in different body parts. The level of *thiglé* that is connected with the body's hormones and internal physical substances like the female and male reproductive fluids is called *dzeyki thiglé*, 'the *thiglé* of substances'. Along with this, we also have *yeshe thiglé* or 'wisdom *thiglé*' and *ngakyi thiglé*, 'speech *thiglé*'. The former operate more on the mental level, whereas *ngakyi thiglé* are linked with the visualization of mantra syllables – all the seed syllables we visualize as part of Vajrayana practice are *ngakyi thiglé*. If you visualize a HUNG in your heart center, that is a Tantric or mantric syllable but it is also a kind of *thiglé*, a condensed or focused point of energy that is solidified through your visualization. The HUNG or OM or HRI is an imagined form, but the energy that it focuses holds an invisible *thiglé*, the essential energy of speech. Visualizing mantras helps us increase our *thiglé* and helps us wake up. We can see from this that *thiglé* are subtle or mental phenomena but are also linked with physical reality, which is why I sometimes describe them as 'psycho-physical'. Sometimes, translators will just say that *thiglé* means semen, the physical reproductive substance. This may be partially true depending on the context but to say that *thiglé* is just semen is wrong. After all, when you visualize a white HUNG syllable at your crown chakra that's obviously not semen, yet both seminal fluid and this HUNG are called *thiglé*.

Then there is also what is called *ma rigpey thiglé* – this is a name for confusion and ignorance in general. Why is ignorance or lack of awareness described as a sphere? When we fall asleep, that state of non-awareness is like a *thiglé*, it is like a black hole that everyone falls into. When you fall into deep, oblivious sleep you are all in the *ma rigpey thiglé*, in that black hole, that sphere of ignorance – you don't even realize you are in the black hole! The reality is that you really get lost in there, just like you can get lost in a dream. *Yeshe ki thiglé*, the *thiglé* or sphere of primordial wisdom is the antidote for that. When you wake up from sleep there is a different kind of *thiglé*, a *thiglé* of wakefulness. It is like a big sphere and through it the black hole of non-awareness turns into a 'light hole,' a cavern of luminous awareness.

So *thiglé* refers to many different kinds of circles or spheres. Even our galaxy is a *thiglé*, just as literal black holes are *thiglé* as well. So there are levels of *thiglé* that complicate any discussion of the subject. For example, in the past I have mentioned to students that the *la* energy is linked with substance *thiglé*, but that this energy is probably more subtle than our physical hormones and so on. Science and medicine deal with and allow for more gross-level *thiglé* – what is known in Tibetan as the *ragpa* level of things, which is opposed to more subtle or *trawa* realities. There is no judgement connected with these terms: gross phenomena have their own functions, potential, power and limitations just as much as subtle ones do. Just like there is gross and subtle *thiglé* we also have the *ragpa* or gross mind of everyday waking consciousness and the more *trawa* or subtle mind that arises when we go to sleep and our awareness withdraws from external gross reality. These are everyday observable realities, so it is very important to understand and experience these things at different levels.

Even some lamas can forget about the layers involved in *thiglé*. Some lamas have gotten so angry at me for saying that *la* is a part of *thiglé*. They have confronted me and said 'How can you say *la* is *thiglé*!? They are two separate things!' But the problem is that even some lamas think of *thiglé* in really narrow ways, as nothing more than just one white ball up there and one red one down there. Sometimes when I ask them about substance *thiglé* and speech *thiglé* it turns out they don't know much about them or have not reflected much on how these different levels of *thiglé* fit together.

Sometimes teachers worry that these topics might be too deep for their students to understand. These are certainly very profound and complex subjects but I think that people need to understand deep things too! If students have access to good, clear explanations about things like the subtle anatomy then it can prevent confusions further down the line. What happens is that someone says, 'Oh, Nida said *la* is *thiglé*!' And then this person goes to someone else and repeats this kind of thing out of context and then all kinds of rumors start! It is a bit like the saying in English, 'a little knowledge is dangerous'. If we encourage people to think in narrow or reductive ways about these sorts of topics, people's minds stop being very open and become closed off. People think, 'Oh no, this is not what I was taught – *la* can't be that! *Thiglé* refers to this and nothing else! That's it – nothing else to it! I know for sure that *thiglé* can't have any link with *la*.' This kind of thinking is not only misleading but it can also close people off from appreciating possible parallels between traditional Tantric Buddhist concepts and scientific findings. While these two systems of knowledge are of course different, there are also some important and interesting overlaps. I will discuss some of these overlaps a bit more in Chapter Five.

A Note on Male and Female Channels and the Nature of Subtle Anatomy

The majority of traditional Tantric Buddhist texts explain subtle anatomy according to men's bodies. For example, in general it is said that the red, solar channel is on the right side of the body and white, lunar channel is on the left (see diagram on page 145). When meditating, both men and women can practice with this visualization effectively. Nevertheless, some texts do show these two channels reversed for women (i.e. the red one on the left side and the white on the right side). This arrangement relates to the development of the fetus in the womb and how the anatomical channels grow in the body. We can thus study the channels in two ways: one way is from the perspective of meditation, which is called *gompey tsa* in Tibetan (the channels of meditative cultivation) and the other is from the perspective of anatomy and medical theory which in Tibetan is called is *chagpey tsa* (the constitutive channels). In meditation practice, the colors and shape of the channels are not fixed but can change depending on the particular practice that one is cultivating and one's own personal meditative experience. For example, while the central channel is generally said to be blue in color, in *Tummo* practice, one visualizes the central channel as red on the outside and white on the inside. This is a special visualization that relates specifically to the *Tummo* practice. Similarly, the red and white *thiglé* are generally described according to the male body in traditional texts as white above and red below, but can be reversed for women as will be discussed in the following chapter.

This is important to understand. People often think that there is only one correct system of channels or chakras and they may even argue about the 'true' color of a specific chakra or channel. The reality is that there are many different chakra and channel systems found in Indian and Tibetan Tantric traditions, and these can change depending on the context and the practitioner. So, to summarize, practitioners of any sex and of any gender orientation can use traditional male-centric versions of the subtle anatomy to perfectly good effect. If you are a yogini who has received transmissions and instructions for these systems and you have become used to them, then by all means you should use them. It is important to know, however, that the Yuthok Nyingthig offers an inverted system for female-bodied practitioners. Female practitioners are encouraged to use it if they so wish and are not already accustomed to other approaches. Whatever system you follow, it is important to be consistent as well as to pay attention to your own inner perception.

CHAPTER 4

Stages of Karmamudra Practice

*Tibetan Vajrayana is really vast in scope. There are so
many methods and practices and sometimes without
a structure it can be really easy to get lost in them.
This was Yuthok's point when he said that because
the spiritual practices of Buddhism are so vast it is
really important that we understand the most essential
practices so that we don't get discouraged
or run out of time.*

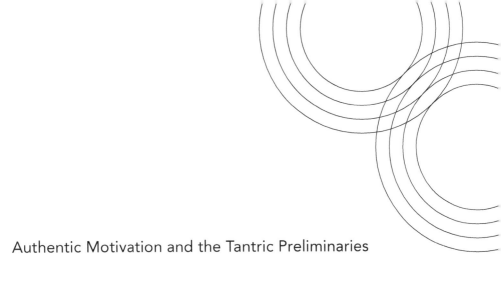

Authentic Motivation and the Tantric Preliminaries

In Chapter Two I gave a very brief explanation of Theravada, Mahayana and Vajrayana Buddhism and how they are connected. When it comes to Vajrayana practice, it is important to understand what preparations and orientations are necessary for practicing in the best and most effective way possible.

There are so many different practices in Vajrayana and sometimes students can get overwhelmed. There are a lot of preparatory prayers for example – sometimes people can feel like they have spent so much of their time doing these prayers that by the time they get to the main meditation they are too tired to even do it! It is really good to do these sorts of prayers, but if people do a great number of them just for the sake of it and without proper understanding, it is very easy to get lost in them, to lose focus and become discouraged as a result. One way of organizing all the practices that are out there is according to the traditional Tibetan division of *jor ngö jey*, or 'preparatory, main, and follow up practices'. In English I like to call this MMD: Motivation, Meditation and Dedication. Motivation refers to going for refuge and generating bodhicitta; Dedication is the dedicating of merit which we do at the end of our practice, and in our case, Meditation is the main Karmamudra practice. We can think of this MMD as a sandwich. All the layers of the sandwich go together and support each other to make up the whole, there is no delicious sandwich without one of the parts. So good meditation comes from good motivation – if your motivation is not so clear your meditation will not work well. Good motivation guarantees a good meditation practice.

In Vajrayana, before engaging with the main meditations we perform preliminary practices, called *ngöndro* in Tibetan. The preliminary practices, which are based on taking refuge and the bodhisattva vows, are purifying, devotional procedures which prepare us for the main practice. There are outer, inner, and secret aspects to the the three 'jewels' to which we go for Refuge. The outer aspect is the Buddha, Dharma and Sangha, the inner aspect is the Guru, Deva (or *yidam*), and Dakini, and the secret aspect is our own *tsa*, *loong*, and *thiglé*. Taking refuge is not about devoting or submitting ourselves to anyone or anything that is outside of or separate from our own inner nature. When we take Refuge it means we understand that we can only find a remedy for our suffering in the enlightened aspect of ourselves, in our own inner primordial awareness. The preliminary practices help stabilize our recognition of this primordial, enlightened aspect of our being and our confidence in it. The Yuthok Nyingthig lineage has its own special *ngöndro* practices, which are unique in many ways.

One particular uniqueness of the Yuthok Nyingthig *ngöndro* and the tradition as a whole is its non-sectarian nature and the concept of 'all-in-one': when one practices Yuthok's *ngöndro* and takes refuge, it is not necessary to visualize a complicated and elaborate refuge tree with all the lineage masters, as is commonly done in other preliminary practices. Instead, one visualizes the single figure of Yuthok, understanding him to be the embodiment of all the Buddhas of the three times. The iconography of Yuthok points to this truth: his right hand holds a blue utpala flower representing the activity blessings of Tara on top of which rests a text and sword representing the wisdom blessings of Manjusri. His left hand holds a pink lotus flower symbolizing the compassion blessings of Avalokiteshvara on top of which rests a vase of nectar of immortality and a myrobalan plant, a jewel and a Vajra, symbolizing the healing blessings of Medicine Buddha, the wealth blessings of Ratnasambhava and the power blessings of Vajrapani respectively. In Yuthok's hair are five flowers representing the five Buddha families, five dakas and five dakinis. By contemplating and meditating on Yuthok's image and taking refuge in him in this way one can gain confidence in his all-encompassing nature and practitioners of other lineages need not feel any conflict or contradiction with their personal paths when practicing this *ngöndro*.

The common preliminaries of Yuthok's teachings (the four thoughts that turn your mind to the Dharma) are identical to those found in other traditions but the uncommon preliminaries are a bit different. The uncommon preliminaries include all the usual *ngöndro* practices but add to these, circumambulation (with Medicine Buddha's mantra) and a

Yuthok Yönten Gönpo, the Younger

very powerful short *Kusali* or *Chöd* practice in which one gives one's own body as an offering to beings. Another special feature is that unlike other styles of *ngöndro*, the Yuthok Nyingthig *ngöndro* does not include separate sessions of Guru Yoga. On one level this is because all of the practices – Refuge, Bodhicitta, the Four Immeasurables, Mandala, Circumambulation, Prostrations, Vajrasattva meditation-recitation, *Kusali* and so on – are all Guru Yoga in themselves. The other reason is because in Yuthok's system there are multiple special Guru Yoga sadhanas that one practices after or separately from *ngöndro*. These include the Creation Stage outer, inner, secret and concise or condensed Guru Yoga sadhanas.

Another distinct characteristic of the Yuthok Nyingthig is that it has a third level of *ngöndro* in addition to the common and uncommon preliminaries. This level is called 'routine *ngöndro*' and refers to practical, everyday activities that are aimed at improving society and alleviating suffering and which are things doctors and healers in particular can perform[19]. These are not special set apart meditations one does in retreat but are things that one can integrate into one's everyday life and ordinary activities and behavior. There is a common proverb in Tibetan that says "If your heart-and-mind is good, then the basis and path of your practice will be good as well." This is so true and is confirmed by Master Yuthok's own statements. Yuthok said, "ff your compassion is great, then whatever you do will be Dharma". These daily preliminaries are all about this, about doing one's work with constant, deep compassion and motivation to benefit others. These are not things that we just do once or twice intensively during set apart times and then abandon, they are practices that we should engage in diligently, all the time.

If loving-kindness is our primary foundation, then any medical treatments or altruistic social welfare activities we might accomplish will also become Dharma. The routine *ngöndro* refers to things that we do to compassionately protect and benefit others. We can think of them as practical and accessible applications of the Buddha's teachings that we can use in the midst of our daily lives. In the *Gyüzhi* or *Four Medical Tantras*, (Gönpo, 2006) the root text of Traditional Tibetan Medicine, it states that the doctor's View should be that of Madhyamaka Buddhist philosophy, her Meditation should be the meditation on the Four Immeasurables and her Conduct should be the Six Perfections. These routine *ngöndro* practices are really important because they benefit beings and also because they show us that *ngöndro* is meant to be something that one integrates into one's everyday life, for the rest of one's life. Today, you will find some people who claim that the common preliminaries just mean meditating once or twice

---

[19] The Yuthok Nyingthig lists the routine preliminaries as: the veneration of the community of practitioners, as well as the cherished spiritual guides and elders; the giving of material offerings to the poor; the dispensing of medicines to the sick; the giving of spiritual teachings to those who lack them; saving sick people and animals from death by means of ransom-offerings (literally 'ritually seducing them away from death'); restoring Buddhist temples and monasteries and so on; improving dangerous roads and paths; expounding the teachings of the Buddha and organizing group practice celebrations and so on.

on mainstream scriptural ideas like impermanence, karma and rebirth and so on, who say that after one has accumulated five hundred thousand rounds of uncommon preliminary practices one is 'done' and does not need preliminaries for the Creation and Completion Stage practices. Some people also claim that when it comes to the particularly profound teachings of Mahamudra or Dzogchen, you don't even need to maintain the uncommon preliminaries, or they will say that since Mahamudra and Dzogchen are such direct teachings one doesn't even need to purify one's mind through *ngöndro* at all. These sorts of claims can be very dangerous, and can end up leading people who don't know any better onto the wrong path. The great 12th century master Drigung Jigten Gönpo taught that "the preliminaries are more profound than the main practices". This is a very enlightened perspective and is how one should approach *ngöndro*.

Tibetan Vajrayana is really vast in scope. There are so many methods and practices and sometimes without a structure it can be really easy to get lost in them. This was Yuthok's point when he said that because the spiritual practices of Buddhism are so vast it is really important that we understand the most essential practices so that we don't get discouraged or run out of time. This is so true. Understanding the essential point of the practices and having the right motivation in practicing them is so important. The underlying motivation of all and any Vajrayana practice that we may do is always bodhicitta. Whatever particular practice we set out to cultivate, our principle and constant aim should always be 'May I attain Buddhahood for the good of all beings.' Bodhicitta means having an altruistic motivation, an altruistic heart.

That is why one of the most important *ngöndro* practice is the prayer of the Four Immeasurables. This is about cultivating compassion, love, joy, and equanimity. We genuinely pray that all sentient beings can always enjoy these things. In the same way, with the concluding prayers where we dedicate the spiritual merit or positive energy that we accumulated through our practices, we pray that we may quickly attain the primordial bliss of Buddha-mind and that through this all beings will also be placed on this level. There is a focus in all of these practices on our (apparent) self and on (apparent) others. With the Six Paramitas or 'perfections' there are four for helping others (generosity, discipline, patience, effort), and two for helping ourselves (contemplation or meditation and wisdom). Whether the focus is on 'self' or 'other' all of these things revolve around cultivating genuine compassion and altruism. Excessive fixation on 'I' and 'me' has psychological and spiritual as well as physical consequences: it closes our heart chakra and creates tension and blockages. His Holiness the Dalai Lama often talks about the physical benefits of compassion and in his book, *The Joy of Living* Mingyur Rinpoche also discusses a psychological study which discovered correlations between risks of heart disease and self-fixation (2007) so it seems like the benefits of these practices work on many levels.

Swift Blessings: The Yuthok Nyingthig's Seven Day Retreats

The general prerequisite to fully practice Yuthok's Karmamudra is to complete at least one seven day retreat of Yuthok's *ngöndro* practice and then at least seven days of Yuthok's Creation Stage Outer or Inner Guru Yoga practices. As mentioned above there are four Guru Yoga practices, as well as an accompanying Dakini practice. Students can do just one of the Guru Yogas, and do not need to do all of them, especially if they are already engaged with other practices.[20] Most students do *ngöndro* and Guru Yoga as short seven day retreats either at home or in a retreat house, back-to-back or whenever time allows. It is your choice if you want to do a solitary isolated retreat or to participate in a group retreat.

The idea that one can do *ngöndro* and receive blessings in just seven days might seem surprising or even impossible to some people. In his song of realization, however, Yuthok says clearly that:

"If you are able to have confidence in yourself, if you can pray one-fixedly, if you can cast off doubts and second thoughts, if you have hope for a place of refuge in one lifetime, then the two obscurations [i.e. of afflictive and cognitive emotions] will immediately be kept in check. Having met me in actuality, in meditative visions or in dreams, I will reveal to you the supreme path of relative and ultimate attainment." (Gönpo, 2005)

Yuthok made a vow that he would swiftly answer the sincere prayers of

---

[20] For more information about the Yuthok Nyingthig's own version of the Six Yogas and for an outline of all of the practices it includes, please see Dr. Nida's book *Path to Rainbow Body* (Chenagtsang, 2014).

practitioners, on pain of his own annihilation. Because of these promises and aspiration prayers, Yuthok's compassion and blessings are especially powerful and fast-acting for beings who need to tame their minds and emotions in these degenerate times. Yuthok makes this clear in a second statement:

"For beings in this degenerate age who don't have the blessing that allows one to practice and accomplish simultaneously, for those who are impatient, lack resolve, and are not able to do long practices – if such individuals have faith in me, hold to my instructions and practice this sadhana which is my own life-force without distraction for seven days, then I promise that I will reveal myself thoroughly: to the superior practitioner in actual life, to the average one through meditative visions, and to the lesser one through dreams." (Gönpo, 2005)

Readers who would like to undertake Yuthok's preliminaries are encouraged to make contact with a convenient branch of Sorig Khang International (www.sorig.net). My commentary on Yuthok's *ngöndro* has been published in English as *The Tibetan Art of Good Karma* (2013). I recommend that anyone wanting to do retreat read this book several times in order to understand the meaning of these practices properly and deeply. The text does not delve into the various Creation Stage Guru Yoga or Dakini practices of the Yuthok Nyingthig but more information about these practices can be found through reaching out to practitioners in this lineage. As an initial step, readers can also read and contemplate Yuthok's song included in the appendices. Reading and meditating on this song is a good and simple way to make a connection with him. Yuthok mastered time and space, he mastered the elements. If you find you experience even a small sudden moment of understanding of Vajrayana – "Ah! I've got it!" – then that is Yuthok's blessing to you. Yuthok's blessing power is to transmit a proper understanding of Vajrayana to benefit you and others. This book and my teaching is merely channelling his transmission. Any way you can find to feel a connection to Yuthok and his blessings, and to the source of all being that he embodies, is important and worthwhile.

Empowerments of the Anuttarayoga Tantra					
Empowerment	Vase	Secret	Wisdom	Word	All
Chakra Location	Head	Throat	Heart	Navel	Base
Syllable	OM	AH	HUNG	SHRI or SVA	SHRI or HA
Practice	Deity Yoga	Mantra Recitation	Karmamudra	Mahamudra	All
Purification	Negative Body Karma	Negative Speech Karma	Negative Mind Karma	All Negative Karma	All Negative Karma
Blessing	Body	Speech	Mind	Knowledge or Qualities	Activities
Five Poisons	Ignorance	Desire	Anger	Pride	Jealousy
Transformation	↓ Dharma State Wisdom	↓ Discriminating Wisdom	↓ Mirror Like Wisdom	↓ Wisdom of Equality	↓ Accomplished Wisdom
Pure Perception	Vision	Sound	Mind	Quality	Action
Realisation	Nirmanakaya	Sambhogakaya	Dharmakaya	Kaya of Suchness	All Kayas
Buddha	Vairocana	Amitabha	Medicine Buddha	Ratnasambhava	Hayagriva
Direction	East	West	Center	South	North

Empowerment, Transmission, and Instruction

In addition to *ngöndro*, Karmamudra, like other Tantric yoga practices, also requires empowerment, transmission, and instruction before one can begin to practice it. The second two of these three are called *loong* and *tri* in Tibetan. *Loong* is a 'reading transmission' – a word for word recitation of the text one wishes to practice from a qualified practitioner of that text, and *tri* is the oral instructions about how to do the meditations involved in the practice. With *loong* we listen and in that way make a connection with the teaching through words. We can think of *loong* as a reading blessing or empowerment. It provides us with a personal connection and continuity with the precious lineage masters of the past, those who have practiced before us. With *loong* the main thing is that we hear – we don't necessarily need to understand what is being said. *Tri* refers to direct instruction and explanation that we receive from a teacher. This information supports us in our practice of specific meditations. This advice can be about how many times to do a practice, or can help us make sense of good and bad signs that arise during our practice and give suggestions or antidotes for bad reactions, and so on. At its heart, *tri* is about understanding, it helps us to understand the essential meaning and purpose of the practices and our experiences.

Empowerment or *wangkur/wang* is a little more complex. An empowerment is a ritual procedure, a kind of initiation that makes use of special ritual substances and objects. It includes music, sights, sounds, smells, and meditation instructions which are transmitted by the lama who gives the empowerment. These days many people know that it is necessary to receive an empowerment to be able to practice specific Tantric meditations, but even so, many people just see empowerments as obscure rituals, as a step or chore they have to get through to be allowed to practice. Others attend empowerments just to receive blessings or some good karma or positive energy. Of course, empowerments do produce very strong blessings and positive energy, but when people think that the most that will happen from going to an empowerment is that they will just have one nice dream when they go to sleep after the ceremony are missing the point of this process entirely. This is a real pity.

When we understand *wang* properly we can see it is connected with *tri*, it is another kind of 'explanation' or 'instruction'. There are so many different empowerments in Vajrayana and they all involve different rituals, substances, deities. But at the base, the real meaning of all empowerment ceremonies is always the same. Empowerments only differ in terms of details – which sadhana deities they revolve around, and so on. Master Lelung understood and emphasized this consistency underlying the diverse details of different empowerments. When we understand this it dispels a lot of confusion around empowerments. Je Tsongkhapa, the great scholar-practitioner and founder of the Gelukpa school of Tibetan Buddhism explained that empowerment is not just a ritual, it is a kind of guided meditation. If you understand what is being taught and conveyed during an empowerment, then there is nothing else – the empowerment contains every aspect of the teachings. It points us to the bliss of our own true nature. Je Tsongkhapa explains that you not only have to receive *wang* with faith, but you also have to understand it with your mind, with your intellect. Many people say they 'received' an empowerment just because they attended the ceremony. But according to Je Tsongkhapa, you have only truly received a *wang* if you have both faith and understanding. To receive an empowerment with only one of these or neither of them means you will be unable to benefit from or appreciate what is being transmitted. These days many students go around collecting or shopping for *wang*. If you have the time and money, traveling to receive empowerments can be good, but if you don't truly understand what empowerments mean, what they are for, then this is really a waste.

Empowerment makes our knowledge and experience ripen like fruit on a tree or blossom like a previously unopened flower. The good news is that our brain, or mind is like that fruit, that flower, the bad news is that it is still unripe and unopened. To ripen our Buddha nature, just like with fruits and flowers we need good conditions: sufficient water, good quality soil, patience and so on. Before we receive an empowerment we are like a beautiful flower that hasn't opened yet. We need certain conditions and supports to open fully. There is light around us, but it is not luminous yet – we can't see it. With empowerment, we make this light luminous and then the flower of our being can open and we can see it. The empowerment process causes the unripe fruit of our body, speech, and mind to ripen. That is why empowerment is called the "ripening" or "illuminating" process. Empowerment is very important because it is a process through which we understand ourselves better. Empowerment is about *us* – it is about the potential of our own enlightened or Vajra Body, our Vajra Speech or energy and our Vajra Mind. Empowerment opens our chakras and introduces us to our ultimate self. It guides us step-by-step through the process of transforming the five poisons – one for each chakra – into the five wisdoms. We enter into the mandala of the Tantric deity around which the empowerment is based and our body, speech, and mind are transformed into their indestructible, non-dual, blissful ultimate 'Vajra' nature. Once we've been exposed to this reality, to this light then if we keep doing the practices transmitted in the context of empowerment, then we will finally reach our ultimate state.

From Darkness to Light: The Real Meaning of Empowerment

If you really understand empowerment then just one empowerment is enough for you to understand your true nature and the true nature of all phenomena. In the Sutric tradition, you have to study philosophy, logic and so many other subjects extensively – for ten years, twenty years, thirty years – in order to come to some realization. There are full curricula of study, but with Vajrayana we don't need to study philosophy as much. There are not that many theoretical explanations in Vajrayana. The focus is much more experiential.

The difference between superficial and real or profound empowerment comes down to understanding. When you gain true understanding through empowerment you experience a kind of 'inner click'. "Oh! That's me, that's my nature! Oh, that's my talent!" Maybe up until that moment you have felt that your anger for example, is not so good. "I shouldn't feel angry!" you think to yourself, you feel guilty, but during an empowerment you realize that in essence your anger is energy – you feel something positive in yourself, the things that you normally feel are negative about yourself change into something positive. If that happens then it is a good empowerment. If empowerment facilitates an inner click like this, then it is long lasting – you have glimpsed a reality that should last your whole life. Since empowerments involve a lot of outer ritual procedures one can miss the point. There are different levels of empowerment but the one that people most commonly encounter involves a lot of material implements and representations. Substances and symbols facilitate inner meditation and realization but we should not get stuck on them. Some people might say, "Oh this vase or this *torma* has so much vibration! It has so much energy! When I touched it I felt the vibration!" That is good but the crucial point is that if you feel that kind of vibration during the empowerment it is ultimately your vibration. And even if we allow that the vibration is in the vase, what is most important is that when the vase touches you and that vibration you feel goes into you, you never lose that special energy. That's the job of the vase: it is helping you to see your nature, to realize that your true nature is like a vase, complete, full of pure blessings, containing everything, absolutely perfect. Once that vase touches you on the head then you have to know that your head is complete and perfect, that it contains everything utterly. And then after you leave the empowerment you have to remember that fact every single day of your life. You have to remember that you are a perfect person. Even when others judge you, when they say that you are stupid or flawed, when they don't trust in you, you trust in yourself because you know yourself and believe in your capacity. That's empowerment.

Once we've received empowerment then we need to always remember that we should empower the good things in ourselves, our fundamental goodness. With empowerment, we are able to see the good in our 'dark' emotions or energy. A number of 'clicks' can happen. As part of Tantric empowerment and Tantric practice we feel our negative emotions but we do not see them as negative. We can look into our darkness deeply and directly and discover light there. Or we realize that our darkness can be transformed into light. Or perhaps we realize that we misunderstood from the beginning – our darkness was never really darkness, it was always light, we just misperceived it as darkness. Ultimately, empowerment is about empowering the good aspects of ourselves, of our minds, empowering goodness rather than negativity. With empowerment we are given the power. The average person experiences more unhappiness than happiness throughout their day. All of our experiences cycle between good, bad, and neutral. Our emotions go up and down in waves. One very simple question we can ask ourselves is whether in our lives, on average, we experience more unhappiness or happiness? How many hours in our day are we happy, unhappy or somehow in between? I've read that according to Western psychology if you're mostly neutral, that is considered good and normal, but I think that's a little pessimistic and stupid. According to Vajrayana, having a baseline of neutral is bad. Neutral is not good enough – we have to feel and thereby find a way to empower lasting happiness.

Some people may be a little confused by this: "I thought Buddhism was all about the 'Middle Way'? Doesn't that mean that we should strive to be neutral all the time?" With Vajrayana we are still between extremes, but compared to ordinary human experience we are aiming a little bit higher than just neutral. Western psychologists I have spoken with told me they value neutrality because at least then their patients aren't on the other side of things, lost in depression and so on, but according to Vajrayana we are humans – we have human feelings. Of course we are up and down, good and bad and so on, but our problem is that for the most part we are a little bit up every once in a while, and then *very* deep down most of the time. According to Vajrayana while we shouldn't necessarily be constantly high we still somehow tend upwards. This is how humans are made. Like my favorite quotation, the line from the Third Karmapa I cited in Chapter Three, "we are born with bliss, we live with bliss, we die with bliss," we were born, we live, and we die with happiness. I like this take on things. If we draw a graph where 'neutral' is a flat line in the middle then somehow the way we should go is a little bit up – we need more bliss, more richness of experience, more happiness. Just saying, "Oh, everything's fine – I don't feel anything!" is what I call a 'potato state'. It is a bit like being numb. This is often how men in particular are trained to experience emotion – don't think, don't feel. Society trains different genders to feel differently, the stereotypical man is frozen in the middle, no thinking, no feeling, meanwhile the stereotypical woman is supposed to be all up and all down! But we are all human and we all have emotion.

If you think about it, when you are unhappy you can always find millions of reasons for your unhappiness. But you also have millions of reasons to be happy as well, so why are you empowering your unhappiness? I think this all really depends on how we think and empower ourselves. For some reason, we humans really like to empower the negative things in our lives. We love to keep empowering and empowering these things, we see the fault with everything all the time spontaneously. It's like an automatic negative empowerment! "Oh! Bad things! Yes, yes!" "Oh, good things? Wait ...Is that true? Is that normal?" And so on. Empowerment is not only something spiritual. We have to find opportunities for empowering our pure vision in our ordinary everyday lives. Even if you attend an empowerment but then forget about all the names of what you received, the technical terms and classifications, every day when you think about yourself you can always ask yourself this question – Am I happy or unhappy? If you are unhappy then you have to investigate that skillfully, and remember that you can empower happiness. Here happiness is the light of our true nature that goes beyond the everyday ups-and-downs, and unhappiness is the darkness of our ignorance, our fear, our worthlessness. You really have to know that empowerment is up to you, it's your choice. It is not karma controlling your life, it's not God, it's not black magic, it's not because others are disturbing you that you can't be happy – ultimate happiness is about your decisions. You make the decision, you make the choice, you empower your choices and your life and that's it! There are so many happy poor people, sick people. It goes without saying that outer conditions and cause-and-effect make us suffer, but ultimate lasting happiness depends on our minds above all else.

Wang is the first of the Tantric transmission trio because it is really the base or the root – it anchors you, it makes you firm, it roots you in your own nature and capacity. If you understand empowerment then both *loong* and *tri*, reading transmission and instruction are already contained within it. If you understand the real meaning of *wang*, it becomes clear that *wang* is like the best psychotherapy. It is a universal psychotherapy. Once you know the real meaning of empowerment then you should empower yourself, you should practice self-empowerment every day. When we are guided in how to self-generate as various *yidams* or meditational deities during empowerment, what these deities are telling us is that we possess this tremendous force – this formidable power of creation and destruction, to generate positivity and destroy all negativities. That is why if you really understand empowerment you get the most positive and strong self-confidence. You get this positive energy for yourself but also for others. I mentioned in Chapter Two that the Tantric approach encourages us to focus on self in a skillful and beneficial way. If you help others with the self-confidence, the positive power and strength of a Buddha then you can really help them. That way, it no longer always has to be, "Oh, poor me! I'm sick, I'm weak! Oh, I'm the victim! Oh, I'm the black sheep!" on and on. Once you receive empowerment you have to say, 'Enough!" to all these stupid thoughts. You have to know and feel that you are good, that you are powerful. Empowerment empowers you so that you believe in your inner force, your instinctive knowledge and power, in your strengths. It becomes impossible for you to participate in self-sabotage.

In the Sutric path, much of the emphasis is on rejecting self and self-attachment. The idea that the root of suffering is clinging to an illusory self and that divesting from our idea of self can free us from suffering is at the heart of Buddhism. Vajrayana agrees with these ideas but instead of just telling us to reject self, it says that when we understand the empty, impermanent, relative and illusory nature of self then we are able to not just get rid of it but empower it. In the world today there are so many selfish people who commit all kinds of negative actions but they are so confident! They are so sure of themselves, so capable and powerful. They are so sure of their importance, their entitlement and they do evil effectively without any hesitation or shame. But then so many good, kind and compassionate people are meek and insecure. These people have so much self-doubt and fear, so much guilt and reservation. "Oh, me? Oh, no, I am not important. I shouldn't do this, I cannot do anything!" and so on. Vajrayana allows us to cut through our guilt, our fear and our shame. Vajrayana says that our sense of self might be impermanent and ultimately illusory but we can still use a strong, positive, confident ego to move through the world. In Tibetan Buddhism there is a form of Chenrezig or Avalokiteshvara, the Buddha of unconditional compassion, who is called 'one thousand armed Chenrezig'. His many hands and arms symbolize his limitless capacity and willingness to help beings and free them from suffering. In some representations, however, this Buddha is shown with fewer arms than he is supposed to possess. You might think this is a mistake but the reason for this is that when we pray before this image and aspire to become what it represents, we complete Chenrezig's set of arms with our own, in the act of developing ourselves. Having the confidence of the *yidam* is referred to as having 'Vajra Pride' in Tantric Buddhism. This does not mean ordinary pride or inflated self-importance. Instead, it is unbreakable confidence and trust in yourself and your true nature and capacities. By realizing the emptiness of our ordinary, everyday selves, we can empower ourselves through the empty form of the *yidam*. We can empower ourselves to help others. For this we need a strong, enlightened ego which we can use as a tool on the Path.

There are in general three levels of empowerment: the highest is the level of the universal, spontaneous mantra, the middle level is the level of the 'mandala of meditative absorption' or samadhi, of the one-pointed concentration, and the third and lowest level is empowerment through the mandala of substances. In the first level, empowerment is transmitted on the level of ultimate or non-dual awareness. The guru transmits the empowerment in a formless way, directly through *rigpa* or pure awareness. The second level works through the power of the guru and the student's meditative attainment – the teacher's mind and visualization is so strong that the student receiving the empowerment can see the mandala as a kind of psycho-physical reality in the air, like a 3D virtual or digital mantra that appears like a psychedelic vision. This is the level of perfect meditation – both the master and the student have pure vision and the guru's power allows the student to perceive the mandala in perfect detail, hovering in space. The third level is the most common one. It is the easiest mode of empowerment, the one which deals with the most basic mandala. At this level we use more physical and tangible ritual substances as supports for the guided meditation of empowerment.

In Tibetan, *wang* also means 'power' or 'authority', and this is because empowerment stimulates our royal power, our 'King and Queen' energy. When we realize our true nature then we are no longer weak, we are no longer helpless. We are in charge. This relates to 'Vajra Pride' when we are filled with confidence and we know that we are the meditational or *sadhana* Buddha. We know we possess Buddha qualities, that we are compassionate, wise, powerful, blissful. During empowerments we often get hit on the head with various things – vajras, vases, texts, images, *torma* offerings – this is a blessing but it is also meant to startle us, to wake us up. Even if we don't wake up during the *wang*, later as we go on to practice we will wake up. Dharma in general is a wake-up call. In any kind of empowerment and any kind of Tantric practice, we start with various supports to help us wake up to who we really are and what we are capable of. So empowerments are not just rituals for granting nice dreams or blessings that quickly evaporate. If we don't understand their true significance then it is hard to go through the levels of practice, as well as through our whole lives with real confidence.

Before empowerment begins we typically rinse out our mouths with saffron water to make ourselves fit vessels for nectar, which is ultimately the bliss of our own nature. Rinsing our mouth like this is about making ourselves a clean container – we rinse the 'glass' of our being because we can't come to an empowerment to be filled with nectar and wisdom with a dirty glass. Through this simple gesture we energetically and karmically cleanse our body, speech, and mind and transform ourselves into a very clear, crystal-clear container. In addition to making ourselves a pure container we also have to listen very carefully to what is being transmitted and not let things escape. Otherwise we are like a container with holes in it, one that leaks the precious nectar we have received. If our container is leaky then when the lama tries to pour the nectar of the teachings into it we lose what we're being given. The first issue is referred to as the problem of poison or impurity – one ritually washes or at least just imagines that one is pure and then knows that one is now a perfect person, fit to receive Vajrayana empowerments. The empowerment is like crystal clear Himalayan spring water produced by the Buddhas and Bodhisattvas. The lama then collects this in a vase and tries to pour it into the vase of our own being. Once we are purified then we receive this clean water in our own container. The second issue is connected with our understanding – if we experience any sort of understanding or if anything clicks in our head during the transmission then we say, "Ok! This is good! Now I can empower my happiness!" Once something clicks then we make the commitment to remember this all the time. This is what it means for our container to not have any holes, this is how we ensure that we don't lose these realizations. Another problem is having a container that is covered. That is our stubbornness, our thick-headedness. The lama tries to pour nectar into our being but it doesn't go in because we are closed to it, our mind is closed. That's why when we receive empowerment we have to open our minds and our hearts. During empowerment something enters into us, all kinds of good things – the blessings of Yuthok, of Medicine Buddha, and so on. We make ourselves open, free from doubt and fear, and we allow everything to come inside.

Through empowerment we realize that our body and chakras hosts all Buddhas and all deities imaginable. In Anuttarayoga Tantra there are four main empowerments that we receive as part of an empowerment ceremony. These are connected with the Vajra Body and are all about transforming the five poisons and opening the five chakras:

First or Vase Empowerment: corresponds with the head or crown chakra. It gives us permission to practice deity yoga and to visualize our body as the *yidam's* body. It purifies our body karma or channels (*tsa*).

Second or Secret Empowerment: connected with the throat chakra. It gives us permission to recite the mantra and prayers of the meditational deity and purifies our speech karma and winds (*loong*). Through it all the 'invisible weapons' and harm caused by words and speech are transformed.

Third or Wisdom Empowerment: goes with our heart chakra. This is the specific empowerment that gives us permission to practice Karmamudra. It purifies our mental karma and ripens our *thiglé*. Karma is ultimately a mental phenomenon, because the essence of karma, of cause and effect, operates through mind. When our mental karma is purified, our *thiglé* or drops are purified and this in turn purifies the winds which purifies the channels, which purifies the body. This process produces the most powerful blissful vibration. Our purified *thiglé* becomes a very powerful, good 'black hole' in which all phenomena can dissolve – the black hole of bliss.

Fourth or Word Empowerment: focused on the navel and base chakras together. This relates to Mahamudra and Atiyoga. Here we use words and analogies to point to something beyond words and concepts, to point to *rigpa*. This empowerment purifies all negative karmas together.

Each of the empowerments also correlates with the transformation of five poisons into five wisdoms:

Vase: Transformation of ignorance into dharma-state wisdom

Secret: Transformation of desire into discriminating awareness wisdom

Wisdom: Transformation of anger/hatred into mirror-like wisdom

Word: Transformation of pride into wisdom of equality, and jealousy into accomplished wisdom

Often when I talk with students or give introductory teachings on Karmamudra, people will tell me that they have received Highest Yoga Tantra empowerments for this or that deity or *sadhana*, but they will say that they have not received the empowerment for Karmamudra. This shows the extent to which many people do not understand what it is they are receiving when they receive any Tantric Buddhist empowerment for a *yidam* or meditational deity practice. If you have received an empowerment for any *yidam* then you have already received the empowerment for practicing Karmamudra using that *yidam*. As mentioned above, the third heart-chakra *thiglé* purifying empowerment of the mind is about Karmamudra. But because many students do not receive any explanations or tri when they get *wang* and *loong* they do not realize this. The third empowerment is always about Karmamudra and there is no Highest Yoga Tantra empowerment without Karmamudra.

Devotion, Intellectual Understanding, and Teaching Tantra Today

Today many students need a lot of *tri* or explanation and theory. Without such explanations, their meditation often doesn't work. This is part of the reason why I think it is so useful to provide general explanations of things like the Vajra Body and empowerment. In ancient times, practicing meditation without much theoretical understanding worked for most practitioners. Even without knowing the exact theory of what they were doing, they were able to achieve great results. This was because they had trust – in themselves, in their teachers, in their traditions and lineages. Today everyone is an intellectual. We all have so many doubts, so many ideas, so much is yes-and-no. A lack of trust in ourselves and our innate capacities and in the capacities of our teachers and fellow practitioners is especially prevalent. Low self-esteem is one of the biggest problems of our times. People do not trust themselves. That is why today, in order to help students practice better and get results, the teachings have to be presented in a way that is accessible to the intellect. If students know the reasons behind traditional practices, things work better. This is a bit like praying. Students often ask me if they should chant Tibetan Buddhist prayers in Tibetan or not. There are many reasons why it is good to chant in Tibetan. Many prayers were received by great practitioners of the past through dreams, visions and profound meditative states. They carry with them a special power which we can tap into if we use them in their original form. Even so, saying prayers in Tibetan is much less powerful if you do not know the meaning of what you are reciting.

We have to accept that we are not living in ancient times. We cannot transmit the teachings exactly how they were transmitted 500 years ago. This is no fault of the teachings, it has to do with the strange humans we have here now! Ancient life was tough but in some ways it was also simpler. Today people have everything they could ask for and they are still unhappy and dissatisfied.

The human mind inevitably changes – that is why I like Padmasambhava's teachings, the *terma* or revealed 'treasure' teachings, because these Tantric teachings are adapted to the time and temperament of the period when they are discovered and transmitted. Today we don't have the same spiritual power of trust or belief like ancient people who had full faith in the words of their gurus, in the teachings, and the texts. When I mention to some people that Yuthok's teachings on Karmamudra are meant for people who are too lazy and undisciplined to practice in the classic way, they are surprised. "Don't we need discipline and devotion to practice Buddhism? I thought devotion was so important – surely we can't just be lazy?!"

Devotion is of course important, but I am not sure that students really understand what the texts mean when they say devotion. I don't think that many students today have truly good devotion. Students today are more analytical. They need more analytical, technical introductions and thorough explanations of meditation practices first and then their devotion develops through practice later over time. In the past people had devotion and trust, and very few doubts. Non-conceptual and non-intellectual teachings worked perfectly, but in the present time they don't work so well anymore. A lot of students put enormous pressure on themselves to demonstrate or prove their devotion. It is worth remembering though that if you have true unwavering devotion then you're probably already enlightened! In today's world we are faced with competing claims all the time. Apple and Samsung both say they offer the best, fastest service. Students today expect to be able to assess and examine which one is faster. They expect to be able to see each product upfront, to investigate each company's claims first before buying the product. We are all suspicious, discerning consumers, that is today's world. So I think that is yet another reason why more open discussion about the principles and mechanisms involved in Tantric practice is important.

Practicing at Your Own Pace and Level

The Dangers of Spiritual Burn-out and Paranoia

Today many people get what I call 'spiritual burn-out', which is a spiritual kind of heartache or stress. People get all sorts of spiritual syndromes. When you bring up *ngöndro* some people will say, "Ooh! I have to finish *ngöndro* as quickly as I can! I have to do all of the practices 100,000 times, 200,000 times, 500,000 times!" And instead of increasing their bodhicitta and purifying and stabilizing their body, speech, and mind they get a panic attack! Sometimes even just hearing the word *ngöndro* can make some practitioners freak out, can make them terrified. "Oh, my God! I didn't finish! I started ten years ago, but…Oooooh no!"

This sort of thing is common. I think some people really give themselves a spiritual heart-attack. This happens because they put too much pressure on themselves when it comes to their spiritual practice. Spiritual practice is all about understanding. Everything begins from understanding – you really need to understand the practices you are doing, you need to *feel* them, experience them, and then *do* them. Doing them just out of a sense of obligation or panic doesn't benefit anyone. Ideally, you should do practices like *ngöndro* in a gentle or peaceful way. At the very least you should do them free from stress or pressure. I'm sure everyone reading this already has enough pressure in their life – we have social pressures, money pressures, work pressures, isn't this enough? Why do we have to add yet another kind of pressure? It really is a very simple question. Spirituality, meditation, yoga – in reality these are things to help you to feel free and relaxed. Less pressure, less stress, more ability to deal with reality and suffering. This is so important. Otherwise all you are doing is running after spiritual practice, after this goal or that goal. You want to get liberation, or you want to get inner peace, or harmony, or whatever, but in the end what you get is a heart attack!

When I mention these things some students think I'm joking. I really am not though. What I'm saying is true. The great Tibetan yogi Milarepa gave the following advice – he said, "Go slowly, and you will arrive faster." And what do so many students do? They want to go faster, and then they never arrive! Or they arrive somewhere, just with a heart-attack or spiritual burn-out. We humans love to complicate and over-do things. But the Buddha's core message I mentioned before was simple: *Don't do bad things, do good things as much as possible, and tame your own mind completely.* In some traditions when you say the beautiful prayer of the Four Immeasurables it is just as something to accumulate, to recite thousands of times. What can often happen is that people just fixate on racking up the numbers, and their recitations are just lies. Lies said over and over, and all that effort is completely useless if they don't meditate on the meaning and motivation behind the words they're saying.

Karmamudra talks about the indivisible union of non-dual bliss and emptiness. When we work with the *thiglé* and melt and unite these, this is what we experience. But this, and 'emptiness' in general can be very abstract for many people. As practitioners, we need to develop and understand compassion and the bliss connected with it before we try to understand emptiness. If we fail to do this, the reality of the emptiness of phenomena, their lack of an enduring essential 'self' can become a merely intellectual concept, disconnected from compassion and bliss from which it is inseparable. We need to build up our compassion, our bliss, and then perceiving emptiness comes later. This is important because people might appreciate the idea that everything is 'empty' and then they think "Oh, well, there's nothing, nothing exists!" and then they become nihilists. If they are stuck with this idea of emptiness-as-nothing-ness then there is nowhere for their compassion to come from, they have shut down their capacity for it. That is why when we do deeply embodied practices like Karmamudra that work with our positive feelings and our heart, then even if practitioners don't fully realize emptiness through the practice they are still at least left with compassion.

At the same time, it is important to make sure we have a proper understanding of emptiness. The view of emptiness is at the heart of Buddhism and comes from the recognition that everything that exists, everything that arises, is produced inter-dependently, and therefore has no independent or intrinsic self-existence. The Buddha taught that when we do not recognize that our perceptions, concepts and sense of identity are empty of self-ness, we treat people, ideas, and objects like they are discrete, permanent and real. We experience attachment and aversion, we cling to our projections and because of this we become deluded and suffer. The Great Bliss of Karmamudra is inseparable from the emptiness of phenomena.

When we meditate on sensory arisings and pleasure as part of Karmamudra, we also observe the arising of these things mindfully and experience them deeply, without clinging to or rejecting them. We observe them directly and perceive their ultimate impermanence and emptiness. Like waking up in a dream, we experience the arisings of our senses lucidly but know that they are like illusions. We allow them to unfold and pass non-dualistically, without attaching to them or limiting them. Bliss without emptiness can easily become more craving and addiction. With Karmamudra, when we look at the ultimate nature of our bliss, what we discover is emptiness. And when we recognize emptiness we understand the non-dual primordial wisdom bliss. So it is very important to realize that while Karmamudra may start with ordinary dualistic pleasure, in the end what it shows us is the empty and transcendent Bliss of our original Buddha nature.

Understanding *ngöndro* provides us with a foundation for both our heart and our mind. When it comes to spiritual matters, we have to be discerning, we have to use our little heads. If you really understand spirituality you won't get involved in spiritual dogmas and paranoias. There is so much spiritual paranoia surrounding Vajrayana, and *samaya* or Tantric vows in particular. At times, traditional Tibetan ways of talking and thinking about *samaya* can really make students paranoid. In essence, *samaya* means 'trust' and 'connection'. It is about relationships. You have a good relationship with your spiritual master, with your spiritual group, and these good relations are like a friendship. The idea is to maintain wholesome, nourishing friendships free from fighting. That is the essence of *samaya*. If you maintain good friendships, if you maintain harmony and good understanding then things go well. Now, of course, as with every other kind of friendship, there can be problems or troubles, but like with any good friendship you talk about these things, you put the effort in and you resolve them. That is why *samaya* can be fixed. *Samaya* can be broken, just like all relationships can be broken or damaged, but in the same way *samaya* can be fixed. If something can be broken for sure it can be fixed as well. That is why there is no point in getting overcome with spiritual paranoia. Our world is full of paranoia and dogmatic thinking already. Being stressed, paranoid and constricted in your thinking does not help you practice Dharma better.

These points apply to spirituality generally. I bring this up because I myself went through experiences like this when I was a little boy as well.

When I was young, I craved spiritual attainment, I wanted to get *siddhi*, *power*, magical abilities, so many things like that. But my teacher told me, "spirituality is like a fruit – you have to let it and yourself ripen. It takes time and happens slowly." When the mango of your mind and your practice is unripe, you cannot put it in the microwave and cook it or just set it in sunlight because "Oh, you just have to make it ripe!" Our attachments and our fear make us agitated and distracted. That is why these words from my teacher are some of the most important pieces of advice about spirituality I've ever received. I was craving everything and he said "It's like a fruit, let it ripen, it needs time, it needs patience. Be patient, consistent and dedicated. Just do whatever little things you can: twenty minutes of practice, one hour of practice every day, just practice these kinds of things and you will reach everything that you need to reach, Okay?"

When we feel craving or paranoia or both, we get lost in our practice. We need to just relax and to not feel guilty – "Oh, I'm so sick, I'm so weak, I'm so bad!" on and on. We should not get stressed from doing Vajrayana meditations or from any meditation or Buddhist practice. With any meditation that you do even if it is not related to Karmamudra or other Tantric yogas, the best way to practice is by feeling the non-dual bliss that is the foundation of all our happiness and joy however much we can. Resting in the state of non-dual awareness should be happy and joyful, not a neutral experience. If we are skillful we can even use our prior memories or experiences of joy to induce this innately human happiness and bliss. We should not be stressed or become like a zombie or a couch potato. The practices we do count when we do them with right motivation and a peaceful and happy mind which isn't tight and fixated. "Oh my mantra recitation is too fast, it's too slow!" Don't worry! Do your best to practice in the best way possible but do not let your paranoia overwhelm you. You have to feel that bliss, the foundation of happiness. Even if you just have one minute to practice, cultivate that and enjoy! The yogi Milarepa said, "Go slowly, don't rush, and you will arrive faster." I really think this is so true and so important.

The Method With One's Own Body and the Method with Another's: Types of Karmamudra Practice and Their Shared Goals

Karmamudra is about cultivating the orgasmic state and experiencing it in a more expansive, free and natural way in the chakras. The methods I will introduce now are derived from Yuthok's Karmamudra for beginners and can be practiced by anyone who is active and healthy, whether or not they have a partner. In Yuthok's teachings there are two levels of practice, as I mentioned in Chapter One. There is the self-practice or the 'method with one's own body' (*ranglü thabpden*) and partner practice or the 'method with another's body (*shenlü thabden*). Whether we practice alone or with a partner, by maintaining awareness during sexual yoga practice we can come to understand the nature of the mind.

One of the reasons why Karmamudra is so powerful is because when we move and transform the *thiglé* through our different chakras we can free ourselves from every possible afflictive emotion or mental state. In the Tibetan Buddhist tradition these are referred to as the *kuntok gyebchu* or 'Eighty Discursive or Conceptual Thoughts'. These correspond with the three poisons of ignorance, anger and desire. The throat chakra is the location of thirty three angers or hatreds, the heart is linked with forty different kinds of desire, and the seven varieties of ignorance or confusion are in the navel. When we really experience the *thiglé* in each chakra we are freed from the corresponding *kuntok*. This is the target of the Karmamudra practices described in important Tantras like the Guhyasamaja Tantra. Ultimately, all Vajrayana teachings revolve around how to remove or rather transform the poisons. There are so many different meditations that have this as their goal but Karmamudra is a distinctly direct practice – the single, silver bullet for transforming the poisons.

The Eighty Kuntok

	33 Conceptual States or Natures Resulting from Anger:
1.	Slight dispassion (for some unwanted object)
2.	Moderate dispassion
3.	Extreme dispassion
4.	The mind's coming and going (inner mental going after some object. The mind going after some external object, chasing after objects)
5.	Slight pain, anguish or grief (suffering coming from some unattractive object)
6.	Moderate pain, anguish or grief
7.	Extreme pain, anguish or grief
8.	The mind at ease or peace
9.	Conceptualization (the mind wild and agitated with thoughts, over-thinking, worry, paranoia)
10.	Slight fear (from some unattractive object)
11.	Moderate fear
12.	Extreme fear
13.	Slight craving (for some object)
14.	Moderate craving
15.	Extreme craving
16.	Appropriation (taking up some sensory object as one's own, completely clinging to it)
17.	Non-virtue (to be in two minds about acting virtuously)
18.	Hunger
19.	Thirst
20.	Slight feeling or sensation (whether pleasant, unpleasant, or neutral)
21.	Moderate feeling
22.	Extreme feeling
23.	Consciousness (conscious awareness of an object)
24.	The basis perceived by awareness or consciousness
25.	Discrimination (conceptual organizing into one category or another)
26.	Shame (that comes from unspoken transgressions, unconfessed non-virtuous conduct, some translators render this 'conscience')
27.	Compassion
28.	Slight love or affection (small desire from an object or focus of affection that does not bring suffering)
29.	Moderate love

30.	Extreme love
31.	Doubt, suspicion or anxiety (an uncertain or wavering mind)
32.	Gathering up (a mind that wants to collect things)
33.	Miserliness (wanting to completely hold onto what one has; some lists have 'envy' instead)

40 Conceptual States or Natures resulting from Desire:	
1.	Desire or passion (for an obtained object)
2.	Desire for an unobtained object
3.	Slight pleasure or joy (that comes from perceiving some attractive object)
4.	Moderate pleasure or joy
5.	Extreme pleasure or joy
6.	Delight (from accomplishing some desire or goal)
7.	Extreme delight or rapture (rejoicing from having experienced the delight above again and again)
8.	Wonder or amazement (such as comes in the face of incredible news etc.)
9.	Laughter (such as comes from when one perceived someone or something attractive and is distracted by that or loses oneself)
10.	Satisfaction (from experiencing happiness)
11.	Embracing (after wanting to embrace)
12.	Kissing (after wanting to)
13.	Sucking (some part of the body after wanting to)
14.	Mental stability (an unchanging mind)
15.	Diligence (exerting oneself after virtue)
16.	Conceitedness (having a high or inflated opinion of oneself)
17.	Completing activities
18.	Robbery (the desire to rob someone of their valuables)
19.	Force (desiring to overcome an opponent, other troops etc.)
20.	Happily/enthusiastically proceeding (on the path of virtue etc.)
21.	Slight courage/boldness (striving after an object confidently and reaching it)
22.	Moderate boldness
23.	Extreme boldness
24.	Aggression/insolence (fighting with superiors without reason etc.)
25.	Flirtation (being charming, posing and putting airs upon seeing an object of attraction)

26.	Spite, ill-will or resentment
27.	Virtue (i.e. the desire to exert oneself in virtuous actions)
28.	Expressing oneself clearly (the desire to be clearly understood by others)
29.	Truthfulness (the desire to express oneself in accordance, without claiming things aren't what they are)
30.	Untruthfulness (wanting to say that something is something it is not etc.)
31.	Certainty
32.	Non-clinging (completely not wanting to take up some object)
33.	Generosity (the desire to give away one's possessions)
34.	Encouragement (wanting to incite others who are lazy or apathetic)
35.	Heroism (the desire to triumph over one's enemies)
36.	Shamelessness (having no desire to refrain from non-virtue etc.)
37.	Cunning/Guile (wanting to deceive or distract others through artifice)
38.	Wickedness (attachment to evil views, love and desire for cruelty etc.)
39.	Wildness (violent unruliness where one wants to scorn or bully others)
40.	Deceitfulness (scheming, not wanting to be honest, upright etc.)

The Seven Conceptual States or Natures Resulting from Ignorance/Confusion:	
1.	Moderate desire or passion (which comes from for something without understanding its essential nature)
2.	Forgetfulness (i.e. deteriorated mindfulness)
3.	Delusion/illusion (caused by attachment to or distraction by illusory appearances which are like mirages or reflections in water)
4.	Muteness (not wanting to speak)
5.	Sadness (caused by a dejected, weary mind)
6.	Sloth/apathy (not delighting in virtue)
7.	Doubt (about karma and the true nature of reality etc.)

There is some variation in the entries found in different lists across traditional sources. In compiling this list I have compared multiple translations, although I have relied mostly on Wedemeyer (2007). I have also translated and placed in parentheses brief glosses for some of these entries from (Zangpo ed. 2008), which reads these conceptual states through a distinctly Buddhist/Vajrayana lens. Such scholastic presentations of the total possible range of conceptual states should be understood as road-maps, traditional frameworks for organizing – and reflecting in various useful ways – on the range of possible human conceptual experience.

Sensual Cultivation:
Karmamudra and the Practice of Extended Orgasm

Karmamudra takes us beyond ordinary desire and perception yet it makes use of our everyday human senses and embodied experience. One of the main things that distinguishes Karmamudra from Mahamudra is that Karmamudra is very focused on physical feelings and bodily sensations. With Karmamudra there is no repression. We use all of our feelings and sensations as resources, as sources of energy. The *thiglé* are just like fuel – we burn them and transform everything. The body is not ignored, there is no self-rejection, no self-deprecation or self-hatred. With Karmamudra, you should like yourself, you should know yourself, you have to feel yourself and use your energy. The more you like yourself, the more you like your partner, the more you are able to feel and expand unconditional love and compassion. That is why if your Karmamudra practice is really strong the bliss that you experience is felt by all sentient beings, not only you.

Karmamudra teaches us to use and cultivate our blissful energy. When we practice Karmamudra we use methods to increase that energy, without blocking it. We think to ourselves, "Okay, the fire is burning, so let's put some more wood on it and let it burn stronger." When this fire burns hotter we get more bliss, and once we have built up a great quantity of bliss, the bliss becomes very powerful. At this point, bliss has the ability to transform suffering. This bliss is true happiness and it eliminates its opposite unhappiness. Bliss is like a light: when you turn on the light, it eliminates the darkness. Of course, some Tibetan teachers will say that the 'great bliss' mentioned in traditional texts has nothing to do with orgasm. If they are monastic teachers, they may not be familiar with or friendly to the concept of orgasm. Some other masters don't like the word orgasm because they say it is too physical, too samsaric. But this is all somewhat ironic, since the great bliss mentioned in the Tantras is in fact referring to orgasm, just a different kind of non-dualistic, more refined orgasmic experience. The Buddha Khorlo Dechok or Chakrasamvara is the constant wheel of bliss – twenty four hours of orgasm! The thing to understand is that there are different levels of bliss and happiness. Ordinary physical orgasms might be short-lived and superficial compared to more refined levels of bliss, but the base of both physical and mental orgasms is the same.

For most people, the precise moment when they experience orgasm typically lasts only five to ten seconds, and if they are lucky maybe eleven seconds, or if they are really lucky maybe even twenty seconds. This is a great feeling but once it is over it's back to "Aaaah, my headache is back" and "don't touch me!" Now let's say your orgasm is ten seconds long. In that moment, where are your feelings of sadness? Where are your feelings of pain? Where is your depression? Your fear, anxiety, anger or confusion? Normally, we have so many of these negative emotions but in that moment of orgasm everything is gone. That is the power of orgasm, the power of bliss. We are willing to allow these split-second fleeting moments of bliss and happiness, but we are much less accommodating of deeper more lasting bliss. In our society today, feeling randomly happy or blissful is considered weird and disturbing.

Normally, for men, ejaculation is associated with sensations in the head and genital areas, or even just exclusively in the genital area. Women on the other hand have internal and external G-spots and the clitoris. There is the clitoral hood and glans, and inner sections of the clitoris that run along the labia majora in addition to the internal erectile tissue. While a lot of these parts resemble men's anatomy, male and female orgasmic responses are quite different. Nonetheless, for the average person whether male or female, orgasm is very brief. The average person gets only a very slight, momentary *thiglé* activation from things like massage, eating delicious chocolate, sneezing and ordinary orgasm. The average female orgasm lasts about seven seconds and the average male one four seconds. So even while you're saying that you're coming, you've already gone! A lot of the early scientific research on orgasm was developed by German doctors. They focused on muscle activation – they explained that orgasm was about a big build-up of tension followed by a release. This is largely true when it comes to ordinary orgasm. A regular orgasm is bipolar, it is almost like using drugs – there is a very high, sudden, short peak then a crash. You go up, briefly, then you come down. Before you orgasm, you want to enjoy the sensations so much, then the orgasm happens, you reach the highest peak of your pleasure. You cry out, "Oh, God, I'm coming, I'm coming!" I think that might be God's favorite prayer. At that moment, you don't pray to God to give you something, your prayer is completely unconditional, it is pure feeling. You just say, "God, I'm coming!" Poor God, He has this great paradise but it is empty – He must be so happy to hear that someone is coming! When you reach that level, the highest peak, you see God, you call to Him, but then you fall back down. And then you are in the darkness. You just visited Heaven, Paradise but then after ten or twenty seconds you are back in Hell. "Don't touch me!", "I need to work!", "I'm stressed," "I have a headache now." This kind of 'post-coital chill' is maybe more typical of men's reactions. Before ejaculation, many men are so kind. But then once they have got what they want, the beautiful angel has already turned into a demon! You thought you were sleeping with an angel, but one short orgasm later and this little angel has become a demon! That's why the sudden shift in behavior that goes with regular orgasm resembles a bipolar disorder.

What can we do about this? Let's say you have an ordinary orgasm once a night. That means that in a twenty four hour period, for maybe just ten to twenty seconds, your mind is completely free from any kind of suffering. That is good but it is also too short. Why can't we extend that? According to Karmamudra, if your practice is good you can increase the level of your orgasm and expand its duration. So, let's say that you can have an hour-long orgasm once per day. Now that's not bad! That's sixty minutes instead of twenty seconds! Let's imagine that all your stress, all your negative emotions, all your problems that have accumulated in the past twenty three hours are like garbage, or better, to continue the metaphor above, like compost or fuel. You can burn all of these away completely in one hour. Then where is your stress, where is your anxiety and fear? That is the essence of Karmamudra. That is why it is a really powerful and profound technique with a very deep meaning, and why it is one of the best meditations. Through Karmamudra practice you can get in touch with your inner bliss and feel a deeper, more extended bliss throughout your life. If you are accomplished in Karmamudra even when you die, you can die in an orgasmic state. With your very last breath you can say "God! I'm coming!" and you will for sure die with a big smile on your face – a sign of your cultivation of Great Bliss-Emptiness.

Typically, our minds are so busy with all the ideas and thoughts of an ordinary person. Yet if you practice Vajrayana properly and with confidence and you really believe that you are transformed, then in that moment you are truly free from yourself. When we transform ourselves through the *Kyerim* or Creation Stage practices we transform ourselves, and then we don't have all the previous thoughts and worries of the ordinary self – we have forgotten them. Once we have transformed ourselves, we are in the state of a Buddha or meditational deity – everything that is, was and will be is perfectly completed, nothing is missing and that is what is called *Dzogrim* or the Completion Stage of Tantric Buddhist meditation. When we practice Karmamudra all the light of our transcendent bliss penetrates the entire universe and all sentient beings. Even ladybugs, humming birds, butterflies flying past your window stop dead in their tracks – "AAAAH! Oh my God! What is that?! Bliss! AAAH!" Karmamudra teaches us to refine and expand our bliss. Even people who do not know about or practice Karmamudra have a sense of this. When they have a really good orgasm they feel like they have such a big heart, that they can deal with any problem and be friends with anyone. Likewise, when couples are in love everything is so good – they experience a kind of pure vision. Their pure perception comes from the love and positive feelings that they are having, from all their *thiglé* growing inside. Unfortunately, in most cases this feeling doesn't last, it isn't sustainable or renewable. People get disillusioned. The *thiglé* butterflies they are feeling get exhausted and then there is trouble! Then they may even try to replenish their feelings with some fake butterflies and they have all kinds of problems.

'Mindful Sex' and Stimulating the Bliss: Karmamudra for Couples and Making Tantric Approaches More Accessible

The exercises that follow are divided into several steps. The first few steps deal with breathing and visualization methods that can be performed either as solo exercises or with a partner. With these methods one focuses on increasing the intensity and duration of the orgasmic state through breathing and meditating. Just by doing this meditation some people have multiple orgasms. Just by breathing for a few minutes it is possible to have ten to twenty mini-orgasms. I know that many people will read this book and they will not be so interested in or involved with preliminary practices, they may skip over everything I've explained about Vajrayana and about all the different aspects of Karmamudra practice. The thing these people are most interested in is union practice, having actual sex with a physical partner. I do not provide in-depth details about union practice in this book. At the same time, even if I had chosen to not put any information whatsoever about union practice in this book, it is still true that most of you non-celibate readers of this book – whoever you are, whether you know about or want to follow traditional Karmamudra practices comprehensively or not – most of you have or will have sex regularly. So I think it is good that people who practice or want to practice Buddhism should at least know something, should at least have some practices that they can do to bring sexual intercourse 'onto the path'.

When it comes to partner practice, people sometimes think the most important thing to understand or to know about is some special esoteric technique or meditation. But really one of the most important things for couples' practice is understanding and accepting your partner. Maybe you have a situation where one partner doesn't really feel like having sex but the other partner really wants to. There are always these kinds of difficulties in relationships I think, these sorts of imbalances between partners. Let's say the wife is tired but her husband really wants to have sex – the husband really wants to ejaculate, for example. Or sometimes the wife really wants to have sex but the husband is tired. If you experience this kind of disharmony, if you encounter these sorts of conditions, then you can do the Karmamudra breathing training described below as a way to release your tension or frustration. When you do these practices together and really take your time, really do these practices in a deep and focused way, then it puts you both in a good mind-set.

It is important to explain these things because so many couples end up fighting and this becomes one of the main causes of separation. Maybe a woman doesn't feel much like being intimate because she's not receiving enough respect from her partner. Maybe the woman feels pressured to have sex even though she is feeling disrespected and disregarded and she ends up falling out of love with her partner. Then there's another situation: in Spanish and Italian there is a proverb that translates to something like 'poorly' or 'badly fucked'. If a woman is very angry and nervous people say that she is poorly fucked by her husband or partner. Here the idea is that if a woman does not get the sexual satisfaction she needs she may become nervous and angry. There is some sense to this proverb. Frequently one's depression, nervousness and so on can be a sign of one's need for orgasm and the healing it can bring. A loss of sexual intimacy or union is one of the main causes of separation and fighting between couples and is one of the main problems couples face. Sometimes people lose interest in their partners – one person becomes interested in somebody else that they think is more attractive, that they get more stimulation from, and so on. Sometimes married partners think, "Oh, I'm married, so I don't need to care about how I dress for myself or for my partner." There are all sorts of possibilities but in all of them the passion and intimacy and love have faded.

As a doctor, people come to me all the time asking for relationship and sexual advice. So many people struggle with these issues and it causes so much suffering. That is why I think it is so valuable to draw from Karmamudra to give people advice about how to have regular *mindful* sexual intercourse. Some of these practices may not be the full or real Karmamudra practice but they are based on similar principles and are things that are accessible and that anyone can do, and which can still transform people's *kuntok gyebchu* and improve their physical and mental well-being. Even if couples don't engage in union practice or have penetrative sex they can make use of the different steps below to integrate more intimacy into their relationship and to resolve stress and fighting between them. This is a really nice practice that can deepen understanding between partners and end conflict. Couples of any kind regardless of sexual orientation should make time to meditate together, to look at each other, to kiss, to hug, to turn sexual intimacy into more of a ritual. This is good whether couples repeat it every day, every night, every second day, or even just once or twice a week. This is all about the cultivation of intimacy and bliss which helps us to realize our true nature. Anything that is respectful and consensual and that generates bliss is good. In Karmamudra we focus on generating bliss because we are targeting the fourth consciousness or mental state that I mentioned before, the orgasmic consciousness. For the waking state we have Illusory Body, for dreamless sleep we have Clear Light Yoga and Dream Yoga for dreaming. There are so many practices for the waking and sleeping or dreaming states but the orgasm part has been kind of ignored, restricted and neglected. So that is why I think that focusing on accessible practices for couples is very important. Focusing on 'mindful sexual intercourse' can bring things down to earth and make Tantric approaches safe and accessible.

Whatever's Convenient, If You're Smart: Some Thoughts on Stimulation, Sex Toys, Anal Sex and Pornography

Anything that couples do – oral sex, anal sex, the use of toys, role-play etc. – provided it is safe and respectful, is fine. If people don't know about these things and they want to experiment with and experience them, according to Karmamudra, that is okay, they can experience them. We can explore and use all of our senses in Karmamudra. Karmamudra says we need to use the pleasures of the five senses. These are important because they stimulate us, they are helpful external factors to increase our bliss which we can use alongside inner *loong* and breath practices. For example, as mentioned above, I always support chanting in Tibetan. *Gyer gom* or 'chanting meditation' is a very ancient and practical method in the Nyingma tradition. Many of us love music and singing, and even if you are bad at singing you can just pretend you're good and still get good results. You have to contemplate what you're chanting, according to your mentality or ability. When it comes to the senses you can also apply your talents to various methods. If you have a good appreciation for sound then you should listen to audio recordings as part of your meditation. I encourage many people today to use audio recordings for meditation. I also once came across a very old book that discussed meditation for blind people. This book said that when they are meditating blind people should not think of colors or forms but about sounds instead. I was surprised to see this acknowledged. Some blind people have a very refined sense of touch, some say they perceive even richer more extensive inner colors than people who can see, kind of like with the darkness retreat. Then again, other practitioners struggle with meditation instructions involving colors and so on. Many people today, whether they can see or not, tend to have so many distracting thoughts. Sound and music is very appropriate for us today. These days listening to music serves as a special aid for people. Listening to good music or chanting and singing while meditating can help people focus their attention and enhance their practice. Whatever works for you is good.

In Karmamudra, anything which brings or stimulates bliss is permissible, but in the end the most important part is respecting and understanding your partner. For example, some straight men love anal sex but some women *hate* it. Many women just end up going along with it because they feel pressured or want to please their partner but they hate the experience and it is painful and distressing. But if the man is very skillful, and the woman is willing and he engages in anal sex in a gradual respectful way it can be extremely pleasurable for everyone. Some women like anal sex – orgasms from anal sex can be very strong and pleasurable for women. In the context of sex between gay men anal sex can also be extremely pleasurable, at least when partners make an effort to make it a good experience through proper communication and preparation. Some straight men may not be aware of how to prepare for anal sex and how to give a good experience to their partner, and this can be a problem.

Karmamudra does not technically forbid the use of things like masturbation, dildos, vibrators, and other sex toys and aids. As will be described below, masturbation is already included when you do Jnanamudra visualization without a partner. The point is that you have to stimulate yourself, make that energy, that fire come up, what is called *detrö* or heat and bliss in Tibetan. Sometimes because we're so involved with physical reality – we eat physical food, live so much in the world of our physical senses – how we stimulate desire also has to be kind of physical in quality. Of course, there are some people who are very good at meditating and for them everything just goes with the mind itself. If you're on that level then that is perfect – meditation, breathing and visualization are more than enough to incite and enhance bliss. If you're not on that level though then more physical aids for stimulation like using fingers, vibrators, toys and so on are not forbidden, they are just a supporting practice or tool.

For some couples doing *la* massage or watching pornography together can also help stimulate their bliss and their heat. These are the same thing, they are just another method. When it comes to porn movies in particular, some people, some parents like to say "Oooh no! Don't watch pornos you're not allowed!" And then ninety percent of teenagers all watch porn movies! Pornography is how most young people learn about what sex is these days. There is nothing inherently wrong with couples watching porn movies together to increase their desire and intimacy, but we need to keep in mind that porn stars are actors and actresses. They are professionals doing a job – they try to make everything seem very real but we should not get lost in that, they know what people want to hear or what they need to see. Porn stars study the design of all this and their acting then stimulates viewers who watch their movies and then buy and watch them again. Pornography might be useful in some cases for stimulating bliss but we should not forget that the pornography industry is a business and that watching porn movies uncritically can also give the wrong impression about real sex. Through porn movies men might get the idea that they should have sex for two or three hours, that they should ejaculate so much and that it isn't good sex if they are not making women cry and scream. Many porn movies can be aggressive and very violent too. The woman is also often the only one making all the noise and the man doesn't make as much noise because he doesn't want to be vulnerable. All these things can give the wrong impression and create unrealistic, potentially harmful ideas. Watching porn is okay for stimulation initially but we should not then get lost in the wrong understanding. There is the danger that people might watch porn movies and then think "Oh yes, women are like this. We have to be rough with them, to beat them, that's what they like!" or "All women like anal sex all the time, I can just use their bodies the way I want," and all kinds of wrong views.

Overall, I think it is very rare for women to get an orgasm from anal sex even though many men want to have it all the time. Many women don't like anal sex because for the most part it hurts them, but men don't care and still like it because that is what they want. People see actors doing all kinds of things in porn and then use this as a model. I know many women who are kind of terrorized by anal sex because their husband has got this idea from porn and he wants it, and the whole situation is so ridiculous. I think in reality, it is very rare that women have real enjoyment with anal sex and anal orgasm. Of course, if some women really do enjoy it and their bodies appreciate it, then it is good. Whatever the case, it is better not to treat anal sex as some kind of violent thing based on porn movies. If a couple does want to use anal sex then they should learn how to give each other pleasure there, clean their rectum and anus thoroughly, take their time, communicate, use lubrication and so on. Ultimately, we have to be careful that porn movies do not contribute to a wrong education and understanding. There is also the danger of porn addiction and all kinds of unhealthy behaviors around porn. When people get addicted to porn then they can no longer feel their inner bliss and their inner world, there's no longer any connection. This is the opposite of what we want to achieve with using different sensory aids to stimulate ourselves to practice Karmamudra.

Whatever or Whoever Produces Bliss:
Points for Homosexual Practitioners

Since Karmamudra is connected with sexuality and sexual desire, people often ask me what I think about homosexuality. This is an important question. In Chapter Two I explained that who your partner is and how you feel pleasure in a consensual and healthy way is all an individual matter. Karmamudra is all about bliss, and whether you're heterosexual, bisexual or homosexual you can still produce and experience bliss – it's exactly the same. When it comes to producing bliss, sexual orientation is no big deal. And if you don't have a partner, if you're single, then as we have seen that is also no problem. As discussed, everyone has the same *thiglé* in their subtle body so anyone irrespective of their gender or sexual orientation can practice the breathing and *thiglé* training explained below. This works perfectly for anyone.

When it comes to the Jnanamudra part, the use of a visualized partner, this is ultimately for stimulating or triggering the rising up of yogic heat. So again, who you visualize as your partner, the exact form or gender of your Buddha-partner that stimulates and provokes bliss in you, doesn't matter – the point is that you generate that feeling. Because traditional representations of union Buddhas in *yab yum* position tend to show a 'female' Buddha and a 'male' one together, some students feel anxious – they think that even if they are homosexual they need to imagine that they are engaging in what looks like heterosexual union when they visualize their Jnanamudra partner. But to do so would be to miss the point of this practice. If a homosexual man visualizes himself in the 'male' Buddha form of Samantabhadra, when he visualizes his partner it is possible for him to imagine another Samantabhadra. Other teachers might have different views, but for me this is completely okay. Karmamudra says that we have to use our senses to generate bliss, so that means we have to imagine what stimulates us and produces desire. That is the key point.

We should not get stuck on the figure we imagine or the differences between conventionally 'male' and 'female' Buddhas. It is true that historically Tantra has prioritized heterosexual perspectives but it is also true that Buddhas' bodies are not like ordinary bodies. When we visualize meditational Buddhas we visualize them as empty and luminous. At the end of the day they are beyond gender and sex, they contain all possibilities. Ultimately what matters is what stimulates you and your feeling, how your feeling is expressed. If you are interested in men and there are many naked ladies dancing seductively in front of you, you think, "Ah! There is no feeling at all!" and then the bliss doesn't come. It's like medicine: if you use the wrong medication for your problem it won't work.

Now, when you go into higher levels of Karmamudra practice which are not addressed in this book, there is talk there about mixing and exchanging of the red and white *thiglé* of the two practitioners, and for these practices there has to be a male practitioner and a female one. Because of the nature of these practices there is not really a way for same sex couples to perform them. Very few people do these practices, however. Also, when it comes to Atiyoga or Dzogchen Karmamudra traditions as seen in Tokden Shakya Shri's sadhana in the Appendices, the essential thing is that you use your own white and red *thiglé* and it is through that that you reach *detong yermey* or indivisible Bliss-Emptiness. There is no mixing of *thiglé* involved here, whether you are practicing this Atiyoga style with a partner or without. In this case both are the same. What matters is what is happening within you yourself, with your own *tsa loong thiglé*, through which you then get *rigpa*. As Shakya Shri explains, we don't need to go through things like mixing and exchanging *thiglé*. The Atiyoga style of practice is effortless – you just have to get the energy, the bliss.

The discussion of chakras and the different blisses or joys in this book does not involve exchanging *thiglé*. For higher classical sexual alchemy practices there has to be male and female and female and male for this kind of exchange and transformation. This is like a chemical or alchemical reaction that then effects a kind of transmutation which, at least according to Yuthok's unique teaching, can produce the Rainbow Body. Tokden Shakya Shri's Anu-Ati style does not need to work too extensively with *thiglé* – it is what we call in Tibetan a *trömay* or 'unelaborated' practice. As we know, classic elaborated partner practice requires intensive yogic subtle body training, so with that there is a lot of *tsa loong thiglé* involved. With that style of practice male and female sexual substances are needed, sun and moon. But with the Atiyoga style that just uses *rigpa* and *thiglé* it doesn't matter. The moon can get his own sun, the sun his own moon, and so on. All the necessary *thiglé* is within any practitioner. When it comes to transgender practitioners the situation is exactly the same. The way in which your gender orientation connects with your desire is an individual matter. In the Yuthok Nyingthig, Yuthok explains that elderly practitioners and people with impotence and damaged channels or people who are *maning* or intersex should make use of Mahamudra instead of Karmamudra. What Yuthok is saying is that if your individual biology makes it uncomfortable, difficult or impossible for you to engage in penetrative sex, you should not worry because you can use the Mahamudra Path to Liberation instead of the Lower Gates Karmamudra one.[21]

The most important thing to understand is that regardless of whether you are gay, straight, bisexual, transgender, cisgender or intersex, as long as you can generate bliss and follow the instructions, you can practice the methods described in this book. In Indian traditions there are representations of Shiva which are androgynous – the single deity has both symbolically feminine and masculine parts. In the mandala of the Tantric *yidam* Chakrasamvara or Khorlo Dechog, there are some Dakinis that are like this too. These goddesses are represented with two different colored halves, white and red, green and blue and so on. This imagery is useful because it really shows how we all have both solar and lunar natures. That is why we can make use of more inner Atiyoga style Karmamudra practices too.

The most important thing to understand is that Karmamudra is a method. The ultimate result of that method is the Rainbow Body, spiritual realization or realization of *lhen kyey dewa*, innately arising bliss. If we understand and remember that, then it becomes harder to fall into the common trap of getting stuck on the 'tools' of the practice. You should not fixate on these or over-inflate them – the chakras, the channels, what you visualize – these are all used as equipment or tools, as a means to an end. They are things that help us travel on the path. When we are traveling we should focus on the journey and not get stuck on the car. We use the car because we have to travel, to reach a specific, important destination. Once we are driving or once we reach the destination there is no point in getting attached to the shape or color of our car or in criticizing others. "Oh! my car

---

[21] The fact that Yuthok lists *maning* alongside these other categories of people seems quite significant. On the one hand, *maning* is positioned as one of several possible medical pathologies linked with a suppressed or non-existent libido. Yet on the other hand, the fact that Yuthok even mentions *maning* when describing Tantric yoga suggests that he accepts and supports the possibility of people who are neither male nor female in a conventional sense doing Vajrayana practices. Given that traditional Sutric texts forbid maning from taking monastic vows this is noteworthy. The traditional term *maning* is not the same thing as 'transgender', although it is sometimes used colloquially today by some Tibetans to indicate something closer in meaning to 'transgender' than to 'intersex'.

is male, mine is female, my car is white, no, mine is red!" and so on. If you spend all your time arguing about how this person's car is a red one, and yours is whatever, on and on, then you may never even drive! You are just stuck there arguing and arguing, 'No! That white car should be red!" Or it should be blue, or whatever. Not only is this a waste of time but it misses the point. So this is very important to keep in mind.

On Ejaculation, 'Achieving' Orgasm and Seminal Retention in Tantra and Medicine

One of the most common associations with 'Tantric sex' in many people's minds is seminal retention, or the idea that men must engage in sex without (ever) ejaculating. Many people have heard about seminal retention but there is often a lot of confusion about what exactly is permissible. Without getting too technical, there are several different kinds of Karmamudra practice, ones which do and do not involve men ejaculating. In some versions of practice, the man is required or encouraged to release his semen into the woman's vagina. Each of these meditation styles involves a different number of refined 'blisses' – four, eight, sixteen and so on – that correspond to the different chakras (See chart on page 234). As we've seen, there are also some small differences in classification between the New Translation schools with their category of Highest Yoga Tantra and the Nyingma Old Translation school's Anuyoga classification. That said, with all these different Karmamudra practices the essential meaning of the integration of Bliss and Emptiness is the same. When it comes to practices for pulling up or reversing the direction of the *thiglé* where one brings the *thiglé* down, retains it, then reverses it back up and then spreads or permeates it out, there are practices in which one only pulls up the white *thiglé* and practices where one pulls up the white and red drops together.

Generally, a lot of Tantric texts will say that the man should fully retain his semen, that he cannot lose even one tiny drop of it. Semen is often described as *thiglé* in the texts, but as we saw in the previous chapter *thiglé* is much more than just physical semen. Sometimes you will hear people say that ejaculation is entirely forbidden in Tantric sex and that the man cannot ejaculate under any circumstances. Some *ngakpa* are certainly known for their skills in seminal retention but that doesn't mean that ejaculation is always prohibited. For the practices where one pulls up the red and white *thiglé* together for example, the man first ejaculates his semen into the woman's vagina and then pulls this up again along with the red essence secretions and spreads this out. These are the mixing practices I described above, which are not taught in this book. There are also other practices in which ejaculating is permitted, which are particularly relied on in the context of the enhancement practices, and for which one absolutely needs an experienced lama who possesses the direct oral instructions.

In his advice on Karmamudra practice Master Lelung also notes that there are certain occasions when it is acceptable or even necessary to lose or release one's *thiglé*. As he says:

"All the traditional texts that teach Karmamudra [the 'method' or 'path of means'] state that one has to do so without 'deteriorating the thiglé', but for those that think that this means that it is thus unacceptable to sometimes ejaculate, this is no problem. Many authentic core texts on Karmamudra specifically teach that one can emit semen at various times when one gathers or 'spirals together' the sacred, Tantric substance of thiglé, like when one produces an heir, makes a precious 'nectar' pill, or confers the secret [mantra/ Tantric] empowerment, and so on. Many lamas of the past practiced this." [22]

Male practitioners may also ejaculate as part of 'enhancement' or 'troubleshooting' practices, what is called *bogdön* in Tibetan. For some practitioners excessively retaining their sperm can cause pain, cramps, and general discomfort. It can also result in incontinence, difficulty urinating, and erectile problems. Some people may also find that seminal fluid is released spontaneously or upon urinating, or that they experience multiple wet dreams and possible emotional disturbances. If practitioners experience these sorts of side effects, ejaculation may be recommended. In the Yuthok

---

[22] In the ancient Indian context, as part of the conferment of the third wisdom empowerment, in addition to explaining Karmamudra meditation techniques, one's guru would engage in Karmamudra practice with his or her consort and then the student receiving the empowerment would be given a drop of the guru and consort's conjoined and consecrated sexual fluids on their tongue. This ritual nectar would trigger an experience of non-dual bliss-emptiness in students as well, thereby introducing them to their own Buddha nature. Today in Tibetan Tantric Buddhist contexts, the guru does not literally perform Karmamudra, and students consume a substitute for this nectar in the form of blessed alcohol, yoghurt, and other substances.

Nyingthig, pain caused by blockages of the channels, winds and drops is listed as the primary 'troubleshooting' factor which may be helped by ejaculating. I discuss this sort of pain that sometimes arises when practicing yoga and different methods for dealing with it further on in this chapter.

Most of the Tantric practices described in the paragraphs above are very advanced, however, and are not addressed in this book. In general, Sowa Rigpa advocates that men should neither ejaculate too much nor too little. That said, there is no single rule or standard for this. Sometimes both men and women experience what is known as post-ejaculation syndrome, where after orgasm they feel weak and tired and depleted. Other people may not really experience this problem. The situation may also be different according to one's age. Whatever the case though, many people find they need time to build up their energy and desire after ejaculation. Some people may not feel sexual desire for a few days after they ejaculate. Maybe after sex they feel depleted and they don't want anyone to touch them, and so on. This is especially the case for men. Some people may feel like their energy and desire is zero for a few days while for others they may feel their desire slowly building up again until they want to have sex again. For this reason, for many people, not ejaculating for a little while can build up the flow and intensity of their energy and desire.

Having said this, we know that not ejaculating can be bad for men's health. Tibetan medicine recognizes that monks who don't ejaculate enough can get specific diseases as a result of this. Tibetan medical views on retention of semen will be elaborated upon in the section entitled 'Karmamudra and Sexual Health' in Chapter Five. Current biomedical views say that young and old men should ejaculate at least twenty one times per month to help prevent prostate cancer and abnormalities. Compared to full seminal retention this can seem like a lot. But the main thing to know is that the best or healthiest amount of times to ejaculate for a man depends a lot on his individual habits and body. If you are not accustomed to ejaculating twenty one times a month or more, it is possible for your body to get used to it. Tibetan medicine says that if you are young and your body and health are strong, even poison can become good food, provided you get used to it. Our bodies are adaptable and resilient, almost anything can become okay for us. If you don't get tired or feel depleted easily, following this scientific biomedical advice to ejaculate everyday or every second day can be really good for you. Doing so is really good for prostate health and prostatitis. Then again, some men might feel tired after ejaculating that many times. So, for some men twenty one times per month is good and right advice, but there also may be a group of people for whom this is not so good. For people who want a general rule of thumb and are concerned about losing *thiglé*, we can say that ejaculating once every three times you have sex or once every five or seven times works, depending on your constitution and how often you have sex. For many men these kind of loose approaches are good for ensuring that one's energy and passion stays more stable.

Other common issues that many men have are erectile dysfunction and premature ejaculation. Men who experience premature ejaculation often think that the best thing for them to do is minimize ejaculation – they say "I need to learn to hold my ejaculation, so I won't ejaculate for seven days, it's better that I learn to hold it." But that is a mistake. For men who really suffer from premature ejaculation it is better if they ejaculate many times. You should not worry too much. Doing this helps with desensitization. Men with this problem should ejaculate many times and later they will feel better. Men in this situation are often over-sensitive and they have a lot of anxiety. That is why if you feel relaxed and empty, then when you have sex there is nothing to empty and this can help men with feeling more long-lasting. The ultimate point with this approach though is that it brings a sort of healing to your mind. You are less filled with anxiety and tension and anticipation, so you can have sex more comfortably, for longer, and have a better experience. When it comes to erectile dysfunction, there can be physical and non-physical causes. Many men's problems with erection are linked to psychological issues and these can be helped through meditation and cultivating of bliss. I discuss these issues a little further in the next chapter.

Issues relating to ejaculation may not be relevant for women, but this broader point about feeling relaxed and comfortable and being free from anxiety during sex is very relevant to women as well. One of the most common sexual problems for women is not finding or experiencing sexual pleasure and orgasm. This can lead some women to push too hard to experience these things and add to their stress and unhappiness. Sometimes when you want something so much, when you push too hard for it, you don't get it. Then one day you give up, and then suddenly you get it, effortlessly! This is especially true of orgasm and sexual pleasure. There is even a joke about this that compares happiness to orgasm. The joke says 'Don't chase after happiness, happiness is like an orgasm: the more you want to have one, the more you don't get!' So many women have the problem of being sexually dissatisfied or of not experiencing orgasm. Women will often blame themselves for this when the problem is really their partner. I know one lady who was not getting orgasms and she was feeling terrible about it. She tried so hard to have an orgasm but just ended up being traumatized by her husband. But later she was really surprised – she got a new boyfriend and now she has five or six orgasms on average every night! She has a better connection with her new partner, he knows how to please her, and most importantly her mind and body are no longer tight and anxious. She's relaxed, and that is one of the most crucial things when it comes to practicing Karmamudra and mindful sex.

Even though the Yuthok Nyingthig Karmamudra
practices are focused on a particular yidam couple,
one of the great things about Yuthok's teaching is that
he says you can still keep whatever secret Highest Yoga
Tantra yidams you may already be practicing and
visualize these instead as part of your meditation.

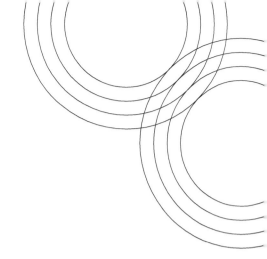

The Actual Practice

When it comes to Yuthok's style of Karmamudra there are five main steps. In this text we will focus on the first three, which can be done with or without partner. The last two steps involve generating bliss with a physical partner. As I mentioned, even if most readers haven't received *loong, tri,* and *wang* or done the preliminary practices, and even if they will not do the full Karmamudra partner training in retreat or anything like that, in any case most of us are laypeople. Most of us are already having sex regularly regardless, so I will give some simple suggestions on how to do the last two steps with your sexual partners in a simple way.

A Word on Yidams or Tantric Meditational Deities

Normally when we practice Tantric yogic meditations we begin by imagining ourselves as some specific *yidam* or Tantric meditational deity. When one receives a Tantric empowerment or *wang* as described earlier in this chapter, one obtains instructions and permissions that allow one to imagine one's body, speech, and mind as the body, speech, and mind of the *yidam* that the empowerment is for. This is all about realizing one's true nature and capacities through the pure and perfect model of the meditational deity or Buddha. 'Self-generating' or imagining oneself as a Buddha helps one to stay grounded in one's underlying wisdom, one's pure awareness, compassion, and bliss. When one practices Karmamudra one imagines that one is uniting with one's consort – whether in the imagination or one's physical partner – as the *yidam*. One's partner is also visualized in appropriate, pure Buddha form. Highest Yoga Tantra and Anuyoga practices typically involve the use of fierce or 'wrathful' Buddha forms.

Even though the Yuthok Nyingthig Karmamudra practices are focused on a particular *yidam* couple, one of the great things about Yuthok's teaching is that he says you can still keep whatever secret Highest Yoga Tantra *yidams* you may already be practicing and visualize these instead as part of your meditation. Yuthok's approach is flexible and non-prescriptive: you don't need to transform yourself into any other kind of deity, you can use the form and mantras of your own meditational deities. Yuthok's teaching is really amazing. For every specific type of Tantric yoga that he teaches he says you can use the *yidam* that you have already been practicing, rather than switch to the Yuthok Nyingthig system. Whatever meditational deity you practice you should remember that the *yidam* is like your secret lover. These days a lot of students in the West are always asking, "So, what's your *yidam*?" This kind of question is connected with the strong thirst that so many people have today for secret knowledge. Empowerment, *yidams* and so on refer to inner realities. Rather than gods or goddesses out there, they point us inwards, towards subtle realities. In general, it is best to keep your *yidam* secret. Such secrecy is necessary because this inner spiritual dimension is very personal and easy to misunderstand, and we need to contain and retain the spiritual energy that we generate through our practices.

Many readers of this book will not have received Highest Yoga Tantra empowerments and that's okay. If you don't already have a *yidam* or are not accustomed to wrathful *yidam* visualization you can do these practices by visualizing yourself and your partner as the union Buddha couple Samantabhadra and Samantabhadri, who are known as Kuntu Zangpo and Kuntu Zangmo 'All-good' in Tibetan. Samantabhadra is the primordial or unembellished Buddha. He is associated with Dzogchen or Atiyoga and he represents our innermost essence. He is our primordial awareness, ever present since before the Big Bang. Unlike many other Tantric Buddhas, Kuntu Zangpo has no special clothes, ritual objects or jewelry. He is a naked, unadorned, and completely shameless Buddha. He transcends both time and space. When you are generating or imagining deeply that you are Samantabhadra you must remember your pure, primordial awareness, your *rigpa* or clear, luminous, limitless completely natural awareness. As Samantabhadra, your body, speech, and mind are completely naked, uncontrived, pure and full of wisdom. This is represented by the colours of these Buddhas. Samantabhadra is represented as blue – this is the deep blue of infinite space. Samantabhadri, who like Samatabhadra is completely naked and unadorned is usually pure white – the white light of complete purity and of the uncontrived, empty awareness beyond all expression, all concepts, divisions, conditions and subjects and objects.

For these practices, sraight cis-gendered men typically visualize themselves as the 'male' Samantabhadra and straight cis-gender women as the 'female' Samantabhadri. As I mentioned above in the section on homosexual and transgender practitioners though, Samantabhadra and Samantabhadri are not really 'male' or 'female'. These are just labels and conventions and what these Buddhas are reminding us is wholly beyond such things. As I explained, readers should conceive of themselves as whichever *yidam* is appropriate for their lineage, training and orientations.

Samantabhadra and Samantabhadri

Step One: Posture, Subtle Body Visualization, and Breathing

The first step involves working with breathing to stimulate and enhance our orgasmic potential. To begin this practice, get a cushion or comfortable seat and sit in any meditation posture that is comfortable for you – on a chair, on the floor with your legs crossed, or in the traditional seven-point posture of Vairocana, for example. If your legs are crossed you can hold both of your knees and sit still, or you can grip anywhere on the leg. Straighten your back and keep your neck slightly down. Close your eyes, and take some deep, slow breaths to relax and focus. The instructions in the Yuthok Nyingthig suggest focusing your eyes straight ahead or pointing them slightly upwards but this is up to you and what works in your own practice. If it helps you to simply close your eyes to minimize distractions do so. You can also use an eyes half closed, half opened gaze. Next, visualize yourself as Samantabhadra, Samantabhadri or your own *yidam*, alone and not in union. Imagine that your body is empty. Your whole form is luminous and hollow, like you are made of light. You do not have any organs or muscles or bones, you are empty like a balloon. Your body is completely naked, free from all physical organs, and it is full of light. You do not have physical tissues or cells. You are also free of the gross elements, water, earth, fire, wind. You have no past, no future. You mind does not wander, it is here and now.

Establishing the Two Thiglé

Now, inside your empty form, visualize the central channel running through the direct center of your body like a thin tube. You can also visualize the two side channels along with the central channel if you are familiar with this. The central channel extends like a hollow bamboo tube of roughly one finger's thickness from the top of the skull to the base of the spine, from your crown to your perineum. It is like a strong straight pillar in a house or a post in a tent. Women can imagine that the central channel ends in their G-spot, or wherever down inside there feels especially good. You should visualize the central channel as straight and transparent, glowing with pure light that is tinged blue. If however, you find that as you set up your visualization the central channel appears to you in a different color, that is okay, just stick with whatever arises.

At the top most point of the central channel is the white *thiglé* or energy drop. This sphere of white energy is described in the text as being like mercury used in alchemy – it is cool, lunar energy and its nature is bliss. This white *thiglé* is positioned in the crown chakra at the crown. It is inside not above the head and rests under the scalp or skull at a point eight fingers' breadth back from the hairline. You should perceive the *thiglé* as a small and condensed sphere, intensely bright, pure and joyful. Then, at the bottom of the central channel in the base chakra located in the genital area is an equivalent red *thiglé*. This red *thiglé* blazes with overwhelming heat, it is like a tiny, mini sun. It glows bright red and is compared in the text to alchemical cinnabar. These visualizations relate to our basic nature. We are made of organic *thiglé*, our life begins in the bliss of union, and the white and red *thiglé* are the genetic, parental essence, sun and moon. If visualizing the white *thiglé* at the crown point is a little difficult for you or you have problems with feeling it in your head, you can touch the crown of your head to encourage yourself to feel that point and the cool, blissful, joyful sensations there. You can do the same with the red *thiglé* in your base or genital area.

As mentioned at the end of the previous chapter, these locations for the two *thiglé* (white in the head and red in the base) is the arrangement that one finds most often in texts. Both practitioners of any sex or gender can use these instructions and get good results. That said, since most texts prioritize male perspectives, this arrangement is also the one most associated with male practitioners and their bodies. If female practitioners are used to this 'white above, red below' method then they should use it. However, in the Yuthok Nyingthig, Yuthok teaches that yoginis who are just beginning the practice for the first time can invert the usual positions and cultivate the red *thiglé* at their crown and the white *thiglé* at their base. This is yet another example of the inclusivity and flexibility of Yuthok's system.

Visualizing the turquoise HUNG

In addition to the red and white drops, in the central channel, at your heart-center in the middle of your chest midway between your nipples you should visualize a small HUNG syllable. This HUNG syllable is one of the mantric speech *thiglé* I mentioned before. In the text it says that the HUNG emerges from reddish-turquoise radiance at the heart-center which is the expression of one's most essential, refined subtle energy and awareness. The HUNG syllable is Yuthok's seed syllable and so you can visualize it as a glowing turquoise color, since this is Yuthok's color.[23] This HUNG is your mind, your consciousness – it means that your mind is manifesting as Yuthok's pure Buddha awareness, that there is no separation between your consciousness and his. As with the central channel before though, if the little HUNG appears for you in any other color, that is okay too. You should imagine this HUNG in detail – take care to visualize the crescent and circle mark at the top of the letter and the *oooo* vowel mark or *shabkyu* hook at the bottom. If visualizing this Tibetan mantra syllable is too difficult for you, you can also just imagine a turquoise-blue energy drop or sphere in your heart center.

---

[23] Yuthok(pa) in Tibetan is more of a title than a personal name. Meaning 'the one with the turquoise roof,' the label was given to Yuthok after he cured the King of the nagas (Tibetan *lü*) or water spirits after the King's daughters appeared to him and requested he travel beneath a lake to their realm to help their ailing father. In repayment for his treatment, the naga spirits made showers of turquoise fall miraculously from the sky onto the roof of the great doctor's house and he thus became known as the man 'with the turquoise roof'.

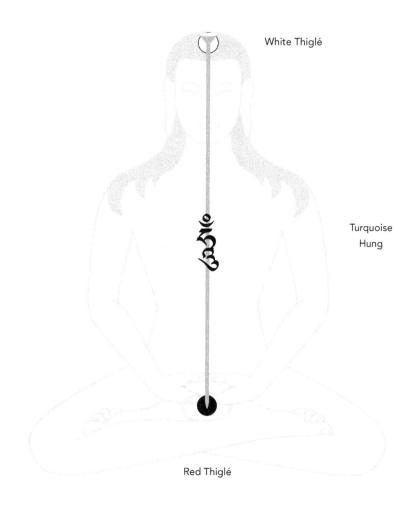

White Thiglé

Turquoise
Hung

Red Thiglé

Visualization for breathing practice

1. Sit in the seven point posture of Vairocana or any comfortable position with your spine straight.

2. Visualize yourself as your *yidam* deity or Samantabhadra or Samantabhadri.

3. Imagine that your body is empty – naked, hollow and luminous, full of light and free from all material substances such as organs, muscles, and bones.

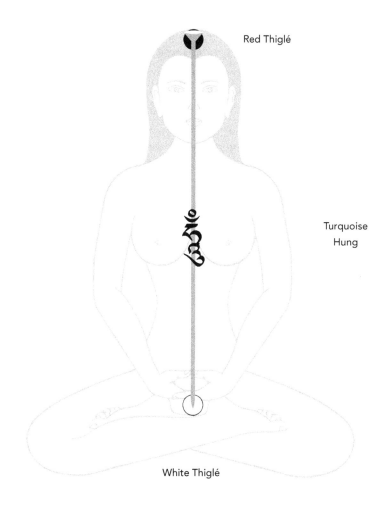

Red Thiglé

Turquoise
Hung

White Thiglé

4. Visualize the central channel, straight and transparent, glowing with pure light that is tinged blue.

5. At either ends of the central channel, at the root and crown chakras visualize the red and white *thiglés* (for men: white in head and red in base, for women: red in head and white in base.

6. At the heart center, visualize a small turquoise HUNG syllable, representing your consciousness.

7. Direct the gaze of your eyes ahead or upwards and practice the breathing. as instructed below.

Working with the breath

Once you have established and stabilized this visualization, you can then move on to the breathing part. Inhale slowly and deeply and as you do, imagine that the HUNG syllable moves down with your breath through the central channel and touches the red *thiglé* at the base or genitals. Breathe through your nose or through your mouth, as is comfortable for you. When the HUNG syllable touches the red *thiglé* the blissful heat and fire in your base intensifies dramatically. Hold your breath and really feel the red-hot blissful heat expand and amplify. Then, when you exhale, the HUNG travels up the channel to unite with the white *thiglé* at the crown. As it moves up, it 'hooks' a little bit of the red *thiglé* energy with the *shabkyu* vowel mark and brings it up to mix with the cool white lunar energy of the *thiglé* at the crown. If you are visualizing a turquoise drop of light and not the HUNG, just imagine that a portion of the red heat energy is taken up by the drop to blend with the white *thiglé*. When the HUNG touches the white *thiglé* the cool white bliss in your head expands and intensifies. Take your time before inhaling again to really feel this sensation in your head and skull. Then, when you inhale again, the HUNG pulls in a little bit of the white lunar energy through the circle at the top of the syllable, like a thread being pulled through the eye of a needle. Once again, as you inhale, the HUNG travels down and unites with the red *thiglé*, and the heat and orgasmic sensation expands in your genital area. Exhale and bring the HUNG up to the crown again, and just continue like this. Each time the mind goes down and up it multiples the *thiglé* drops. Just keep moving the HUNG or the essence of your mind, your point of awareness, up and down with your breath, stimulating and increasing the *thiglé* and your sensations. The key thing is to hold your breath as you breath in and out to give yourself some time to fully focus on both *thiglés*. Keep your gaze and eyeballs rolled up, and from time to time remind yourself again that your body is the deity's body – don't think about your physical organs or body, your body is empty like a balloon and made of light, you only have an external layer or surface skin.

Important points and troubleshooting

This breathing meditation is a very simple exercise but it is also very important. That is because it involves our desire and is tangible – when you breath and touch the *thiglé* points with your breath, awareness, hands or all of these, you really feel them. You really feel strong physical sensations. By touching and stimulating those points you should really start to feel something. At first this might feel like some kind of ticklish, tingling, or blissful sensation. If you don't feel anything at first don't worry – this just means you need to repeat the exercise and carry on practicing. If you have some scarring or physical damage or damage to the channels you may not feel very strong physical sensations but you can at least generate mental sensations initially and build them up from there.

When you inhale, part of the white energy goes down and when you exhale part of the red energy goes up. The *thiglé* in both chakras don't move at all, only the HUNG moves, taking small portions of the hot and cool, sun and moon, mercury and cinnabar energy up and down with the breath. When you inhale, you feel the heat. When you exhale, you feel the bliss. For this exercise you need to be focused but also relaxed. With this, I explain to students that Karmamudra is like café latte, milk and coffee mixing. Of course, if you have too many distracting thoughts while doing the breathing then it turns into a cappuccino! Don't worry though, cappuccino is still Okay, just keep practicing! This exercise involves mixing the two energies but the main thing is to learn to feel the sensations above and below distinctly. When you think of the lower point, it should also be joyful and blissful, but the focus is more on heat. You can also feel heat in the white light of the *thiglé* at the crown, but the energy there is more joyful. In the beginning, when the red energy goes up, you should mostly feel bliss and when the white energy goes down, you should just focus on feeling heat. When you practice more and more, both tips of the central channel will experience bliss and heat at the same time. In the beginning the most important thing is to separate and distinguish the sensations of the two chakras. Slowly as the two energies mix more and more, the heat and bliss will unify. When the red energy goes up, you will feel very blissful, yet at the same time, you will also feel heat. And the same goes for the other direction. Just do the practice slowly.

You keep breathing like this until you feel an intense build up in the base. For men recognizing this sensation is easy – according to the text, you know you are making progress if, when you inhale and bring your awareness down into the base, the heat expands and it feels like you're about to ejaculate. This is easy for men because of their ejaculatory response – they have a lot of stupid little tubes down there that always want to get something out! For women, they focus on building up their sensations until they start to feel some sort of orgasmic spasms in their genital area when they inhale. The idea is that with each inhalation you should feel such heat and bliss that you feel like you are on the verge of climaxing but *as soon as you exhale this sensation should totally disappear and be replaced with the cooler feeling of bliss in the crown chakra*. This may take some time to refine and master. In the beginning, you should just focus on moving your mind between the head and the genital area. Once you have become familiar with this process and have some control over your mind when you think of the sensations in your head area, your genital area will become empty, and the focus will move from there completely. The same thing goes for the genital area – when you inhale all of your focus and sensation moves to the base, away from your head, and you no longer feel strong sensations in your crown chakra. In the beginning, some students may have difficulty just feeling anything at all. So, at first just focus on building up the sensations. Put your hand on your genital or pelvic area and inhale and exhale. Where do you feel more heat, in your head or your genitals? Where do you feel more bliss? Can you feel both clearly and distinctly, with equal intensity? You have to practice until you feel both energies. Once you have practiced a lot, you will be able to distinguish the sensations and you will only feel cool bliss in the head area when you focus there on the out breath – the lower part will be empty. Likewise, when you inhale and bring your mind down, you will only feel the orgasmic heat, and will not feel anything in the head area anymore.

When you can experience this it means your practice is slowly working. Being able to alternate neatly between the sensations in the base and crown chakras, when you can make the heat and orgasmic bliss as intense as possible in the lower parts one minute then smoothly refocus on the bliss and only slight heat in the crown with the exhalation of breath then this is the main sign that your meditation has become fairly stable and grounded. Some students who are familiar with Tummo Yoga get a little bit confused and they think that you have to imagine the red lower *thiglé* as a tiny flame or fire. In *Tummo* inner heat practices, the red *thiglé* is visualized as a fire.

While *Tummo* and Karmamudra are definitely connected, in this case it is best not to mix practices. When we do Tummo training the fire blazes up and melts the white *thiglé* which drips down and makes the fire blaze up even more. For this first step, when you visualize the red and white dots or drops, they should appear as two small circles or spheres. Do not visualize a flame or think of a fire when you visualize the red *thiglé* and do this practice. The crucial thing in this context is to combine our visualization of the two red and white drops with our breathing. Part of the red light from the red drop rises up to the head. This isn't like a fire flaming upwards. Instead, you have a drop or sphere of glowing light, and then another smaller dot or fragment of light which rises up or separates out from this when it is taken up by the lower 'hook' of the blue HUNG syllable. The main point is that your mind or awareness, which is centered in your heart at the start of the practice, travels up and down, touching and amplifying the sensations at the location of each *thiglé*. A small portion of the red drop goes up with the blue HUNG and mixes with the white drop, and this then intensifies feelings of bliss in the crown. Then the same thing happens the other way around: a portion of the white drop descends, mixes with the red drop at the base chakra and intensifies its heat. This is like when a single drop of water falls into a larger body of water and causes ripples to appear – when the little turquoise mind-drop goes down, blissful heat multiplies and 'ripples out', when it goes up, bliss intensifies.

Heat and bliss, heat and bliss. You must combine and synchronize these with your breathing. You can hold the breath for a while, before you exhale. As you do more and more meditation, your breathing will slow down. For this you must really use and train your breathing. Combining mental concentration and visualization with breathing makes your meditation practice much more powerful. Over time, as you practice breathing, you will slowly but surely be able to enhance your inner and outer holding capacity, your ability to hold each inhalation before exhaling, and to hold your lungs empty before the next inhalation. When you have more inner holding, it means your mind is also 'held' or focused securely. It means that your mind is relaxed, that you are able to control your mind. This is called 'catching' or 'seizing' the mind through breathing.

While breathing and visualizing, to enhance the practice women can touch their right big toe and men their left big toe. Grasp the area above the nail, where the hair grows and this will help with the exercise. Also, after you have practiced combining the bliss and heat with your breathing for some moments, you can also touch specific sensitive spots parallel to each other on both sides of each ankle. Touching these points enhances your meditation. Then just lightly touch and massage both your calves and feel where the most sensitive spots are. After feeling around there for a little bit you can then continue meditating. Then take a break and use both hands to lightly massage both knees. Then return to meditating. Don't change your position, keep your back straight. These touch and massage breaks will help focus and amplify your practice. As I already explained, with Karmamudra meditation we don't have as many concentration problems, our meditation is more blissful and spontaneous. So, when you do this step, you breathe and visualize and keep a particular mental focus and just repeat this many times. Maybe you will find that you feel very good, and then you just stop your inner and mental movements and contemplate. Contemplation means meditate, and to meditate means to be mindful. The breathing and visualizing has made you feel so joyful, so nice, so blissful. Just keep this feeling of bliss in your mind and be mindful of it for as long as possible. Just relax and just feel it, alert but loose. Observe the blissful orgasmic feeling, hold it as your sole focus, feel and perceive its nature. Touching these special points aids with this mindfulness. Then when you want to build up your feeling again, just do more breathing, over and over. Refine and intensify your bliss and contemplate its nature mindfully.

Some students worry that a practice like this, which feels so good, can become addictive. But if this kind of Karmamudra practice becomes your addiction, then that is the best addiction you could possibly have! In the Sutra tradition desire is said to lead us to suffering, but this is when we don't know how to control our desire. For sure, if we don't know how to control our desire and don't understand its ultimate nature, it can absolutely lead us to a disaster. The point of these Karmamudra techniques though is to teach you how to control your desire, how to increase, enjoy and deal with your desire. We have to be able to build up and amplify our desire so that it becomes our sole focus – then we can meditate on it in an undistracted way and perceive its pure, empty nature. The more bliss we cultivate the easier it becomes for us to be mindful, to understand and control our desire.

Some students experience numbness in their base chakra when they practice this method. This is interesting. Sometimes physical injuries or trauma can affect the channels. If we have certain physical issues, these can affect our meditation or our inner feelings. In certain cases, this can be due to previous surgical operations that students may have had in the area. This is an issue that often affects women in particular. For example, C-sections, injury during vaginal birth and episiotomies can all affect women's experiences of sexual desire or bliss later on. With C sections and episiotomies there is direct physical trauma and scarring as a result of the cuts, but even with natural birth or vaginal delivery, the pelvic and genital areas can sometimes go into a state of physical shock because of the pain experienced during these processes. The good news though is that we can rebuild sensation in these areas through meditation, so I think that if you want to regain sensitivity around scar tissue or areas of injury, this meditation can really help. If in the beginning you feel only numbness, don't be discouraged. Just focus gently but firmly on your breathing, and use your mind and imagination as best you can to stimulate sensations in the crown and base. With time both your control and your feelings will increase.

Normally, if students practice a little bit every day, about ten to thirty minutes a day, it takes about one month to gain proficiency. You will know you are on the right track when you feel the bliss moving upwards when you exhale and moving downwards as you inhale. It should feel like a strong sensation: when you exhale it's here, when you inhale it's there – you will have physical sensations. As the root-text says, when you focus on the lower part, the feeling should be so strong that you almost experience orgasm. Then, if you can quickly and easily switch and transfer your awareness and all of your feeling up into the head chakra and your feeling of orgasm in the base chakra goes away, then that is the end of Step One and you have mastered the technique. The main point is that you have become the master of your own mind – whichever of the two locations you meditate on, you are ultimately able to keep your mind wherever you want. This is one of the really good and important outcomes of this meditation. It is an indication that your *loong* is moving precisely and smoothly with your mind in the Vajra Body, that you have mastered or tamed the 'wild horse of your *loong*. As with the metaphor mentioned in Chapter Three, our untrained consciousness is a man without legs and our uncontrolled *loong* is a blind horse. But when the horse has been tamed it listens to you and you can direct it where you need.

At the beginning of this book I mentioned that Karmamudra is about the practice or cultivation of orgasm and explained that orgasm is not only physical orgasm. I mentioned how we should be more mindful when we experience orgasm, so that we can experience the many sensations and feelings that are possible with orgasm, and which are much subtler and more refined compared to rough physical orgasms. These subtle feelings are more powerful than those associated with ordinary orgasm and they can transform our minds, and destroy our anger, sadness and fear. This breathing method is an introduction to this subtler orgasm, it is the first step towards this kind of practice. Breathing like this and learning to build up your heat and bliss allows you to feel yourself and your energy better, in a deeper, subtler way. When your mind is relaxed you are able to control it, and with this breathing our mind becomes more subtle. In the later stages of Karmamudra we need to feel the different levels of bliss or orgasm in each of our chakras. As we saw, empowerment opens our five chakras, and then with Karmamudra we learn to feel the great bliss and light of each chakra individually and deeply. In order to experience all of these blisses or joys we need to have a firm and subtle mind. This breathing training brings this subtlety and allows us to put our mind somewhere and have it stay there.

You can cultivate these subtle sensations whenever is convenient. Sometimes when we fall asleep we get a strong sensation of bliss or emptiness, so it can be useful to practice this breathing and visualizing when we are lying in bed before we go to sleep. You can lie down on your right side – this is the best lying down position to sleep in for the channels and winds – and you can use your hand to help guide and focus your breathing and visualizations. Often as you fall asleep the orgasmic sensations become more subtle and intense and this can be good to familiarize yourself with. Even if you don't practice this exact method, it is still important to include the central channel in your visualizations. From time to time, throughout your day, recall that special, pure HUNG energy in the central channel. This is also useful for *Bardo* Yoga training, which teaches us how to prepare for having control over our subtle consciousness when we die. As it happens, the feelings involved in this meditation are very similar to those that arise when we die, and a very similar breathing meditation is recommended in *Bardo* Yoga for before death. This meditation also involves the two *thiglés*. If you are good at this simple Karmamudra meditation then, the moment you are dying, you will not have any fear or confusion. Since you know that your exhalation is sending up the red *thiglé* and filling you with bliss and since you know that with each inhalation you are sending down the white *thiglé* and feeling full of heat, you won't die with fear, you will die with orgasm instead! This sounds a bit like a joke but this really is a good death, it is the absolute best and most helpful way to die.

Visualisation for men

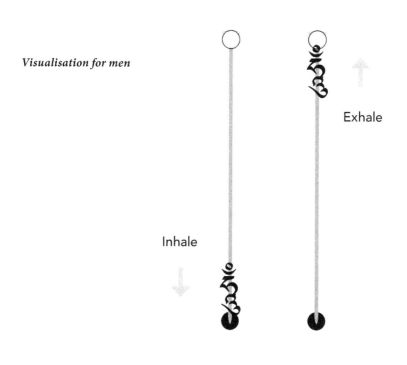

Exhale

Inhale

White *thiglé at the crown*

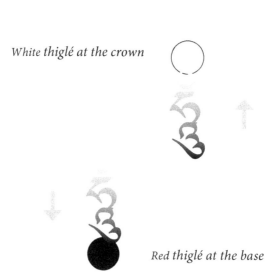

Red thiglé at the base

Steps of breathing practice (for men)

1. Sit in the seven point posture of Vairocana and do the steps of visualization as described on page 212. Breathe through your nose or mouth, as is comfortable.

2. Inhale slowly and deeply. As you inhale, imagine that the turquoise HUNG syllable at your heart moves down with your breath through the central channel and touches the red *thiglé* at the base of the central channel.

3. Hold your breath at the top of the inhale and feel the heat in your base intensify and expand.

4. Exhale slowly and deeply. As you exhale, imagine that the HUNG travels up the channel to unite with the white *thiglé* at the crown. As it moves up, it hooks a little bit of the warm red *thiglé* energy with the *shabkyu* (vowel mark below the HUNG) and brings it up to mix with the cool lunar energy of the white *thiglé* at the crown.

5. Hold your breath after exhaling completely and feel the cool white bliss in your head intensify and expand.

6. Inhale again: as the HUNG descends the central channel it pulls a little bit of the white *thiglé* from the head down with the circle at the top of the syllable to mix with the red hot energy of the *thiglé* at the base.

7. Repeat the cycle of breathing several times in a focused and relaxed way.

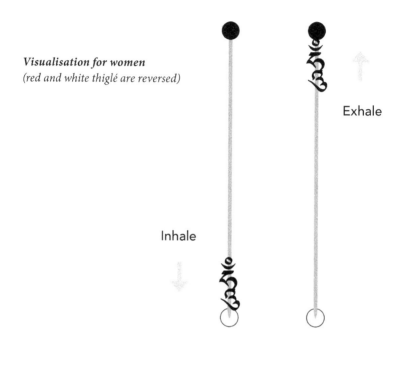

Visualisation for women
(red and white thiglé are reversed)

Exhale

Inhale

Red *thiglé at the crown*

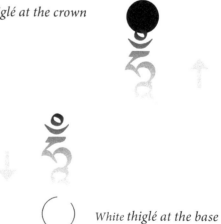

White *thiglé at the base*

Steps of breathing practice (for women)*

1. Sit in the seven point posture of Vairocana and do the steps of visualization as described on page 213. Breathe through your nose or mouth, as is comfortable.

2. Inhale slowly and deeply. As you inhale, imagine that the turquoise HUNG syllable at your heart moves down with your breath through the central channel and touches the white *thiglé* at the base of the central channel.

3. Hold your breath at the top of the inhale and feel the bliss in your base intensify and expand.

4. Exhale slowly and deeply. As you exhale, imagine that the HUNG travels up the channel to unite with the red *thiglé* at the crown. As it moves up, it hooks a little bit of the cool blissful white *thiglé* energy with the *shabkyu* (vowel mark below the HUNG) and brings it up to mix with the warm solar energy of the red *thiglé* at the crown.

5. Hold your breath after exhaling completely and feel the heat in your head intensify and expand.

6. Inhale again: as the HUNG descends the central channel it pulls a little bit of the hot red *thiglé* from the head down with the circle at the top of the syllable to mix with the cool blissful energy of the *thiglé* at the base.

7. Repeat the cycle of breathing several times in a focused and relaxed way.

*If women are accustomed to practicing in the manner described for men above with the red and white *thiglé* reversed, they can continue to do so.

Step Two: Looking, Smiling, Touching and Uniting with the Jnanamudra

The second stage of practice involves intensifying one's sensations and bliss through the imagination. For this step one imagines a partner or what is known as a Jnanamudra. Like the first step, this step is also for practice by oneself. It is a self-stimulation technique.

For this method you visualize yourself as your *yidam* with a pure Vajra Body like before. Visualize your central channel and two *thiglés*. Just like with Step One, it is very important to fully generate yourself as a perfect being in your perception. There can be no complaints – it is impossible to be too old, too stupid, or too weak for this practice when you are truly manifesting as a perfect and primordial Buddha. When you have arisen as the deity the next step is to imagine that there is a beautiful Daka or Dakini in front of you. This is your imagined consort. If you are generating yourself as Samantabhadri, Samantabhadra or whoever, imagine your partner in whatever form suits you. The idea here is to progressively engage with your perfect partner in your imagination to intensify your bliss. We do this according to the four traditional stages: *Tawa* (Looking), *Göpa* (Talking/Laughing), *Khyüpa* or *Rekpa* (Embracing/Hugging or Touching), and *Jorwa* (Uniting).

The four stages are traditionally connected with the four classes of Tantras in Vajrayana. If we understand this it can help us appreciate a little more about the deeper meaning of each of these categories. *Tawa*, *Göpa*, and *Khyüpa* are connected with three lower Tantras, or the Kriya, Charya, and Yoga Tantras respectively. These Tantras do not include instructions on Karmamudra union practice, and this is because *Jorwa* is connected with the Highest Yoga Tantras. That is why the three lower classes of Tantra do not include meditations involving Buddhas in union. We can think of these Tantras as a family of sisters. *Kriya* Tantra is all about appearances or the look of things: it is all about making your altar, your shrine, your temple and outer visual offerings and forms clean and perfect. You also wash your own body and make this clean. These external factors create conducive conditions. Charya Tantra on the other hand, is about inner thought processes. The first sister says,"Oh, it's so important to clean your room, to have a nice house" and so on. She is focused on external conditions.[24] Then the second sister says, "No, how you think and how you feel internally, your inner feeling is what is important!" So maybe even if your shrine or your temple isn't so clean, if your mind is, then that is most important. And then the third sister, Yoga Tantra, intervenes and says "Wait, no, they're both equally important!" With the Yoga Tantra, there is touching or embracing of factors. Ritual cultivation is 50/50: it is about half external and half internal preparations. Each sister is a little smarter or more sophisticated than the next – the first one says "Clean your house!", the second one says, "No, no, no! Clean your head!" and then the third one says, "Clean them both!" With each sister different methods become permissible or obvious. So when it comes to the stages of Karmamudra, one sister or level says, looking is enough, then another says, no you can laugh and smile, then the next says, no, no, you can hug. This depends on the level of desire. With each level the feeling intensifies.

With the last, oldest sister we are in the domain of Anuttarayoga Tantra, which talks about sexuality, about union. She is the biggest most mature sister. As I explained in Chapter Two, she goes beyond just external and internal realities or even a balance of both, and says, "Wait – we have to know what is our problem is, and then we have to realize that that is our talent." This is the essence of Vajrayana, the path of union, of the 'super sister' of non-duality.

Tawa / Looking

Now, sometimes when students imagine their Buddha consort they look at traditional pictures and come up with an accurate enough approximation of what they see, but their visualization is really flat and boring. Even if you visualize a Buddha Jnanamudra correctly it is useless if it does not excite you in any way. I think part of the problem here is with styles of representation and people's ideas about Tantric Buddhist imagery. If you read traditional texts that describe Tantric Buddhas like Vajrayogini, Vajravarahi, Kurukulle or Chakrasamvara these texts are very evocative and well written. The deities are described in an extremely sexy way. Now, maybe what sometimes happens is that certain painters who perhaps don't get this idea then paint *thangkas* or religious tapestries and then these end up not looking that sensual. But

---

[24] The Tantric methods described in the *Kriya* class of texts focus on the proper way to make altars and prepare offerings for external Buddhas. They emphasize the need for the practitioner to maintain bodily and mental purity, to avoid certain foods, and to practice celibacy as part of ritual practice.

according to the original texts, these images are meant to be extremely sensual and sexy. They are meant to stimulate you just from observing them, just like the texts can stimulate your mind, just by reading them.

Vajrayana is all about actively engaging our creative imagination and Tantric teachings are very visual. If you use visual stimulation well it can be very effective and transformative. When I was a child in Tibet, I remember watching performances of the *Bardo Thödöl*, the cycle of teachings that most people know today as the 'Tibetan Book of the Dead'. When I was young people would dramatize ideas from this visually as a sort of theatre. I remember these still so clearly. People would represent the anguish of a dying mother in a darkened room, there was a statue of a woman with representations of her sense organs and holes in the statue and a candle would be placed inside and light would shine out. She was distraught about her children, her children would cry out and say, "Mother, don't leave us!" and there were different lamps to represent the different colored lights of the elements and sense-consciousnesses that appear in visual form to the mind during death. These educational displays made such an impression on me.

Almost all men watch erotic movies, people all over the world read pornographic literature and so on to get turned on. We are visual beings and the porn industry and special movies is a booming, global industry. As I discussed above, porn movies are just acting, they're contrived and often quite stupid but the stimulation is still so powerful, that kind of stimulation can sometimes make desire come. So our visual sense is very important. Nowadays, there are so many naked ladies in advertising and commercials. Naked women mainly attract straight men, and these adverts are mainly aimed at them, but that's still the general human mentality. If you are a straight woman, let's say there are five men in front of you: a young one, a slightly older one, a sexy one, one with a very big belly, an old one, and so on. They are all humans and attractive in their own ways but your feelings toward them is different. Maybe you look at one of them and you really like him – suddenly heat is running up and down through your body. You don't want to see the others anymore. Maybe even if you leave and go home, you can't stop thinking of the guy you like, maybe you even dream of him! It's the same for anyone. Visual meditation is so powerful because when we are attracted to something we are focused: attraction produces powerful concentration. Looking and watching is part of the warming up or foreplay process. It is a bit like a strip show. If we like a person we see or we are watching a nice strip show, we don't have any concentration problems. We are not thinking: "What should I do tomorrow?" Our concentration is in the present – it is dripping with the saliva from our mouth, or better still, with fluids coming from other parts of our body! Where is our concentration problem now? So, looking and watching is really important.

So the first step with our Jnanamudra is to visualize our beautiful, perfect partner. If people can get aroused by watching silly porn movies, then now we are directing and watching our own special, high-quality movie in our minds. You should visualize your partner in the most appealing and stimulating way possible. Gaze upon your perfect, secret partner's form. Study every inch of their form and feel what sensations arise in you. Contemplate those feelings, be mindful of them. Look at your partner with desire and let them look back at you with a powerful, flirtatious, stimulated gaze. Feel the heat arise in you, be mindful of it. Let your desire come as it will, don't try to block it, don't feel bad about your desire. It is there to be transformed and used, it is homeopathic. Using this desire releases and liberates it. We don't want to destroy or repress or suppress our desire, we want to use it. We are all humans – we all have desire, it's not something bad or wrong. Your meditation should be very nice and very joyful.

Some students have trouble generating sexual arousal through visualizing the Jnanamudra and sometimes want to imagine an ex or current lover who turns them on while doing this meditation. If you have good memories of a former partner or a current one who turns you on it is okay to re-invoke these positive thoughts and images when you do this meditation but you have to visualize your Jnanamudra as a perfect and pure Buddha-being. You can call to mind some former love to stimulate yourself but in your mind you must think of them as a Buddha-being. Just like you yourself generate as the deity, they too are not an ordinary person.

Göpa / Talking and Laughing

The next step is talking or laughing – expressing ourselves. We've been looking at our Jnanamudra partner and they have been looking back, and our heat and arousal is increasing. If your Jnanamudra smiles at you, you need to smile back – if you don't they will be bored! Now we move to engaging in conversation back and forth – "Wow! You're looking so amazing tonight, wow, you look great!" This is not the time or the kind of meditation to fall asleep in! Don't be boring and fall asleep! If you are bored and fall asleep then you are letting your Jnanamudra do everything. This is the time to be creative. Talk to your Jnanamudra and hear them engage in conversation with you. As you look and smile at and chat with each other your desire and heat should increase. The *Göpa* stage is all about smiling, about facial communication, and about combining this smiling feeling and exchange with words as well. This is also the best time to use dirty words. I give a fuller explanation of dirty talk in the section on couple's practice below, but for now the main thing is to be free and spontaneous. Say whatever stimulates your heat and desire, and don't block any sounds of passion that come out.

Khyüpa or Rekpa / Embracing and Touching

Now we move onto the third step of self-touching. This is similar to masturbation. Some people really need self-touching to arouse themselves, while other people do not really need it. This all depends on your mind power. With each step the process, and our heat and arousal gets stronger. First you use breathing, then imagination, and now you get to you use your best partner, your hand. Of course in the Sutric path and the monastic tradition, masturbation is thought of in quite a negative light. As we saw with the nun and her demon in Chapter Two, monastic people often feel really guilty when they masturbate in secret. But according to Karmamudra, you are allowed to touch and stimulate yourself in order to enhance your feelings. This is not about rushing or proceeding directly to ejaculation and orgasm – it is not a short-cut but a way to stimulate ourselves, to make a fire, to light the wood and get it burning, and to continue to stoke that fire.

In his text, Ju Mipham suggested that practitioners do *la* massage to increase feelings of sexual desire. This is very good approach because it relies on direct physical stimulation, and many people have problems with visualization and with becoming stimulated through their imaginations alone. If you are a little weak at the breathing method, and your imagination is also weak, then physically stimulating yourself can help you feel sensations of arousal much stronger. As you touch yourself you can also do the breathing exercise and imagine that you are touching your Jnanamudra and being touched by them. You can do this in all sorts of ways. In the Kamasutra there is talk about eight or nine major erotic locations. Of course where you feel the most sensation is an individual matter: many people are sensitive on their lips, others on their ears, necks or shoulders. Breasts and nipples are sensitive for almost all people. Some people may also be sensitive around the navel area or around their kidney and thighs. Some people may also be sensitive on their hands or feet and sometimes head. It is good to know your own locations, and if you have a partner you can tell each other which of the eight spots you like to have touched the most. Some people like touching and hugging with aggression, maybe a little pain, this too is a personal question. When you practice with the Jnanamudra you can experiment with touching each other in the same way.

Jorwa / Uniting, and Working with the Chakras

All of these methods up until now – breathing, visualizing, and engaging in a deep and mindful way with your own sensations and a Jnanamudra – have been geared towards stimulating your heat and bliss, and towards deepening your feeling and understanding of your own desire and energy. I once had a student who was in his forties. He thought he was too old to practice and that he was too old for this kind of energy to come back. He had programmed himself this way, he was sure things were not working. But I explained to him that it was important that he did not rush but instead train step by step. Breathing, visualizing, looking, smiling and talking, and then touching. When he did this his energy returned. As you work with these methods your sensations and your blissful heat grow and expand. Your *thiglé* also become stimulated and multiply throughout your Vajra Body.

Now, once you have gained some practice with generating heat and bliss in this way, and with amplifying it with physical stimulation, you can also begin to work with and use your five chakras.

When we get aroused heat and bliss naturally arise in our bodies and minds. This heat then rises up and melts the white lunar, mercurial *thiglé* in our crown, and this *thiglé* then drips down from our crown chakra into our throat chakra, then our heart chakra, then our navel and base chakra. As the *thiglé* passes and circulates through each chakra we experience more and more refined levels of bliss and awareness. With ordinary, more physical

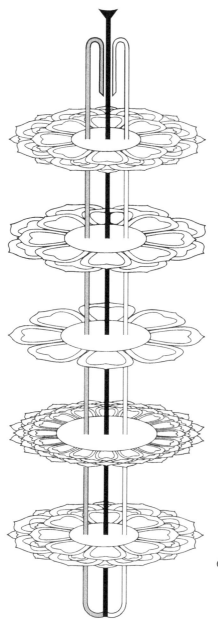

Head
32 petals (White)
བདེ་ཆེན་འཁོར་ལོ་
Dechen Khorlo
Chakra of Great Bliss

Throat
16 petals (Red)
ལོངས་སྤྱོད་འཁོར་ལོ་
Longchö Khorlo
Chakra of Enjoyment

Heart
8 petals (Blue)
ཆོས་ཀྱི་འཁོར་ལོ་
Chökyi Khorlo
Dharma Chakra

Navel
64 petals (Yellow)
སྤྲུལ་པའི་འཁོར་ལོ་
Trulpey Khorlo
Chakra of Manifestation

Root
32 petals (Green)
བདེ་སྐྱོང་འཁོར་ལོ་
Dekyong Khorlo
Chakra of Sustaining the Bliss

The five chakras

arousal and orgasm our crown *thiglé* is stimulated a little and starts to vibrate and drip down, but many people usually never feel more than a little sensation in their heads and maybe their throat area. With Karmamudra we can extend and refine our orgasmic sensation by working consciously with our chakras.

The five chakras are 'channel-wheels' positioned in the central channel. According to the traditional texts, the head chakra is white and looks like a thirty-two petalled lotus, the throat chakra is a red flower with sixteen petals, the heart chakra is blue with eight petals, the navel is yellow-gold and has sixty-four petals gold, and the base chakra is green and also has thirty-two petals. If you are not familiar with visualizing and working with these chakras in the traditional way, then you can just focus on the *thiglé* melting and dripping down to the area of each one. As you build up the heat and bliss, and eventually unite with your Jnanamudra, you should visualize the heat of your arousal rising up and melting the *thiglé* at your crown. As this happens, your bliss increases, and the *thiglé* drips down and collects in your throat chakra. If you like you can touch and massage all around your throat – the middle, and both sides as you imagine this. Focus and concentrate on the bliss building up in your throat chakra. You can help with this training by holding your breath for as long as is comfortable – feel the bliss and heat intensify in the chakra. Sera Khandro describes this progression briefly in her text in the Appendices. A special refined form of bliss is generated in each chakra.

Depending on the system one is working with there are four, eight, sixteen, or even thirty two blisses or joys. In the throat chakra there is 'bliss', in the heart chakra 'supreme bliss,' 'special bliss' in the navel and 'primordial bliss' in the base chakra. You begin by counting downwards from the throat chakra as the first bliss down to the base, and then, in some practices back upwards again from base to head. Traditionally, when you practice Karmamudra in a focused, comprehensive way in retreat you spend ten days at a time training the bliss at each chakra, starting with the throat and then progressing onwards.

You cultivate this blissful energy and let it fill up and activate your throat chakra for ten days, until when you imagine the bliss, it goes solely from the head to the throat. You meditate and visualize yourself as the deity, then stimulate yourself while imagining being with your Jnanamudra

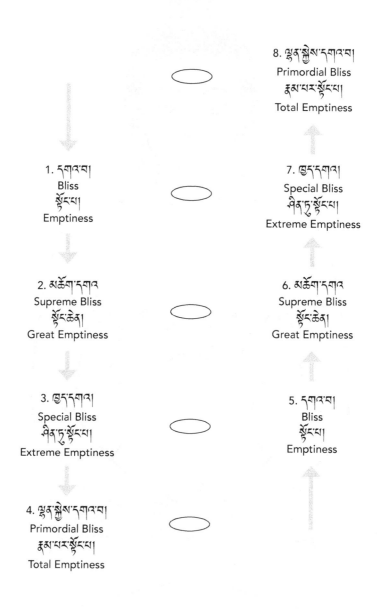

The five chakras and corresponding Eight Blisses and Emptinesses

partner. You focus all the blissful feeling in your head chakra, then imagine white drops of blissful light dripping down only as far as the throat chakra. This is how you learn to guide the bliss in your body. Normally, as the white *thiglé* drips and drips and fills up the chakra, the blissful awareness there expands like water ripples. After ten days of practicing this, for the next ten days you practice sending the energy down from the head chakra to the heart chakra. Then the following ten days you send it from the crown into the navel chakra, and then, for the following ten days from the head chakra into the base chakra. That makes forty days of practice. By the end of this you will be able to hold your bliss in each chakra separately, one by one. Through experiencing the various 'joys' associated with each chakra that come from sending the *thiglé* up and down we come to understand emptiness and experience *detong yermey* or indivisible Bliss-Emptiness. When the bliss comes then you watch the nature of the bliss and then you know that it is empty. We are free from fixations. Of course, you have to remain undistracted. That is why Karmamudra is very sophisticated but also very dangerous if pursued without proper concentration, motivation, and understanding. It is important that throughout our practice we remain focused on the nature of our bliss and our awareness, that we recognize correctly the basic nature of our minds and experience for ourselves the indivisibility of bliss and emptiness.

To help with this process, I offer some step-by-step instructions below which you can use as a guide for performing this Karmamudra meditation with the *thiglé* and chakras, whether you do so alone or as part of couple practice. This is a version of *thiglé* melting practice that I have shared with students who are not trained in advanced Karmamudra or *Tummo* practice:

Visualization

1. Visualize yourself as Samantabhadra, Samantabhadri or as your personal *yidam*, whether peaceful or wrathful. Your body is empty, perfect, and full of light. This is the true nature of your human body. You have gone beyond the misunderstanding of seeing yourself as an imperfect, limited, physical human form, now you reach back to your original state, to the state of the light body, of luminosity, purity and perfect completion.

2. Visualize the white *thiglé* (or red for women's visualization) situated at the crown of your head, filling your head with light. Imagine the *thiglé* as a tiny but infinitely bright three-dimensional sphere, a white moon inside your skull. At the same time, imagine that there is a very hot, tiny red sun or flame either behind or four fingers' width below your navel. The moon is very white and very bright, it is cool and ecstatic, while the beautiful three-dimensional sun or flame at the navel point is blazing hot, radiant and blissful (this fire at the navel is a little different to the red thigle visualized at the base of the central channel in the men's breathing exercise). Stabilize these visualizations, relax and feel the cool and hot blissful sensations that radiate from these *thiglé*. Your body is that of the *yidam*, your energy flows perfectly, and your mind is full of joy.

You should maintain this visualization throughout the four stages of Looking, Laughing, Touching and Uniting, whether practicing alone or together. If you are doing couples practice, you can sit together and do these visualizations together. It is up to you whether you want to incorporate the Union stage into this meditation or not. Depending on your schedule, how you're feeling that day, or your expertise in the practice, you can either just sit together and visualize, visualize while masturbating or engage in penetrative sex. As you progress through the stages of Looking, Laughing and Touching or Embracing you meditate on the inner heat that arises.

Imagine[25] that this sun or flame in your navel blazes – This is the inner fire that is linked with *Tummo* Yoga. This tiny little flame or bright shining sun burning under your navel or inside your belly is the essence or condensation of all your sexual heat and arousal. Imagine that this fire increases and shoots upwards. Its heat and light reaches the white *thiglé* in

---

[25] The verb 'imagine' has unfortunate etymological baggage in English. The word typically used for these kinds of meditation instructions in Tibetan is *sam*. This term, which can mean 'think that', 'perceive that', 'consider that', has a broader scope than the English 'imagine' and is not specifically associated with the visual mode. Intensive visualization is the backbone of Tantric practice but readers are reminded that all of the senses can and should be rallied in 'perceiving' and establishing elements of the Vajra Body during meditation. So, if readers find it difficult to visualize or 'see' these forms, they should not be discouraged and should remember that 'imagining' may be just as much, if not more about hearing, tasting, smelling and just generally 'feeling', 'focusing' or 'knowing' than about seeing.

[26] Some texts describe the white *thiglé* as being like butter that is progressively melted by the inner fire.

your head and starts to melt it. The white *thiglé* moon is like ice, not as cold but just as pure and beautiful.[26] The fire of your bliss travels up from your navel to your head and the frozen 'ice' of the *thiglé* starts melting.

Descending the Thiglé

3. As the *thiglé* melts it drips down and begin to collect in your throat area, within the throat chakra. These drops pool in your throat like intensely luminous drops of moonlight and you experience a special, refined form of bliss. This bliss is similar to the sensations you feel when you start hugging, kissing, or caressing your lover – it is extremely pleasant and joyful. While this occurs you still feel the heat and natural energy of the fire in your body, rising up. The more that this heat comes up the more the bliss of the white *thiglé* melts and drips down. Meditate on this bliss in your throat chakra for some time, experiencing it as inseparable from emptiness.

4. As the fire rises up the inexhaustible white *thiglé* melts more and more and begins to drip down into your heart-center. The bliss expands strongly, it doubles in strength or intensity as it moves to the heart chakra. And all the while the heat of the *Tummo* fire continues to intensify, increasing your bliss, your joy, your pleasure. Meditate on this mounting ecstasy!

5. The white *thiglé* continues to melt more and more and drops down to the navel chakra of 'Special Bliss'. With each chakra the bliss gets stronger. Each of the chakras are filled completely in turn, and then one by one they overflow and pour down to the next one in the sequence.

6. After some time the *thiglé* drips down to genital area and you experience extremely strong bliss. Meditate on the bliss that you feel as the *thiglé* drops into the genital chakra. You are free from worry, from bad memories, all your traumas and wandering thoughts. Your mind is calm and joyful.

7. After you have meditated on the bliss in the genital chakra for a while take a deep breath. Inhale and hold your breath while pulling in the navel and contracting your anal sphincter. Holding your breath like this will increase your body temperature and your bliss. Hold your breath as long as you can and then when you can't hold your breath any longer, exhale slowly. Breathe slowly and gently – don't strain yourself. Then inhale and hold your breath

in the navel again. See or perceive the fire located there shooting up. The more the fire increases the more joy and bliss you experience. The *thiglé* melts and drips down rapidly and you feel extreme ecstasy.

Raising the Thiglé

For the next stage, the *thiglé* starts to go back upwards from the base or genital chakra to the navel. As before, as the circulating *thiglé* nectar reaches each new station or chakra, your bliss becomes even more intense and refined.

8. Move the *thiglé* nectar from the base to the navel, then from the navel to the heart, up to the throat chakra and then back to the head. Meditate on the bliss-emptiness in each chakra.

9. When the *thiglé* returns to the head imagine that your entire body is filled with *thiglé*. Your body is like a pure, crystal bottle filled with *thiglé*, radiating and vibrating joy and bliss. Where there is *thiglé* there is joy, where there is *thiglé* there is bliss. You no longer just experience *thiglé* in your chakras but through your entire body – through all your sense organs, through your skin, your fingers and toes – everywhere.

As you rest in this state of pervasive bliss you are freed from all the types of anger. You are freed from all possible desires, from all addictions – you feel so blissful, you don't need to drink alcohol, smoke, work, take drugs or do anything at all other than abide in this perfect experience. In this state, you xperience perfect inner clarity and are freed from all types of ignorance or confusion. This indivisible bliss-emptiness exists throughout your body, your mind, it pervades through space, through everything in existence, through past, present, and future. It is the nature of all Buddhas.

This ecstatic bliss and feeling comes from your mind and *thiglé* but now you don't need to meditate on the *thiglé* as before. All you need to do is just experience the limitless bliss of your naked mind. Don't try, just relax, let go. Your mind is like a crystal or a body of still, clear water. Look into space. Your view is as vast and unencumbered as space, it is free from directions or center, from any reference points at all. The nature of your mind is like all pervasive space, free from categorizations of good or bad. It is light, pure sunlight shining limitlessly throughout all space. It is what is called 'the union of clarity and emptiness'. The nature of your mind is pervasive, it transcends time and space. You can't put your mind in a box or imprison it in limited space. It is limitless, free from time and space. It is free from existence and non-existence, it is beyond good or bad, beyond any categories or boundaries. It is transcendent and blissful. If your mind stays, let it stay, if it moves around let it move around. The nature of mind is free from either one location or movement.

However you experience your mind, your thoughts or your emotions, let these be in a very free way. Whether your mind stays or moves around, its nature is bliss. Even if your mind is thinking thoughts, its thinking and those thoughts too are blissful. If you find your mind is at rest, then let it stay blissfully calm and peaceful. Your mind is free from shape, from color, free of all qualities. It is universal, transcendental, clear, transparent. Don't limit your mind or imprison yourself, don't judge yourself – your mind is totally free from space and time, it is free from pain and suffering, free from hopes and fears.

When you experience this state you are like a Buddha, you are resting in Buddha mind. When you experience yourself as a 'normal', limited person your mind is in parts. Your consciousness has been placed into boxes – happy moments, unhappy moments, worry, no worry. It is as if your mind has been fragmented into many pieces. When you are in this state, the ineffable, transcendent state of Samantabhadra, you are free from the boxes or capsules of self and concepts. In this state there can be no doubt that you are a Buddha. The nature of your body is the rainbow body, the nature of your winds and energy is enlightened wisdom energy and the nature of your mind is Bliss-Emptiness.

This stage is very important. In Atiyoga, clear, quartz crystals are used as an analogy for the nature of mind. Like a crystal, the nature of your mind is clear and pure, totally transparent and limpid. Any light that shines on a crystal is refracted through it and appears as rainbow light. The crystal allows all and any colors to manifest. This is like our mind. Our mind is the crystal and the light is our awareness, our mind's activity or thinking. Light shines on and through the crystal and all sorts of colors or displays are manifested. But the light does not change or influence the crystal in any way. The crystal takes the light, the light shines through it and a full spectrum of visible colours is produced but the nature of the crystal never changes.

It remains transparent. Like the surface of a mirror that reflects images but remains unchanged it stays just as it is. So, this is like our thoughts.

This is how our mind works according to Atiyoga. Atiyoga says that whatever we experience, whatever appearances or 'colors' arise, we should just relax and let our sense organs experience it. If you hear nice music you should enjoy it, experience it and let it arise fully. Then, once the nice music has stopped or is finished, you are no longer attached, you no longer experience craving. "Oh! Where is that music again, I want more!" You're no longer craving – you experience the music fully, relish it in the moment it appears. Even if there are bad noises – traffic noises, say – these come, you experience them and then you let them go. This is the meditation of and on the five senses or sensorial experiences. Our lives are based on sensory experience so this meditation is extremely important. [27] If you know how to handle these experiences without fuelling craving or aversion then your life becomes rich – amazing and beautiful. If you don't know how to handle these five sensorial experiences, however, you get into trouble. You eat something sweet then you want it more, you want it more and more and more and more and more, and then you are addicted. If you don't have that sweetness your life no longer functions. That's the definition of addiction. You can't function normally without certain substances and experiences – alcohol addiction, drug addiction, work addiction, gambling addiction, whatever it may be, it's all the same. So, I really like this analogy of the crystal. Atiyoga says that if there is light we should let it shine through our crystal. When there is light, let there be rainbows, when there is no light, no rainbows, that's also okay. The crystal remains pure and unchanged. In darkness or in light the crystal's nature never changes.

From time to time in your everyday life, you can use the simple meditation of imagining your head, your eyes, your heart, or your entire body as a clear crystal or pure, still, luminous lake. This can help connect you to your natural peace and clarity, and what is called *rigpa* in Tibetan, our innate, pristine awareness beyond all qualities and elaborations. Recognizing the true nature of our mind is very important, whether you

---

[27] What Dr. Nida is describing here parallels Shakya Shri's instructions in his Atiyoga style Karmamudra teaching included in the Appendices: "Maintaining the View of the ultimate reality or nature of phenomena, work with the creative energy of the senses and train repeatedly [to perceive] every form, sound, smell, taste and tactile sensation as the magician's illusory display [that they truly are]." [See p. 295].

practice Karmamudra or not. To help readers recognize this state, I include below a short summary I compiled of the special Mahamudra/Atiyoga *trekchö* instructions found within the Yuthok Nyingthig:

གཡུ་ཐོག་སེམས་ཁྲིད་རིག་པའི་ཡེ་ཤེས་མ་བཤུགས་སོ།

'The Primordial Wisdom of Pristine Awareness':
Yuthok's Teachings on the Essential Nature of the Mind

གཡུ་ཐོག་སྙིང་ཐིག་གི་ཡིད་ཆོས་སྐྱར་འཆར་བའི་ཁྲིད་ལ།
རིག་སྟོ་བདེ་ཆེན་ལམ་དང་སྒྲེང་སྒོ་རྣམ་གྲོལ་ལམ་གཉིས་ཡོད་པ་ལས།
ཕྱི་མ་རྣམ་གྲོལ་ལམའམ་སེམས་ཁྲིད་རིག་པ་རྗེན་མའི་སྙིང་བསྡུས་ནི།

There are two direct or oral instructions (*tri*) in the Yuthok Nyingthig for manifesting the mind as Dharmakaya or the Ultimate Reality Body: The Path of Great Bliss of the Lower Gates [i.e. Karmamudra] and the Path of Complete Liberation of the Higher Gates[(Mahamudra]. The latter, the Path of Complete Liberation, is a distillation of *sem tri* instructions, that is, teachings on the essential nature of mind or naked, pristine awareness (*rigpa*).

ཐོག་མར་ཟླ་གཅིག་ལ་སེམས་གནས་པའམ་འཇོག་བསྒོམ་བྱ། དེ་ནས་ཟླ་གཅིག་ལ་སེམས་འཕྲོ་བའམ་འགྱུ་བསྒོམ་བྱས་རྗེས། འགྱུ་གནས་གང་རུང་གི་སེམས་རོ་མཐར་ཕྱིན་པར་དཔྱད་བསྒོམ་གྱིས་ཟླ་གཅིག་ལ་ཉམས་སྐྱོང་ཐོན་པར་བྱ། དེ་ནས་རིག་རོ་ནི་གཤམ་གསལ་ལྟར་སྟེ།

First, for one month, one meditates on the mind in its resting or 'abiding' state. Then, one meditates for another month on the mind in flow or motion, on the proliferation or radiating of thoughts. After this, one meditates by investigating exhaustively the essence or 'true face' of the mind either at rest or in motion, analysing these to their ultimate conclusion. One does this for another month, until meditative experiences arise. Then one meditates on the essence or face of pristine awareness (*rigpa*) as described below:

སྣང་སྲིད་འཁོར་འདས་སེམས་སུ་ཐག་ཆོད་བྱ།། སེམས་དེ་ཡེ་ནས་གདོད་མར་སྦྱོས་པ་
ཐལ།། གཤིས་ཆེར་མ་གྲུབ་སྣ་ཚོགས་མདངས་སུ་འཆར།། འཆར་བཞིན་འཆར་མཁན་གཞི་རྩ་བྲལ་བར་གྱུར།། སྨྲ་བསམ་ཤེས་བརྗོད་བློ་ཡི་ཡུལ་ལས་འདས།། ཐམས་ཅད་འདུས་པའི་རིག་པ་གཅེར་བུར་ལྡང་།། སྣང་བ་ཕྱི་དང་རིག་པ་ནང་མ་ལུས།། ཡེ་ཤེས་ཟངས་ཐལ་མ་ལུས་གཉིས་སྣང་མེད།།

"Confirm for yourself that all that exists and appears
in Samsara-Nirvana is in the mind.
The essence of mind is primordially unconditioned,
it is always and already free from all mental elaboration.
Though it has no basis at all, it shines forth in a myriad of colors
Yet even as it manifests it is entirely devoid of any 'manifester',
is wholly without any basis or root source.
It is beyond anything that can be spoken or thought of, understood
or expressed, it is wholly beyond the realm of the conceptual mind.
It is the bright and vivid naked awareness which subsumes all things,
Outer appearances don't just stay on the outside,
rigpa does not just exist on the inside,
Primordial wisdom does not just pass unobstructed
between inside and out,
Pristine awareness is transcendent –
It is completely free of duality, devoid of the perception
of an object out there and a perceiver in here.

ཉིན་མོངས་དན་པ་སྐྱེ་བྱ་སྐྱེ་མཁན་བྲལ།།
ཡེ་རྗེ་མ་བཞིན་གྱི་གནས་ལུགས་དེ་ནི།། མཐོང་རྒྱ་མེད་པའི་ཆོས་ཀྱིས་མཐོང་བར་བྱ།
ཉམས་སྐྱོང་རིག་པའི་ཡེ་ཤེས་འགྱུར་མེད་འཆར།།
སོ་མ་ལྷག་པ་མ་བཅོས་རང་མདངས་ {བཟོ་མེད} སྐྱོད།
རྗེན་ཁྲོས་མེ་བའི་དང་ལ་མ་ཡེངས་བསྒྲངས།།
ཚེ་འདིར་ཀུན་བཟང་དགོངས་པ་མངོན་འགྱུར་ར {ཐེ་ཚོམ་མེད}།།

242

It is devoid of any 'rejecter' who rejects bad afflictive emotions
and mental states,
It is the underlying basic condition of being, the primordial is-ness –
Perceive it, without perceiving anything at all!
Meditative experience of the primordial wisdom
of natural awareness manifests unwaveringly,
Let go into this natural, unrestrained, uncontrived,
and spontaneous self-radiance of being without trying to make it happen,
Maintain this bare, loose and relaxed state without distraction,
And you will without a doubt actualize the Buddha-mind of
Samantabhadra in this very lifetime.

ཅེས་གཡུ་ཐོག་གསར་མ་ཡོན་ཏན་མགོན་པོའི་གསུངས་ཆོག་བཅད་དུ་བསྡུ་མཁན་ནི་སྨན་པ་ཌི་
རྒྱ་ཡིན། ༢༠༡༢-༡༠-༡༠ལ།

*From the teachings of Yuthok Yönten Gönpo the Younger (Gönpo 2005),
summarized in verse by Dr. Nida on the 10th of October 2017.* [28]

Additional Advice

Normally the *Tummo* fire is not directly mentioned or explained in the context of Karmamudra practices. With *Tummo*, we visualize the red *thiglé* as a tiny blazing flame which flares up and melts the white *thiglé* in the crown. If some readers are used to visualizing *Tummo* fire then that is fine, but in general when we do these Karmamudra practices we get automatic, real, physiological heat from our cultivated arousal. That heat is similar to the heat generated in *Tummo* practice. Normally when we are active our body generates heat. Heat comes with excitement, stimulation, movement and arousal and so on. So, for this practice it is possible to just imagine that the heat we are already experiencing as part of our arousal is melting the *thiglé*. Or sometimes even without that heat you can visualize that the white

---

[28] Readers who would like to learn more about Yuthok's Ati Yoga teachings are encouraged to consult Dr. Nida's *Mirror of Light* (Chenagtsang, 2016) and *Weapon of Light* (Chenagtsang 2017).

thiglé itself is melting and dripping down. If you are used to working with visualizing fire that is okay but generally speaking when we are aroused in any case the heat is there, so it is not essential that one actually visualizes fire blazing up from the the navel. Body heat from bliss and excitement is already there and the white *thiglé* is already dripping, so the idea is to just work with this more mindfully according to your own training and capacity.

It is important to keep in mind that you may not always feel the bliss and heat as strongly as at other times. If you have not had sexual contact for a while, then you are likely to have stronger sexual desire. If you had sex recently, your sexual energy might feel lower. In general, the more sexual desire you have the better you will be at doing Karmamudra practices. The idea is to learn how to use that desire for your meditation to make you more focused and to improve your concentration. If you already have a lot of sexual desire, visualizing and nurturing bliss and heat will be easy for you. You may at times be able to climax or ejaculate in the usual way with your imagination alone but remember that you should not be trying to have a regular orgasm that puts a stop to your desire and ends your meditation. Your goal is not to climax or ejaculate, even though this may occur. What you want is to be able to control and expand your orgasmic response.

If you are really turned on, you should pause. Sometimes your mind is so powerful that it can make you ejaculate or climax, so if you are feeling like you might be on the verge of coming and you can't control it, you can stop the practice, get up, walk around, take a cold shower or do whatever you need to cool down. After you have cooled down, you can start again. Of course, you are encouraged to ejaculate (see the section above for more information on ejaculation) and can have more regular short orgasms, but through your training you should control it so that it is not as often. When we don't have a regular orgasm and cultivate a more expansive orgasm instead, our sexual energy remains and grows. This is the case for both men and women. Once you climax or ejaculate, that kind of energy often disappears. The heat that you cultivate through these practices should be like a joyful fire that makes your mind more clear and awake. It has very strong qualities. It can make you a happier person. If you find that the heat is too strong, you should back down a little bit and pause and then you can start again. Alternatively, if you don't have enough sensation, you can massage and physically stimulate yourself, just not to climax.

In his text, Yuthok says that if yogis or yoginis feel the urge to climax they should do some physical yogic exercises. One exercise mentioned is called the 'Liberated Lion'. To do this pose, press down on the flaps of your ears and seal them with both of your thumbs, then clasp your lips in between the pinkie and ring fingers of each hand to seal your mouth, seal your nostrils shut with each middle finger, and press your eyelids down and seal your eyes with your two index fingers. This forms parallel lines across your face. Inhale, close all your orifices, hold your breath and then rotate your head and torso in a circle five times clockwise and then five times counter-clockwise. Swing your head and upper body quickly and smoothly in a gentle arc, holding your breath until all repetitions are complete. You can do this exercise either sitting or standing. When done, unlock your fingers and exhale forcefully from your mouth and nose, making a loud HAAAAA! sound. This yogic exercise is more for the upper part of the body.

An even easier exercise to do is to lie down on your back with your knees bent, inhale, and lift your lower back into the air. You can use your arms to push up your body. Hold your breath while keeping the spine lifted, then exhale and release the posture. Alternatively, if you have received transmission and instruction, you can do Bumbachen or 'vase breathing' as well. This important yogic exercise involves holding and churning the breath in the lower abdomen.

Sometimes when you do the Karmamudra breathing exercises you might feel some tension or pain in your body. Sometimes you feel it in your head, in your chest or in your back or you might feel pain in many different areas, accompanied by a sensation of blockage. One of the effects of doing these meditations is that your energy starts to move better, but sometimes, as the energy moves it can get stuck and cause pain and blockages. This is what is called *tsa soog*, *loong soog* and *thig soog* in Tibetan, 'pain caused by channels, by winds and by *thiglé*'. When you send the *thiglé* up and down its energy can sometimes get stuck and cause discomfort. If you feel pain, you can do the following exercise as well: sit cross-legged or in the lotus position and with your arms straightened and your hands pressing on the ground, lift up your whole body with your hands. Lift your buttocks and tailbone a few inches off the ground and then drop your backside firmly but gently back onto the ground. Be sure not do this too hard so that you do not to hurt yourself. Hold your breath as you do the exercise, raising and dropping your buttocks down twenty one times in quick succession before exhaling. This is called the soft *beb* or 'dropping down' exercise. It is an excellent cure for energy blockage and for resolving feelings of pain in the body.

When you are doing these practices it is okay if you have a mini-climax or orgasm. Very strong, sudden and explosive climaxes can dampen your desire. They have that bipolar quality I mentioned before – they are very sudden and very high and then you are very low and very tired. Mini-waves or peaks of bliss and stimulation can sometimes be good, however. These can be used to continue building up more orgasms, and extending our bliss. Our goal is to build up these mini-orgasmic waves until they become stronger and stronger, and to hold these for longer and longer periods of time. If you know how to do this you can keep an orgasm going for more than one, two, three, six, or maybe even twenty-four hours! Can you imagine going to work with a mini-orgasm in your mind? Everyone will wonder why you are so happy, everyone will be thinking to themselves, what is it about this person, they seem so cool! If someone makes a disparaging comment about or towards you, you won't care. This is the aim of Karmamudra: to extend and refine our bliss.

Most of the time we think that the aim of sexual intercourse is to have a regular, short orgasm. This kind of orgasm is a powerful experience of course, but once that powerful experience is done and gone, it evaporates. We experience a high sudden peak of happiness, followed by a very low trough or dip, and then sleep. Some people object that we don't need to learn about sex or talk about and do research into orgasm because it is just a natural, mechanical response not worth our time. The Karmamudra yogis and yoginis of the past did a lot of research to understand what orgasm is. They wanted to know how many levels of orgasm humans are capable of, how humans can enhance their orgasms and experience them better, how they can use them as a powerful tool to transform their energy and mind. I encourage anyone who is skeptical about these matters to do their own experiments. Skepticism about amazing claims is good and natural. That is why I recommend that skeptics do three months, or even better three years of Karmamudra retreat. Spending time in retreat allows you to develop your own body, energy and mind, which then allows you to see for yourself what you are really capable of.

If you want to seriously practice Karmamudra together as a couple then you need to set aside three or four weeks of time to do a couple's retreat. That way, you can really feel the energy of Karmamudra. Think of this month long period as like your honeymoon. Some of my students have a bad reaction to this – for example, most honeymoons are only one week in Romania! As always, I advise these students to then just do as much as they can, as thoroughly as they can, within the time that they have. You can do a one week Karmamudra retreat – that is also good for developing a strong base in the practice. You can also do solitary retreats of varying length, and of course, practice regularly at home in the midst of your daily life. Typically, however, when you go on a Karmamudra retreat as a couple, this is something that you should keep secret and not talk about openly. There are practical and energetic, spiritual reasons for this, similar to how one should keep one's personal *yidam* private as I discussed above. One traditional name for Karmamudra retreat in Tibetan is *sangchö* or 'secret conduct'. If you want to practice together you need to find a perfect, undisturbed place – maybe somewhere in nature, or at a holiday resort. As always, if you would like to engage in intensive retreat practice you should do so under the guidance of your guru and have a clear idea of what is required.

In conclusion, there are three main steps for training the mind through desire: breathing, imagination, and physical stimulation. This is a soft way to train ourselves but it provides crucial preparation for partnered practice. Once you have mastered your own body, energy, and mind, partner practice can be extremely powerful.

Step Three: Partner Practice and Tips for Couples

In this section, I would like to give some suggestions for ordinary couples who want to apply some of these techniques and have sex more mindfully. I believe this is truly important. Vajrayana tells– us that we have these four states of being and awareness – the waking state, deep sleep, dreaming, and orgasmic states. These make up the full spectrum of who we are and all we can perceive. Every day we wake up, every day we have deep sleep, every day we dream, and many of us have orgasms every day as well. Orgasm is an inherent part of ourselves and our human experience, so why don't we practice Karmamudra methods every day? So many Vajrayana practitioners do meditations while they are awake, they train for the *Bardo* and practice Dream and Sleep Yogas, but then they when it comes to the state of orgasm they neglect this. Orgasm is just one more opportunity to understand and gain control over our minds, to realize our basic nature.

Of course, the problem is that many people don't experience that and that is why they are so stressed and unhappy. Even for people who are having a lot of ordinary orgasms and quick, mindless sex this can end up just contributing to their unhappiness, attachments and addiction. So I really believe that even if you are physically tired, short on time, and so on, you and your partner can still take a few moments before going to sleep to just sit and practice the breathing meditation explained above together. Couples can sit together and inhale and exhale at the same time and visualize together. Then, if they are excited and both want to they can move onto Looking, Laughing, Touching and Uniting practice, or else they can just go to sleep. These procedures might not be the full, traditional, ultimate Karmamudra practice, but it is easy and powerful and a part of Karmamudra too. Readers can get a taste of what is possible with these practices, and maybe go on to do the Yuthok Nyingthig preliminaries and receive teachings to go more deeply into these spiritual practices.

When one practices Karmamudra all of the *kuntok* are spontaneously stopped, you don't have to do anything. I think many people know this instinctively. When people are very angry, when they are very stressed or nervous what do they do? They masturbate! If they masturbate well and have a good orgasm then they feel so relieved and feel like everything is okay. This is connected with the *kuntok*. These are conceptual states or mental afflictions, and they are the root cause of all our suffering. And all of these can be dissolved through Karmamudra.

When couples are having sexual intercourse, if they imagine their *thiglés* melting and dripping into their chakras then they can also eliminate all of their *kuntok gyebchu* as described above. So many people are beset by the three poisons, they are filled with desire, stressed, angry and confused – this is our samsaric nature so this is a really good practice for sexually active people to be doing. If couples can do this practice it will go a ways towards reducing and eliminating all the *kuntok gyebchu*. If we work with it skillfully, sexual experience can become a kind of eliminator or transformer. It changes your mood, your bad feelings, it is a good pain killer – it has so many positive capacities. It is my belief that anyone can apply these principles and benefit. That is why it is so important for couples who have frequent sex to engage in *mindful* sexual intercourse based on practices and ideas from Karmamudra.

The four traditional stages of looking, laughing, hugging/touching and penetrating that I have outlined above for the solo practice all apply to the importance of taking time as a couple too. They are all about cultivating intimacy and romance. These methods are not about just five or ten minutes of sexual activity where one partner just tries to fulfill their needs as quickly as possible. Even if you aren't a great Karmamudra adept, taking this approach is really good and important. It doesn't matter whether you are an old or young couple, it is like food. Humans need variety. You can't just say, "Oh, I always eat pasta! It tastes fine the way I always make it so I'll just eat it like that every day!" Sometimes you have to change the way you make the pasta or maybe you decide to eat pasta but you eat it in a different bowl or in a different location. You need variety, so you can enjoy different flavors and tastes. So, for couples, it is good to sometimes change locations and so on. It is good for couples to really find an ideal space for sexual intercourse, to find and set aside good time to be together. Sex should not be about the two of you just adding your individual stress together and expressing your frustrations onto each other or using each other selfishly for your needs. "Okay, I want to have sex, I want to ejaculate!" It is really essential to have mutual understanding and respect.

All of the four stages used in solo Jnanamudra practice and all of the possible procedures for increasing enjoyment or bliss in your mind through the five sensory contacts apply to partnered practice as well. When it comes to doing Karmamudra with your partner, **'Looking and Watching,'** and physical appearance is also very important. Both partners should dress very well and alluringly for each other. I know a woman who is in her fifties, and she likes to change her style, her hair color and her jewelry on a regular basis. In this she is a lot more like a younger woman. When I asked her why she did this, she told me that she does these things not only for her own enjoyment but for her husband as well. She told me: "When I keep changing, for my husband, it's like I'm a new girl each time and he never loses his interest in me!" I thought this was very smart. This is in line with what Kamasutra teaches – you always have to be attractive to your partner. This is not just the woman's responsibility like some people think. Even if you have been married for twenty years, thirty years, if both partners play skillfully with their appearance and with their visual creativity and imagination then they will both still have a fresh feeling for each other. If you engage artfully and artistically with your sexuality, there is always a way to play, to feel sexy, and you will never get bored. You will always have energy and desire that you can use in beneficial ways.

Talking and Laughing is a crucial part of partner practice too. Sexuality is an art, which means you really have to be an artist with your desire and sensuality. Artistry can be about appearance, how we dress, use makeup and so on, like with the previous step. When it comes to speaking, artistry can be about kind and soothing or pleasant words and conversation. Smiling, talking and verbal communication also goes along with listening to music, lighting incense, eating delicious food and other methods for engaging the five sense organs. This is the moment when you can eat and savor just a little bit of chocolate and burn incense or put on perfumes if you enjoy that. Whatever contributes to your overall desire, your overall enjoyment, works here. Remember, with Karmamudra you really have to cultivate and savor sensory pleasure. So, if you like to eat chocolate keep a small piece of chocolate in your mouth, let it melt slowly, savor it mindfully. Your tongue is connected with the sense-consciousness of taste – the more the chocolate stays on your tongue, the more your brain will be satisfied. If you don't savor the taste and you just swallow it mindlessly in one go, your mind will still be full of desire for more chocolate. Your mind will still be unsatisfied and have the desire to taste more chocolate even if your stomach is already full of it. This mindful way of savoring sensory pleasures is key to the practice of working with and transcending ordinary desire.

Eating delicious, sweet substances and saying sweet words can stimulate desire but even communicating in a rotten way can be very powerful and sensual. As with Jnanamudra, dirty talk can be very useful and important for partner practice. Exactly which 'dirty' words work to increase your and your partner's desire is quite an individual thing. What stimulates one person might make another person run away! As it happens, in his texts Lelung Rinpoche uses the exact terminology used in English: the Tibetan term *tzok tam* literally means 'dirty talk'. Lelung was a real expert in this. You might think this is a bit shocking or silly, but this is a really interesting subject for scholars of Tantra. Everyone knows that when we are being intimate, kissing or touching or engaging in sexual intercourse, our speech or voice becomes like music, free and spontaneous. Everyone also knows that if there is a good song or good music playing you can dance better, and when it comes to sex, all our dirty words and the sounds that we make during intercourse are the same kind of encouraging soundtrack. If you're having sex and your partner is moaning "Ah! Ah! Ah! Ah!" you can feel that energy. It is so powerful that even if they are faking, that music can still affect us! It is a real art. In his Kamasutra-Karmamudra text Ju Mipham says: "Don't block your voice." Whatever noises you make, this 'AM!' or 'HAM!' syllable, whatever it is, whether they are heavenly or hellish sounds, Mipham says to let them come. He explained that those are the vibrations of our channels. He said that we should feel free to let them come, that we should not stifle them out of embarrassment or fear. I think that normally (and especially as far as straight porn movies are concerned!) men believe that it is more important that the man gets the woman excited, that he makes her cry out, and so on. But men's verbal vibrations are important for their partners too. Whatever your sexual orientation, the sounds you make with each other are very powerful. As Mipham says, these uncontrived and spontaneous sounds of desire are in fact the innately produced mantra-sounds of the channels in our subtle body.

Another aspect of 'talking' and expressing yourself is the importance of having open conversations with your partner so that you can understand each other better. A lack of open and respectful communications in relationships is one of the main causes of divorce. When couples do not have much sexual contact, there is not much of a base for relations. The combined absence of good sex and good communication very often leads to problems and separation. Partners might become interested in other people, they might think someone else is better sexually or looks better, or they might become more attracted to someone who makes them think that they understand them better, or can listen to them or support them better. Naturally, partners may end up divorcing in these situations. Getting divorced once when things don't work out is okay, but getting divorced a second, third, or even fourth time, I'm not so sure! These days it seems like there are some people who are always busy getting divorced! That is why I think that the ideas and basic practices of both Kamasutra and Karmamudra are good for married people. If couples do not have open conversation, it is very hard to understand one another and mutual understanding is so important. It might be true that a couple is having a lot of sex, but this is not worth much without a shared understanding.

When it comes to sexual intercourse, one problem heterosexual women often face is that men don't want to take the necessary time to warm up their partners before having penetrative sex. In addition, men often don't want to try the positions that the women they are having sex with might like. They only want to do the positions they like. A third problem is that men reach their orgasmic peak and ejaculate really quickly on average, and so are finished before women are even getting started. For this reason, in many cases women think men are too quick to climax, although in some cases, women may feel that men take too long. When men understand their partners and their needs and desires, then taking too long shouldn't be a problem, but if a straight man doesn't understand his partner very well she might be laying there thinking "Oh my God! When is he going to finish?!" Meanwhile the man is there thinking, "Oh, wow! I am doing such a good job,I have such amazing stamina, oh yea!" The same applies to gay men or women who don't understand their partners. If your partner is tired or not so aroused, and they say so, then you can pause for a bit, maybe drink some tea, watch a porn movie together for a little while. These are ways to communicate with one another and to re-connect.

With **Hugging and Touching** as well as **Uniting**, communication is also key. Anything can work here, but the most important thing is that you understand one another and know about one another's sensitive areas, and how you like to be hugged, kissed, and touched. The third and fourth stages are when you really intensify your feelings, and this is when it is most important to meditate deeply and with clear concentration and focus. As feelings arise and expand, look firmly and directly at the essence of your bliss and perceive its 'true face' or nature. When the white *thiglé* drips into your throat chakras and fills them with bliss, touch your throat, really try to feel the sensation and focus it there. When you do this somehow your mind stays there, and the *thiglé* in your throat shine brightly and joyfully, radiating out white light like the moon. Stay focused and meditate! When the *thiglé* drops down to your heart chakra, for example, keep your mind as vast and open and pure as the limitless clear blue sky.

At times, you will experience profound feelings of great bliss in your and your partner's body, at other times you will even experience such feelings outside of the apparent limits of your body, in the table, throughout the house, in the trees outside, in everything you see. Everything exists in and as bliss. That is what is called 'pure vision'. Your mind experiences the bliss so strongly and purely, that even when you look at an object, you think that there is bliss in that object. When you start to get these experiences, that is a sign that your Karmamudra is functioning. This kind of experience leads naturally to the theory and experience of emptiness. This is *detong yermey*, the inseparable union of bliss and emptiness. We experience intensive bliss but at the same moment, we know the true nature or state of our experience and what we perceive is emptiness. We feel that bliss in our body very strongly but even as we do that bliss is inseparable from the state of emptiness. It is like waking up in a dream, it is completely the same. When you have a lucid dream, even as you are dreaming you know that your true nature and the nature of all the appearances in the dream is empty as well – empty or devoid of any intrinsic, permanent, independent 'self' who experiences. Everything arises beyond attachment to subject or object categories. That is why the final or ultimate goal of Karmamudra is the achievement of the final goal of Buddhism: realizing completely the true nature of all phenomena. With Karmamudra we find this emptiness or 'self-less-ness' through bliss. Selflessness or *dakmey* in Tibetan means our own personal selfless-ness and selfless-ness of all apparent phenomena.

CHAPTER 5

Medicine, Science, and Health

Today it is common to hear biomedical doctors say that many diseases are psychosomatic in nature. Biomedical doctors accept that the mind can cause illness and suffering and recognize that stress is a major contributing factor to a variety of physical health problems. But strangely these doctors are much more reluctant to admit the reverse, that the mind can not only cause, but also cure disease.

The Inner Science and the Healing Science

In the Tibetan language, Buddhism is often called *Nangdön Rigpa*. This phrase literally means the 'the science' or 'true understanding' (*rigpa*) of 'inner' (*nang*) 'matters, meanings or realities' (*dön*), or put more simply, the 'Inner Science'. Tibetans also describe Buddhists as *nangpa*, or 'insiders'. This has been interpreted to mean that most Tibetans have historically identified as Buddhists compared to non-Buddhist outsiders or foreigners, but it also has a deeper meaning. To be a Buddhist means to look inwardly for the cause or meaning of phenomena and experiences. If we practice inner self-study, which is the essence of Buddhism, we are necessarily dealing with our mind. The Buddha talked about '84,000 mental afflictions', describing a whole range of different emotions and how to work with them. As humans we are rich with emotions, feelings, thoughts, ideas and fantasies. All these things are part of what is called the inner dimension of being, and this study of the inner dimension is called *Nangdön Rigpa*. The good news is that to address these 84,000 mental afflictions, it is said that there are 84,000 dharmas, countless methods to work with this vast variety of different thoughts and emotions according to the individual's particular mentality.

There is another term in Tibetan, *Sowa Rigpa*, which means 'the Science of Healing' and is the Tibetan name for the ancient medical system which is practiced not only in Tibet, but also in other Himalayan regions such as Bhutan, Ladakh, Nepal, Sikkim, as well as parts of Siberia and Mongolia. This unique tradition has incorporated elements from great foreign medical systems of India, China, Ancient Greece and Persia, while retaining its own distinctly Himalayan character, shaped by both Buddhist and pre-Buddhist thought. Sowa Rigpa has the fourfold aim of preventing illness, curing illness, extending life, and cultivating happiness. These days, colloquially, I often like to translate Sowa Rigpa as 'the Science of Health and Happinesss' which, though not a direct translation, accurately captures this rich medical system, which provides tools not only for working with the physical body, but also with our complicated psychology on a very deep level, recognizing that mind and body cannot be separated.

On a more spiritual level, we can translate Sowa Rigpa as the 'Nourishment of Awareness,' since another meaning of the word *sowa* is to 'nourish' while *rigpa* refers not only to a 'science' or 'system of knowledge', but also to our innate primordial awareness, as the term has been used in this text. I use this translation of Sowa Rigpa when I am discussing the Yuthok Nyingthig spiritual tradition and its close association with medicine and healing. Two 'treasures' have been attributed to the great Yuthok Yönten Gönpo, the first being the *Gyüzhi*, the *Four Tantras*, which is the root medical text of Sowa Rigpa, containing an explanation of the basis of both health and disease; an extremely sophisticated understanding of anatomy, physiology, embryology, and pathology; a highly effective diagnostic system with emphasis on pulse and urine diagnosis; and a wide variety of treatment modalities including a regimen for diet and lifestyle, herbal medicines, and external therapies. The second treasure of Yuthok is the *Yuthok Nyingthig*, the cycle of Vajrayana Buddhist teachings discussed in this book. While it is not necessary to be a Buddhist practitioner to study or receive benefits from Tibetan Medicine, we can consider these two treasures of Yuthok to be two sides of a coin, which together offer a complete set of methods to bring about total health and well being, not only of the physical body, but of the complete system of body, energy, and mind. The ultimate goal of the Yuthok Nyingthig practices is of course complete spiritual liberation, however, the relative benefits of greater health and vitality, longevity, improved diagnostic and treatment skills and so on that the practitioner can obtain along the path, should not be underrated.

Today it is common to hear biomedical doctors say that many diseases are psychosomatic in nature. Biomedical doctors accept that the mind can cause illness and suffering and recognize that stress is a major contributing factor to a variety of physical health problems. But strangely these doctors are much more reluctant to admit the reverse, that the mind can not only cause, but also cure disease. Traditional Tibetan Medicine or Sowa Rigpa also recognizes psychosomatic problems as being one of the four classes of disease and and calls these diseases which have hard-to-pin down causes but deeply felt and tangible effects 'illusion diseases.' The other three classes of illness according to Tibetan Medicine are: karmic or inherited diseases; diseases caused by an imbalance of more or less subtle constituents that make up the patient's body and being, such as the traditional three humors of wind, bile, and phlegm (*loong, treepa, beken*); and 'provocation' diseases which traditionally refer to invisible spiritual forces that can negatively affect the health of the individual, but that according to Biomedical principles, could also refer to unseen pathogens like bacteria and viruses.

For each of the four causes of disease, Sowa Rigpa offers a specific solution. For the 'illusion diseases,' education is required: a disease created by the mind cannot be healed by medicine, but only by the mind itself. 'Karmic' diseases can only by cured through one's own actions and by planting positive seeds that over time can reverse the effects of negative actions that may have been committed prior to this life. Diseases brought about by an imbalance of the three humors can be treated by the methods described in the *Four Tantras (Gyüzhi)*, the root medical texts of Tibetan Medicine.

Wind / Loong

Bile / Treepa

Phlegm / Beken

The three humors or dynamic energies of loong, treepa, beken (wind, bile and phlegm):
According to the teachings of Traditional Tibetan Medicine, the imbalance of these has its
roots in the three mental poisons of desire, anger, and confusion respectively.

Tree of Treatment:
*The four methods of treatment taught in the Gyüzhi (Four Medical Tantras)
and the additional method of 'spiritual healing'*

These volumes describe four main methods of healing: diet, lifestyle, medication, and external therapies which include techniques such as *Kunye* massage, moxibustion, cupping, acupuncture, and many more. There is a fifth method of healing which is not mentioned in the *Four Tantras* but which is nonetheless an important aspect of Tibetan Medicine, and this is spiritual healing. For diseases caused by provocation, if these provocations are spiritual in nature, generally only spiritual healing methods, such as certain ritual practices or mantra healing, will help. Spiritual healing methods also include practices for working with body, energy, and mind, such as physical yoga practices, mantra recitation and breathwork, and meditation, many of which we have discussed in this book. The methods of healing in Sowa Rigpa are incredibly diverse and effective. For those interested in learning more about Tibetan Medicine, I recommend reading my book, *The Tibetan Book of Health: Sowa Rigpa, the Science of Healing* (Chenagtsang 2017). Various issues related to sexual health and well-being can be addressed by diet and lifestyle choices according to the *Four Tantras*, Tibetan herbal medicine, external therapies, as well as spiritual techniques for working with body, energy, and mind. Some practical advice is given in the section entitled 'Karmamudra and Sexual Health' however it is important to consult with a qualified Tibetan Medicine practitioner to clearly understand the causes and the nature of one's particular concerns.

It is important for us to rethink how we deal with the health of our mind and our body and to utlilize the many methods from ancient healing and spiritual traditions. In modern times, we are faced with an epidemic of mental disease. Usually when we talk about epidemic diseases we think of sicknesses that are caused by physical microorganisms. Yet today, especially in developed countries, epidemics are often mental in nature or origin. There are millions of people around the world today afflicted by and diagnosed with depression. One would think that as the amount of psychological research and psychotherapists increases in the world, the number of patients would decrease, but it often seems like the opposite thing is happening! Here, the Buddhist teachings of *Nangdön Rigpa* can be very effective. With this approach, we don't have to wait until somebody gets depressed, has anxiety or suffers a panic attack. The way to treat a patient is not to wait for them to become mentally ill – this 'inner science' offers a way to prevent the mental illness and to deal with it before it adversely affects our lives. Karmamudra can serve as part of the solution to the mental and bodily afflictions that plague so many people today. Some people may assume that since Karmamudra is about sex it is mostly physical and has only limited relevance for psychological issues. By now it should be clear that this is not the case. The 'inner science' of Buddhism allows us to look deeper into the unknown and sometimes dangerous human mind. Our minds are profound, complex and extremely complicated. For this reason, we need a powerful method for working with them, we need a very powerful kind of energy to deal with the intensity of our mental afflictions. Buddhist inner science can provide us with the deeper understanding and more profound knowledge about the human mind and emotions we so sorely need.

In Chapter Two I explained that the Vajrayana view is that our ultimate nature is bliss. We are born with bliss, we live with bliss and we die with bliss. These days it is not uncommon to meet practitioners of Vajrayana who have been practicing for twenty years but who are still deeply depressed and taking anti-depressant medications. I find this a little sad and confusing. It seems like these people have jumped onto the path and have become involved with all kinds of practices without really understanding the basis of the path, without comprehending the meaning of the Vajra Body or the nature of mind. Of course, psychiatric drugs may help some people and mixing or confusing the Vajrayana view with mental issues, by mistaking delusions and hallucinations for visions and signs of accomplishment or special abilities, can cause problems. In some cases, certain Vajrayana practices can interact badly with mental conditions, and so we must be careful and sensible. That said, Dharma practices can be used to help us with many of our psychological problems. Some teachers disapprove of the re-labelling of Dharma as 'self-help' or just psychology. It is true that the Buddhadharma can be thought of as a religion, and it is a complete path to ultimate liberation. For many people that is exactly what it is and should be, but at the same time, today so many people are unhappy and unhealthy, and as a result they do not have the mental stability, well-being and confidence to practice Dharma in a deep or dedicated way. If simple Buddhist practices can help these people become more happy, healthy, peaceful and stable then I think that is good too. Buddhism of course has more ultimate goals, but if people can benefit from Buddhist meditation practices in more short-term, relative, worldly ways, they will be in a better position to practice Dharma well, in truly beneficial ways.

The Science of Tantric Yoga

Finding Common Ground Between Tantra and Medicine

In the previous chapter I explained how we can use a Jnanamudra partner as part of our meditation practice. The Jnanamudra is our best, secret partner – spiritually or energetically it is our perfect partner. Through generating our perfect wisdom consort or 'seal' we are able to build up very subtle sensations and emotions and to refine our feelings. When we do these special practices we begin to acquaint ourselves with the Clear Light consciousness of our subtle mind. There is a link between the Clear Light yoga of dreamless sleep and Karmamudra. Yogas of sleep and dream familiarize us with different stages of sleep and different experiences of mind and consciousness. Over time we learn to navigate, understand and control these states and experiences. Karmamudra is exactly the same. This is really amazing. For most people, ordinary deep sleep is like a black hole or a coma - you wake up and say to yourself, "Huh?! Oh! What happened?!" Nowadays, thanks to machines we know about the various stages of sleep, we have a sense of what these are, how they correlate with brain activity and so on. Yet centuries ago, even without sophisticated machinery, yogis and yoginis were able to explore these various stages and states of consciousness. How did they know about these things in such fine detail hundreds of years ago? They knew these things because they really examined and deeply meditated on their own consciousness, on the diverse potential of their own minds. The rigorous empirical contemplative investigation of these practitioners is why Vajrayana explanations are sometimes very close to medical ones.

Tantric yoga and medical science are obviously not identical. But I do think there is value in keeping an open mind and investigating overlaps and correlations. Scientifically speaking, we know that the experience of orgasm needs endocrines and hormones – the hypothalamus sends specific hormones to the testes and ovaries and stimulates changes in the body and mind. This is very similar to how *thiglé* are understood to enter into the blood and travel to specific centers in the body. The hypothalamus of the brain connecting with and influencing the reproductive glands is also very similar to the way that the *dechen khorlo* or crown chakra of 'Great Bliss' is made to interact with the 'Bliss Sustaining' chakra in the genitals in the context of Karmamudra practice. The *dewey tsa* or 'bliss channel,' which is the main channel used in Karmamudra practice, is also said to protrude out of the vagina following extended periods of stimulation, and it is said to increase bliss during practice. This is reminiscent of the clitoris, and shows that Karmamudra experts were talking about the clitoris and its importance to women's sexual pleasure centuries before Western scientists even acknowledged its existence.

Correlations like this suggest to me that the flow of *thiglé* is somehow connected with hormones and that chakras correlate in some fashion to the endocrine system. Things like hormones and glands are physical, scientifically measurable phenomena, but when we meditate, when we change the colors of seed syllables and chakras, when we visualize light and so on, this somehow has an effect on our physical structures and substances. Noting these kinds of correlations can help to legitimize Karmamudra texts and practices scientifically. It can make clear that Karmamudra makes sense scientifically too, that it has some kind of empirical basis. Very subtle aspects of Vajrayana like the Clear Light mind are beyond the capacities of current scientific technology to measure or analyze. Still, there are many things in Vajrayana that can be verified and measured using current scientific methods, and who knows, there may be more sophisticated machines in the future that are able to measure more subtle levels of consciousness. I myself have participated in scientific research relating to Tibetan Dream Yoga and I strongly advocate for continued dialogue between Vajrayana practitioners and scientists. I think these collaborations are very important.

In many cases today it can seem like religious tradition and medical science are fundamentally opposed. There are so many different religions in the world, but whatever tradition you might be involved in, one thing remains equal and that is that we are all human. We all have basic biological drives like the drive to eat food, and our desire for sex is equally biological. For this reason, having sexual desire isn't something bad or negative – it's normal and innate for us. But then, when culture, religion and society tells us to repress and suppress these urges and when we then really try to do that, our sexuality can turn into a disorder, it can become sick or diseased. What this means is that we lose control, we don't know how to handle our sexual impulses and desires. This is the reason why, as we saw in Chapter Two, the Anuttarayoga Tantra says that sexual desire is a really powerful energy, a strong force, which if embraced, can be used as part of our meditation practice, either alone or with our partners. Once this desire or energy force becomes our tool then it's a little like a car. Suddenly we have a very swift vehicle which we can drive in a careful and skillful way. Directed like this we avoid harming anyone, we don't sexually abuse people or misuse our sexuality. We can have fun, we can drive, fly, explore – there is nothing wrong with that because we are guiding our energy mindfully. In fact, Anuttarayoga Tantra tells us that this energy is so powerful that if we know how to direct it, it can free us from desire entirely. It is a homeopathic remedy. We cure poison by using poison, poison liberates poison. That is why knowing how to handle this energy is so very important.

In a certain sense, the meditations of Vajrayana are very medical in how they teach us how to understand and work with ourselves and our energy. When we study medicine, anatomy and physiology and so on, we have to examine the naked human body. We can't investigate this human body of ours with clothes on. Instead, what we have to do is cut into this body, peer beneath surface appearances and look inside to study what is occurring, to understand the body's structures and functions. So, in a way Vajrayana is very similar. Like medicine, it also asks the question, "What is the ultimate, basic nature of humans in their most naked, undressed form?" Many religious traditions do not talk about 'naked humans'. They shy away from this direct medical sort of talk about sexuality. Often when the subject of sexuality comes up, these traditions will say, "Oh! Sexuality, don't talk about that! Cover up, cover up!" Then everything is covered and the only thing these traditions can talk about is our clothes – our outer trappings, our ornaments, fashions and conventions. They may talk endlessly about what clothes or jewelry we should wear, which styles are correct or inappropriate, and so on, but they may never discuss the realities of our naked nature. Vajrayana is a really, really naked tradition. It deals in depth with and explains our naked human biological functions and inner psychological functions and processes in all their extreme complexity. The ultimate goal of Vajrayana is to fully understand our nature, to understand how our human subtle energy body, our energy channels and human mind function. When we know all these things and gain mastery in meditation techniques then finally we wake up, we achieve Buddhahood.

Karmamudra and Sexual Health

Some of the most prevalent health issues related to sex are erectile dysfunction and premature ejaculation for men and low sexual desire, lack of orgasm, sensation or sexual pleasure, and suppressed menses for women. Infertility, sexual shame, embarrassment, and other psychological and emotional problems also affect many people today. Nowadays, there is so much stress in the world and many men experience impotence as a result of psychological issues. Psychological issues also play a role in limiting women's experience of sexual pleasure. Biomedicine and Tibetan medicine have different and overlapping views on the possible causes of these conditions. According to biomedicine, erectile dysfunction is often linked to stress, overmedication, and issues connected with blood circulation like cardiovascular diseases and diabetes. This is not totally out of line with Traditional Tibetan Medicine, but in this system, erectile dysfunction is also linked with cold and heavy diets, cold and sedentary lifestyles, kidney dysfunction, weakness of metabolism and certain emotional states. 'Cold kidneys' is also a major cause of low sexual desire in women, according to Sowa Rigpa. Of course, there can be several causes for having erectile dysfunction and low sexual desire, and these can operate singularly or together.

In Traditional Tibetan Medicine sexual and libido-related disorders are called *rotsa* problems. *Rotsa* can refer to problems of infertility as well as issues linked with low sexual desire. Male and female infertility has a range of physical and psychological causes, so it is important to make use of the right medical treatments. When a man has erectile dysfunction people will often describe this as a *rotsa* problem. Discussions of *rotsa* often center on men's issues and concerns, and traditionally the subject of *rotsa* has been strongly linked with medical treatments aimed at helping men to produce more children, and especially sons. Despite this, women also experience sexual dysfunctions, and these can be explained in terms of them having depleted *rotsa* as well. Having little desire for intercourse and struggling to experience sexual pleasure or orgasm is much more common in women than men after all, so I think it is very important that we don't neglect or ignore the subject of women's *rotsa* as physicians.

While some *rotsa* problems are hereditary, some people lose desire due to psychological issues. Whatever the precise cause, such problems can bother couples for a really long time, and then this secondary stress, along with the use of incorrect medicines or treatments can, quite ironically, end up affecting couples' *rotsa* even further. When *rotsa* problems are hereditary – which is usually easy enough to determine – other than using chemical drugs and other medication or treatments to improve circulation, it can be quite difficult to find anything that helps. Some general things that can cause problems with *rotsa* include: overuse of chemical medicines, abuse of recreational drugs, bad quality food, over-exertion, staying too long in cold and humid climates, kidney disease, and nervous and blood disorders. Male and female *rotsa* can be affected by more social or mental factors as well. This includes things like psychological trauma, extreme stress, shame, and grief, so medical treatments that restore psychological well-being are very important too. It is very important for patients to receive thorough consultations and tests to see whether their problems are mostly physical, mental or energetic in nature.

Cold kidneys refers mostly to problems on the physical level. This condition relates to circulation: when our kidneys and genital organs are too cold, there is not much movement of heat through them and this can lower the libido. This sort of problem can be chronic and systemic or more temporary. Eating a large meal and having digestive problems, which is also connected with inner metabolic heat, can also contribute to a dampened libido. Treatments for this sort of problem involve warming up the kidneys through diet, exercises and medicine. Doctors may prescribe warming foods and drinks, things like ginger and cardamom tea, and other herbal medicines which warm up and stimulate the body and improve digestion. It is as if a part of our vital energy is frozen and we need to thaw it out and warm it up. External therapies such as moxibustion and warm salt compresses are also very useful. These treatments focus on the kidneys, but it is also possible that a patient's nervous system might be fragile or weakened and this can also cause problems with libido and the flow of vital energy in one's system. If certain kinds of *loong* energy aren't moving adequately, this can lead to cold kidneys. Many Karmamudra texts suggest that one take *loong* medicines or receive treatments for this sort of problem. *Kunye* massage and *hormé* (a warm herbal compress therapy known as Mongolian moxibustion) are excellent therapies for imbalances of the wind humor.

Getting older can also be related to decreased libido. Generally speaking, women begin to cease menstruating from around fifty years of age, although this can also happen earlier or later due to sickness or genetics. Women may experience shortness of breath, over-heating, sweating and insomnia, as well as anxiety and mood swings. Desire for sex may decrease. These symptoms might last for anywhere from a few months to one or two years. It can be preferable for some woman to decrease the frequency at which they have sex, and to take good quality traditional Tibetan herbal medicines for wind and bile disorders during this time. Some women also find that hormone replacement therapy helps them during this part of their lives. Women who are no longer menstruating but do still feel desire in the post-pregnancy phase of their lives can, and are encouraged to, continue to have sex without fear of pregnancy. This will make for both a happy body and mind! The moment when men's sperm declines is somewhat more indefinite. That said, by consuming nutritious foods and certain medicines and extracts, it is possible for men to increase their potency even up until the age of ninety. From about seventy years on, men's sexual organs tend to gradually get weaker and their sexual desire decreases. Some men don't enjoy hearing this but if you're a Buddhist you should know that the fact that everything in this world is impermanent is undeniable!

In any case, if you're an older person who still has a strong libido and a healthy body then there's no reason to block your desire. Older men who have a strong desire for sex but whose penises are less than serviceable can still take medicine and experience pleasure. Traditional Tibetan herbal medications are a bit weaker in potency at first but work well in the long term and tend to have fewer side effects. Chemical, biomedical drugs are stronger but if you take too much of them they can become harmful and potentially threaten your life. Chemical aphrodisiacs can also be risky for people with high or low blood pressure or for people who have heart diseases. In some cases, men have also died during sex due to overdosing. For patients who feel faint after sex, who have experienced strokes and suffer from partial paralysis, or who have kidney or liver disorders, these medicines can end up doing more harm than good. In general, it is wise to be very careful of store-bought drugs. One should not just consume whatever random thing one happens to buy. One should absolutely consult with qualified doctors and not rely on erroneous or inappropriate medicines just based on one's own or other unqualified people's opinions or ideas. Given that many Karmamudra texts suggest that practitioners make use of herbs or make remedies for impotency, I think that if partners are having difficulties with arousal or erections, it can be okay at times to make use of certain chemical medicines. I am not an expert in these substances but I have talked with biomedical doctors who specialize in prescribing these medicines and I am told that pharmaceuticals like Viagra, Cialis and so on do not cause great physical damage to the body if used as prescribed and in moderation. If physical problems are at the root of low libido and erectile dysfunction, then medicines, whether biomedical or otherwise, can certainly benefit, and other therapies like moxibustion, the use of hot compresses and massage can be very useful as well.

As with low libido and erectile problems, male and female infertility can have many causes. Some readers might be wondering if infertility has any effect on students' ability to practice Karmamudra. This is a little difficult to answer in an overarching way, since there are many different reasons why someone might have problems with fertility. Infertility may be linked with aging, a lack of heat, inflammation or problems with the organs and channels. It can also be a result of *tsa loong thiglé* problems and thus require more energetic treatments. So, in some cases infertility might affect a student's ability to practice Karmamudra but it may also not have much of an impact. In addition to describing strategies for treating infertility, Traditional Tibetan Medicine also has a series of general recommendations for when to avoid sexual activity to prevent health issues down the line. The medical Tantras do not generally recommend sex during pregnancy or menstruation. Due to the loss of blood, physical, mental, and emotional discomfort, as well as weakness that some women sometimes experience when they are menstruating, the *Four Tantras* state that sex should be avoided during this time. In a similar vein, it is said that one should avoid having sex when one is sick, feeling weak, mentally incapacitated, or during periods of extreme grief. That said, this is not a hard and fast rule. Often boys new to sex are afraid that if they have sex with a woman when she is menstruating they will get some kind of infection or 'pollution,' but this is silly. If a woman who is menstruating has sexual desire, wants to have sex, and both partners are disease free and in good physical health, then enjoying sex is totally appropriate. Conception also may not occur if a woman has unprotected sex while she is bleeding. That said, not all bleeding may be menstrual bleeding. Some women can bleed a little during peak ovulation, and ovulation may occur during bleeding or after. Since every woman's body, and every man's fertility, is different, having sex during a woman's period is not an advisable form of contraception. If you do have sex during menstruation, vigorous or extensive intercourse may produce a lot of bleeding so it is best to cover the bed with a towel or extra, absorbent layer. After sex, both men and women should wash their genitals and as always pay attention to proper hygiene. When it comes to having sex during pregnancy, this can also be fine, provided the expectant mother is willing, comfortable and in good health, and as long as her partner knows how to engage in intercourse in a skillful way. If her partner does not, sex during pregnancy can cause pain, pressure or trauma so it is taught in the *Four Tantras* that one should refrain from sexual intercourse at this time. Still, if expectant parents have desire, it is not a problem to have sex. Some traditional experts explain that having sex from behind or from the side during pregnancy can actually make childbirth easier, but all of this comes down to the mother's physical and mental state of being.

When it is most advantageous for one to engage in sexual activity is highly relative. Traditional Tibetan medical tradition notes that the frequency and timing of one's sexual activity can depend on the season, one's age, one's general physical strength and one's overall body type or psycho-physical constitution. As I touched on in the section in the previous chapter on frequency of ejaculation, knowing one's own body and tendencies is key to making healthy and realistic choices. Ultimately, when it comes to having a healthy libido, what is most crucial is that we make an effort to engage in sex in an ethical way. If one can follow a diet that agrees with one's constitution, if one can meet a partner with whom one is really compatible and whose interests align with one's own and who one can talk with honestly from the heart, then that's the best situation. When you find a karmic partner that is destined for you, who really aligns with your body, speech, and mind, the two of you will be harmoniously connected in your heart and mind. A lot of your mental suffering will be cured and you will be freed from *rotsa*-related problems as well. So, take care of your heart and mind carefully!

Another important point regarding sexual health is the topic of excessive retention of semen, as mentioned in Chapter Four. In the discussion on lifestyle recommendations in Chapter Fifteen of the *Explanatory Tantra*, the second volume in the *Four Medical Tantras*, it is advised to avoid extreme behavior in various activities and to respect the body's natural rhythms. For example, it is cautioned against both excessive fasting or over-eating, sleep deprivation or indulgent over-sleeping, suppressing the urge to urinate, or forcing oneself to urinate when there is no urge, and so on. Both suppression and its opposite are said to immediately disturb the natural flow of *loong* energy in the body, leading to many other health problems. In regards to sexual activity, it is said that if men overly suppress the urge to ejaculate, the semen will leak by itself and genital disorders, blockage of urine, the development of stones in the urinary tract can result. Impotence may also occur. In order to prevent or treat such problems, the text advises for men to ejaculate as well as to eat nourishing foods and drinks such as sesame oil, milk, chicken, and to drink some mild alcohol. Of course if one trains very gradually in the spiritual practices, then these problems can also be avoided, but in general for most men, it is advised to practice the path of moderation in this regard.

Like a Dog Eating Lungs: Differences Between Men and Women's Sexual Tendencies and Responses

In the previous chapter, I mentioned that in some Karmamudra texts it is noted that some women can lose sexual desire after childbirth. These texts suggest that women can regain and rebuild their sexual energy and desire through Karmamudra practices. As I mentioned, the trauma of C-sections, episiotomies and so forth can damage women's channels and dampen their ability to induce sexual desire and bliss for a while. But the causes of women's low arousal are rarely purely physical, they are often psychological, emotional, as well as social, and have to do with cultural norms. Women are often the primary care-givers of babies, they also have to spend a lot of time breast feeding, they may not be sleeping enough while caring for infants, and so on. Many women lose sexual desire following child-birth for these reasons as well. For some women, sexual desire may come back quickly, but for others it can take much longer. I have seen many husbands get the idea that their wives are 'married to their babies and not to them' because of this. I think this is a typical male misunderstanding, men simply do not understand what women go through. They don't understand the experience of pregnancy or delivery, of C-sections, what it's like to undergo birth-related surgical operations, the extreme exhaustion some women experience from producing milk, from breastfeeding, from not getting enough sleep because they have to remain mindful of their baby's needs twenty-four hours a day, on and on. And then in spite of all this, husbands are still selfish and think: "I'm feeling turned on and you don't want me? What is your problem?!" without any thought for the exhaustion or stress new mothers might be feeling.

I sometimes think that one advantage of same sex partnerships for women is that in some cases women understand women more easily. As a fellow woman, your partner understands well the needs of the female body. Men often have difficulty understanding women. Women sometimes experience different feelings and emotions during their period that men don't understand. Even when couples have real understanding and a strong loving and respectful connection, it almost always takes longer for women to feel aroused and ready for sexual activity. You could say women need more sexual *ngöndro*, 'preliminary practices' or foreplay. This is part of the warming up process. There are various yogas called warming up yogas, and this is what women, or at least many women need. This is one of the major differences between men and women's sexuality. Some men might think that the warming up part is boring, or maybe some men are overly excited and want to skip the warming up process altogether. This kind of thinking and behavior ensures that there is always a gap between men and women and their sexual experience. That is the problem. In many cases, women will just give in and have sex with men without being excited, without getting wet, without really wanting to have it or even getting any of their own pleasure, they just do it because they want to make the man happy. There are so many cases where sex is like this. If women said to their male partners "You know what? I actually don't like having sex!" the majority of men would think "How is that possible?! We have had sex regularly for the past twenty years!" The answer would be that the woman just wanted to make him happy or just wanted to satisfy him and get it over with. There are many cases like this.

Worse still, research shows that many women expect that they will experience pain or a lack of pleasure as a normal part of sex, which ends up being about prioritizing men's desire and fulfilment. I have heard it said too that something like at least twenty seven percent of all women in Western countries do not experience orgasm during sex. Some women have experienced sexual trauma in their past and are disconnected from their sexuality and capacity to arouse bliss. One of the most important aspects of experiencing powerful, profound orgasms is letting go. To let go, one has to feel comfortable, relaxed and safe, and not overly pressured or anxious. One of the best solutions for people suffering from low or blocked desire and arousal is *la* massage, as described on p. 134, which was recommended by Ju Mipham. Ultimately, *la* massage is about relaxing, warming up, connecting. Any therapy that helps one to take things more slowly, focus in, and refine our sensation so as to more easily let go can be very beneficial.

Some descriptions of orgasm make it sound quite mechanical and simple but in reality the autonomic response in the human body is rather complex. 'Orgasm' comes from the Greek word *orgasmos*, which means to swell or become excited. Swelling and excitement are certainly a part of orgasmic response, but there are many other aspects. There is a sudden discharge of accumulated sexual tension, rhythmic muscular contractions in the pelvic region and spasms in multiple areas, and general euphoric sensations. We also make different body movements and vocalizations. Orgasm is experienced by males and females and is largely controlled by the involuntary or autonomic nervous system. That said, male and female orgasm is quite different. After climax we experience a state of relaxation known as the 'refractory period'. Researchers attribute this to the release of the hormones oxytocin and prolactin, as well as endorphins, which are like morphine made inside our bodies, our own painkillers.

Generally speaking, however, males and females experience the refractory period a bit differently. The stereotype is that after climaxing females tend to want to spend more time bonding, kissing, hugging and so on, whereas after ejaculation males experience a kind of dip or 'post ejaculatory chill' which makes them tired, irritable, want to go to sleep or makes them dislike being touched, want to pull away and so on. Of course, everyone is different, but this general trend is something many of us are familiar with from our own experience and from popular culture. Today, scientists are starting to understand more about these different reactions in terms of hormones. We now know that the male and female hormonal responses post-climax are quite different and this seems to correlate with these different tendencies. There also seems to be some possible correlation with Tantric practice – these side effects experienced post-ejaculation/

orgasm may be one reason why Tantra states that men should not lose their semen unnecessarily while practicing. These scientific findings are interesting to think about and will hopefully increase our understanding of orgasm and sexual experience in the future.

When it comes to orgasm, women's orgasm is generally stronger than men's. How many orgasms can a man have in one night? Normally men don't experience multiple orgasms, or very rarely, unless they have trained in producing these. But women can have multiple orgasms naturally and easily, often every five or ten minutes or so. Almost every woman has the chance to experience powerful multiple orgasms. This is the base of Karmamudra. That is why I think that Karmamudra is more powerful or easy to accomplish for women. In a way, women seem to be more gifted at Karmamudra. I have already explained how Karmamudra is normally always described as more of a men's practice, as something not so much for women practitioners on their own terms. Traditionally, many Karmamudra texts emphasized extensive Karmamudra training for male practitioners, but not so much for female ones. Moreover, in the past, more men had the opportunity to practice Karmamudra and Tantric Buddhism and so most practitioners were men. Everything was focused on men seeking out suitable, naturally endowed female partners with whom they could train. This is actually quite ironic because if you look at what actually happens in everyday life, the approach of Karmamudra seems way more suitable or aligned with women and their bodies. Women normally take more time to get aroused, and Karmamudra is all about taking your time to build up sensation. Women typically respond well to Looking, Talking, Touching – all of these warming up practices. Women's partners have to wait until they are sufficiently wet before they can just dive in and start having sex. They have to take their time, to play around with and stimulate their partner until she is ready, and then it is okay to proceed. Most women feel that it is normal and right that they should need some warming up. This all lines up perfectly with Karmamudra – if you really look at the way Karmamudra is designed it really fits more with this orientation.

But even so, most men don't care about this. They approach sex with their partners just like men approach sex when they go to see a prostitute: "Okay, I paid you, you're naked, now I'll fuck you." These poor girls aren't required to have any feeling of pleasure of their own, they just need to service the man. It is like pornography: "Okay, somebody paid me to do a job, so now I need to perform this or that sexual act, and so there's not really any feeling, there doesn't have to be." A lot of men are able to do this – they can have sex and get gratification without much preamble, without much warming up or feeling. Of course, it is possible that a woman can go to a male prostitute and say, "Okay, I paid you for twenty minutes. You do this and that" but it does seem like heterosexual men and women generally have different approaches or natures in this. Things may be different for homosexual couples or for couples with less traditional gender dynamics, but broadly speaking Tibetans typically say that men and women's orientation to sex is different. There is a saying in Tibetan used to describe the way that men approach having sex, I think it might have been something that Ju Mipham said: "like a hungry or starving dog wolfing down an (animal's) lung". The way that men go about having sex and fulfilling their desires is like a hungry dog eating an animal's lung. The lungs of an animals are puffy – they are a spongey kind of meat that looks substantial but is mostly just filled with air. So it is not even that nutritious or filling. And then when the dog eats it, it just goes "HAB!" And then the whole thing is gone! There's no process of chewing and enjoying, the dog doesn't savor the meat or even really taste it. It's just "HAB!" and then it's finished. Dogs are actually like that, when they're really hungry they don't chew, they just wolf their food down, one bite and it's gone.

I think this is really apt. In most cases men's sexual appetite really is like a dog eating an animal's lungs. In contrast, women tend to have a more gradual style: there's looking, smiling, touching, hugging and then when the lotus is wet, that means that the body is ready. And then, if there's penetration, it means that the lotus is open and prepared, you don't need to use any of those industrial-grade German style lubricants – sometimes I think it can get kind of ridiculous – male engineers sitting together and thinking, "Okay, we want something fast! We want sex now! No waiting! The woman is dry? We'll fix this problem!" But then when you come right down to it, in most cases it is not really the women's problem, it is the man's! Ultimately then, as far as I am concerned, the best way to practice Karmamudra is for men and women to practice in a perfectly matched way. It is crucial that couples understand each other's bodies, psychologies, and needs and that whether we are engaging in worldly or wisdom sexual practices we do so in an equal and balanced way.

Generally speaking, I think that if men learn Karmamudra they will be able to have much better sex. If they get some training in Karmamudra practices, then they won't just jump into sex as soon as they feel arousal and ejaculate quickly. Karmamudra encourages men to take more time with their warming up process. Even if their arousal is quick and easy, the slowing down and focusing that Karmamudra requires can be really good for men. It can help them to truly feel and experience all the subtleties and flow of their energy and pleasure. I suspect that one reason why there are so many cases of men raping people is that many men have been taught to have a very angry and forceful attitude towards sex. They are aggressive with their sexual feelings, they are not gentle and sensual, there's no intimacy, no romance, no passion or love there. They just jump, grab, and fuck. It's crazy. So many men take this approach in their relationships with their partners and end up never feeling satisfied and just become more and more angry and destructive. It is true that sexual energy is very powerful. It is often very forceful and overwhelming, and as we have seen already if you misuse it you can easily harm others. But by training in Karmamudra it is possible to engage with and direct that same forceful, intense energy differently, and make both yourself and your partner happy.

Concluding Remarks

The profound practices of Karmamudra have been surrounded by misunderstanding both in the past and in modern times. I have tried my best in this book to clarify the many misconceptions about Karmamudra that still circulate broadly today, and to share these ancient teachings in a way that is simple, direct, and suitable for contemporary audiences. My presentation here has not always been completely traditional - nonetheless, my goal has been to honor these ancient traditions by explaining appropriate aspects of them in a new and modern way. In general, Karmamudra is a very high-level and secret practice, but there have also been several very great and important masters such as Drukpa Kunley, Ju Mipham, Lelung Zhepai Dorje, and Yuthok Yönten Gönpo, who have shared these teachings more openly and publicly. My goal in writing this book has not been to utterly unveil a secret teaching but rather to increase awareness about an important subject, one that if understood and used well can bring much benefit and healing to people. In general, sexuality is a very sensitive topic and in many cultural contexts it is not something discussed openly. This sort of restriction has been the cause of so much suffering and pain. But sexuality is a very normal part of life for all lay people, so it is essential that we have a better understanding of it. As a doctor, I like to compare sexuality to a great and powerful medication, one that has the potential to bring physical, energetic, and mental benefits to countless patients. Sexuality can bring healing and inner peace for so many people and can serve as a key to genuine happiness if used properly.

Concern about public health, social well-being and education has informed my writing about sexuality and Karmamudra for some time now. I have included excerpts from my Kamasutra or so called 'Treatise on Desire' text throughout this book and in the Appendices. I wrote this three-part teaching in Tibetan specifically for a Tibetan audience a few years ago. I was concerned about the general lack of sexual education in Tibet and felt it was important to share something with Tibetan communities, especially the nomad communities with whom I grew up, who don't have access to the same kind of information people in the West have about things like sexual health, erotic pleasure, and psychology. Because Tibetans love poems, I wrote this in verse, in the hopes that more people would read or listen to it. The first part of the poem focuses on sexuality for ordinary people with an emphasis on hygiene and other important issues that there is a general lack of awareness about in some parts of Tibet. The second part focuses on sexuality from a medical perspective and talks not only about Traditional Tibetan Medicine but also general issues of concern such as sexually transmitted infections. I have not included these two chapters in this book, since it is geared towards a Western audience who already has a greater level of awareness about these things. I have however, included the third part of the poem in the Appendices. This is the spiritual part of the poem and it discusses Karmamudra practice. I sincerely wish that this book may bring awareness and benefit for many people.

CONCLUSION

Dedicating the Merit

Shanglon Dorje Duddul.
The special protector of the Tibetan Medical Tradition.

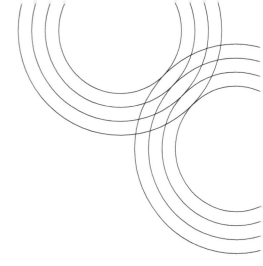

བསྔོ་བ།

Dedication

དགེ་བ་འདི་ཡིས་མྱུར་དུ་བདག །
ཚོགས་སྦྱོ་བདེ་ཆེན་འགྲུབ་གྱུར་ནས། །
འགྲོ་བ་གཅིག་ཀྱང་མ་ལུས་པ། །
དེ་ཡི་ས་ལ་འགོད་པར་ཤོག །

May I, through the virtue and merit (of this book)
Swiftly accomplish the Great Bliss of the Lower Gates
And may every being without exception
Be brought to this level of accomplishment as well!

ལྷན་སྐྱེས་བདེ་ཆེན་རིན་པོ་ཆེ། །
མ་སྐྱེས་པ་རྣམས་སྐྱེ་གྱུར་ཅིག །
སྐྱེས་པ་ཉམས་པ་མེད་པར་ཡང་། །
གོང་ནས་གོང་དུ་འཕེལ་བར་མཛོད། །

May precious, innately-born Great Bliss arise in all those
In whom it has not yet arisen,
And for those in whom it has, may it not decline
And increase ever further!

བཏུད་བྲལ་ལྷུན་སྐྱེས་བདེ་བ་འདི། །
སེམས་ཅན་ཀུན་སྙིང་ལ་སྐྱེ་བ་དང་། །
ཆགས་ལྷུན་མ་གྱུར་ཐམས་ཅད་ནི། །
བདེ་ཆེན་ས་ལ་སྐྱུར་འགོད་ཤོག །

May this ineffable in-born Bliss
Arise in the hearts of beings
May all desire-filled beings who were once my own mother
Be swiftly brought to the level of Great Bliss!

རོ་རྗེ་འཆང་ཆེན་གཡུ་ཐོག་པ་ཡི།།
བསྟན་པ་དར་ཞིང་འགྲོ་ལ་ཕན།།
མཆོག་དེའི་འབངས་སུ་སྐྱེས་ནས་ནི།།
དུས་རྟག་སྤྱི་བོས་མཆོད་པར་ཤོག།

May the teachings of the great Vajra-holder Yuthokpa
Spread and benefit beings,
May I be born in his retinue as his student
And forever bow my head to him in reverence!

ཟབ་ལམ་བླ་མེད་རྒྱུད་སྡེ་ཡི།།
དགོངས་པ་རྟོགས་ཤིང་ཉམས་སུ་ལོན།།
སྲིད་པའི་བར་དུ་གནས་གྱུར་ནས།།
འདོད་ཆགས་འགྲོ་བ་གྲོལ་བར་ཤོག།

May I realize and practice
The enlightened intention and perspective of the profound path
of the classes of Highest Yoga Tantras –
For as long as samsara remains
May all beings who desire be liberated!

བླ་མ་ཡབ་ཡུམ་སྐུ་བརྟན་ཞིང་།།
འཕྲིན་ལས་རྣམ་བཞི་མཁའ་ལ་ཁྱབ།།
ཟབ་ཆོས་བདུད་རྩི་སྨྱོང་ནས་ནི།།
དོན་གཉིས་ལྷུན་གྱིས་འགྲུབ་གྱུར་ཅིག།

May the bodies of the gurus in union remain firm
And may all four aspects of their enlightened Tantric activity
[utterly] pervade space –
Having tasted the nectar of the profound teachings
May I effortlessly accomplish the Two Truths
[of relative and ultimate reality]!

འདོད་ལྡན་རྣལ་འབྱོར་ཕོ་མོ་ལ།།
ཕན་འདོད་རེ་བས་བྲིས་ན་ཡང་།།
གསང་སྔགས་ཁྲོམ་སློགས་ཉེས་པ་གང་།།
མཚམས་པ་ཆོས་ཀྱི་དབྱིངས་སུ་བཤགས།།

I have written this with the hope and wish
That it will benefit yogis and yoginis who are filled with desire –
Nonetheless, whatever faults I may have committed for disclosing the
Secret Mantra too openly, for having 'shouted it in the market place'
I confess them – may they be liberated into the dharmadhatu,
the ultimate space of emptiness!

Concluding verses from my 'Treatises on Desire'

APPENDICES

Karmamudra Texts

Lelung Jedrung Zhepai Dorje

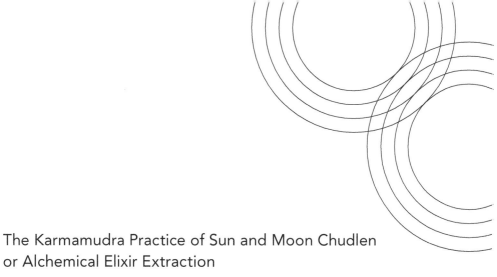

The Karmamudra Practice of Sun and Moon Chudlen or Alchemical Elixir Extraction

(Lelung Jedrung Zhepai Dorje, 1697-1740)

The *chudlen* or alchemical elixir extraction method of extracting of the sun and moon and lineage supplication prayer that was bestowed as a pure-vision by the one and only Goddess Nyima Zhönnu, or 'Youthful Sun'.

"I pray to the spontaneously-arisen Lady, the actual youthful sun, whose Dharmakaya or ultimate-reality body is Vairocana, whose enjoyment-body is the Mighty Lotus Pema Wang, and whose emanation-body is the Lotus-Born Guru's consort the Great Mother Tsogyal, the Victorious Lake of Wisdom! Let the Path of Means [i.e. the method of Karmamudra] be honed and purified! Let the magical technology of the sexual yoga of Samsara-Nirvana be accomplished as naught but the genuine expression of great desire! To Sharwa Chagpa Dorje Chenpo, the Great Vajra of Arising Desire, I pray! Let the method of Karmamudra be honed and purified! It is the distilled essence of the consummation of the Vehicle of the Great Secret, the path of the union of wisdom and means, of the primordial wisdom of emptiness and bliss! May all the practices of the preliminaries, the main, and follow-up procedures be brought to completion, and may they ripen and liberate my mind! May bliss be born from the sight of beauty, from enchanting and side-ways glances that rob one's wits, from gentle caresses on the surface of the skin! May I meet with the lady whose body and mouth are sweet-smelling, whose nipples are hard, who has the grace of a swan! May I meet with this loving companion, she whose lotus (i.e. vagina) is round, warm, and blooms expansively, is pure and profound,[29] she whose channels are wholesome, whose voice is sweet, whose great compassion is vast and expansive! May I meet with her, she the wise adept of Tantric yogic conduct who refines and preserves the secret teachings!

Let me meet with the supreme secret *mudra*, who in becoming exceedingly aroused, is skilled in the mood and demeanour of intoxication, is trained in the method of desirous union and is fond of sex, and who without guile, deception or hypocrisy, abandons all jealousy! May all those lineages of the two-stage path be purified! May all outer, embodied and disembodied demonic obstacles be without sustenance! Inwardly, may my vital force increase and may my four elements be in balance! On the secret level, may my channels, drops, winds, and subtle mind be serviceable! Setting up our bedroom for the practice of bliss in a remote retreat-spot, may we proceed to engage in exceedingly intimate union! Once we are aflame with passion like nothing ever before, may our forms blaze with the splendor of exceeding intoxication in body, speech, and mind! Engaging in the 'arrow', 'bow', 'tortoise', 'tiger', 'fish', and 'lion' - in all and every possible sexual yoga position and activity, and spending our time practicing day and night without pause, may we perfect the capacity for bliss-emptiness! With our minds made rigid through maintaining arousal without getting irritated or sick of it, may the female partner satisfy all desires without obstruction! Solely through the union with the magnetizing [karma]mudra, may I pass through the ground, path, and enhancement practices and may I consummate both experience and realization!"

This is the lineage supplication prayer of the supreme [sexual yoga] method which the one and only goddess Nyima Zhönnu bestowed as a pure vision and which she said was required, and which the man Chagpa Dorje, intoxicated with desire, prays continuously as his Vajra-armour.

---

[29] *Zlum rgyas drod ldan padma dam zhing zab.* This is a wonderfully loaded phrase by Lelung, which works on many levels all at once. As is typical for texts on Karmamudra, Lelung refers to the consort's vagina as a lotus flower or *pema* in Tibetan. He lists five separate adjectives to describe the lotus, all of which have ingenious double if not triple meanings. Round/circular, extensive/expanding and hot/warm can be read as referring to observable physical features of the aroused sexual parts of a woman, but also to certain features of a flower (rgyas means expansive but is also used as a verb to describe the unfolding of leaves or petals). At the same time, these terms have associations with meditative or yogic realization and practice: wholly purified, natural, uncontrived Buddha nature is also expansive or rgyas and 'endowed with heat' is a synonym for yogic accomplishment. The two terms 'pure' and 'profound' also have double meanings – the first in addition to meaning 'sacred' can also mean 'tight' and *zab* or profound could also suggest deep in a more physical sense.

Here follows the 'The Sexual *Chudlen* or Alchemical Elixir Method of the Sun and Moon' proper:

Emaho! Amazing! I, the yogi Chagpa Dorje, bow to the three roots, the ocean of Victorious Buddhas! During my thirty-fourth year, the noxious year of the male iron dog (1730/31), on the 29th day of the *chuto* lunar mansion month [i.e. roughly the sixth month][30] in the great pleasure-garden of the Dakinis in the eastern part of the region of Olga, the fortunate disciple Dorje Serdok ['Golden-colored Vajra'] brought together the ingredients for the pure Tantric substances and nectar and we summoned Lhachik Zhönnu and the dakinis of the three abodes as guests. Many Dakinis and Dakas and the precious Guru gathered for the Tantric feast, many Vajra-armored Tantric 'siblings' [practitioners who took Tantric empowerments and vows together, assembled]. White offering scarves soared through the air and rained down upon this garden of delight. The celebrants sang and danced auspiciously, and when offerings were made to the dakas and dakinis, the blessing-power came down onto everyone and they blazed with the light of positive spiritual experience.

I spent the whole night that night in a state of meditation without any fixed reference point. At one point, when I nodded off back to sleep for a little bit, I beheld Lhachik Zhönnuma in the form of a beautiful, smiling woman. The experience of insatiable desire grew within me. She flashed me slanting glances from the corner of her eye, and I was energized with subtle trembling [by her transmitted gaze]. Through all kinds of speech that kindled the great bliss of arousal my hopes were at last fulfilled. She lay on her back and I removed her lower garments to the right, and from the fluids of great secret bliss born from the midst of her lotus, a cascade of the water of desire was revealed, boiling forth. She advised me in revelry and enjoyment, moaning with sounds of pleasure, and once done, as we experienced orgasmic bliss, speaking lovingly she instructed me as follows:

---

[30] Tibetans use an extremely diverse set of calendrical systems for reckoning the months of any given year. Here Lelung is using a system made popular through the introduction of the Kalachakra Tantra into Tibet in the 11th century. This system names the months after the lunar mansions in which each full moon of the year occurs (there are roughly twelve). The 29th day of the lunar month is the day designated for protector-spirit offering practices.

"I am the woman trained in sex, she who by relying on the magical technology of sexual yoga pulls all beings of the three realms under her sway, eliminates all adverse conditions, and accomplishes all things. So should there be a yogi, he should undertake the sexual rite with me. There are three stages to this: the preliminary congress, the main practices and the post-coital activities.

For the preliminary congress, in your 'bed' or retreat-place of bliss, enlist an attractive woman who is endowed with all the necessary qualities. Her pure, clean body should be sweet-smelling and her bhaga (vagina) warm. Her tender flesh should be soft to the touch, her voice pleasant, and she should express herself freely and spontaneously. Her dirty talk should have the power to transform minds. While she should be fundamentally modest, her arousal should seldom be contrived. She should be heartfelt and of little jealousy, and she should have a strong sexual appetite.

While calling me to mind, the woman should prepare *serkhyem* or 'golden' libation offerings for the protectors. Get the bliss seal or consort to do these preliminary rituals with you. Imagining that this woman is the very embodiment of me, close your eyes, scrape your nails across her skin and say whatever feels appropriate. Talk dirty to her, joke with her, and incite arousal and bliss through all kinds of extended foreplay. Touch and firmly massage her lower parts with your hands. Sinking into her, press against her and begin the so-called 'intimate activities'. Cover her in kisses and lick and suck with your lips and tongue as foreplay and then, when she's clearly experiencing arousal, remove her underwear as she lies on her back. Penetrate her vagina right between her knees. Enter her with her legs bent and her genitals spread open to work her bhaga well. Smiling, kiss her there? and with your vajra [i.e. penis] erect and firm, penetrate her and rub towards the top of her bhaga repeatedly until [both of your] bliss intensifies. This is what is known as *nyeweh jor*, 'the intimate activities' or the preliminary practices for drawing nearer.

For the main practice, the yogi should see himself clearly as Chagpa Dorje and the woman should feel with great conviction that she is me. Then, once you've performed the 'secret blessing of fire and space', in a state of '(vajra) pride of desire', push your vajra deep into the bhaga so that it's completely absorbed into it, and twist it to the right, to the left, thrust it upwards, and straight in. Send it out like an arrow then draw it back in like a bow. Pull it out once more and massage her with it by rubbing and pressing it against the area around the mouth [of her vagina] in various ways. Having delighted her with this massage, enter her again like a leaping tigress.

Hold your pose majestically like a lion, flick your hips lithely like a fish darting to and fro. Using the movement that's like the inching gait of a tortoise, clasp her neck with your hands. Fold both her legs behind your knees and press down with your hips and penetrate her. Slowly and gently inspire bliss and rest wordlessly in your own true nature or essence of being. Without losing control of your seminal-essence, keep your inner most mind tightly focused. If you don't know the yogic exercises for drawing up or reversing and the spreading out *thiglé* or seminal energy drop then, when at last the *thiglé* starts to descend enter her, and concentrating on directing your *thiglé* as a cloud of offerings that delights all the Victorious Buddhas and Bodhisattvas, ejaculate. Don't just pull your vajra out, let her bring her pleasure to completion [as she likes etc]. Having finished, lick your and her conjoined sexual essence and take up some with your ring-finger and taste it. This is the most supreme *chudlen* or elixir-extraction that dissolves all obscurations.

For the post-coital stage, once you have accomplished the main practice, do not separate right away but stay together embracing. Kissing each other on the cheeks and feeling great love and tenderness for one another, retain the bliss you are feeling. These aforementioned things are the most essential points for generating bliss easily.

By applying carraway, saxifrage, spikenard, shellac resin, black agar-wood and deer-musk mixed with sesame oil to your and your consort's navel, the point below the navel, the outer parts of her vagina, and your private parts, you will bring these erogenous zones to perfection. By boiling together as a decoction the fat of a vulture, a sparrow, a swan, and a wild-ass and by applying this mixture repeatedly to the vajra and lotus, this will make them warm, serviceable and potent. If you mix ginger, long black pepper, and cloves with the fat of a wild ass and rub this into your waist/loins and the hollows of your kidneys, this will resolve cold disorders.

Even when you get up and part from each other, keep holding one another's hand and maintain body contact. Touch each other and eat delicious foods [barring ones that deteriorate the quality of the *thiglé*] and enjoy yourselves together. Feed each other food with your tongues and mouths and relish the taste of them. Make use of *chudlen* extracts and

Nyima Zhönnu, the Treasure Dakini of Lelung Zhepai Dorje
Image: Courtesy Dr. Nida Chenagtsang
Pehar protector temple, Samye Monastery, Central Tibet

fortifying medicines made of wholesome and appropriate ingredients. Through all sorts of activities - singing and dancing, playing music, and talking dirty to each other - apply yourselves diligently to the method(s) of generating bliss. The kind of bliss one can experience is degraded through things like exhaustion, over-exertion, worrying and over-thinking, mental/ emotional anguish, and extreme aggression and hatred, so abandon these things and your bliss will get stronger and more powerful. Don't get mixed up with people and things that violate your Tantric vows. If you find that you do, do rituals to purify yourself and clear away any pollution. Confess your faults with 'The Confession of the Expanse of the View'. Practice this, my sexual ritual!"

This very embodiment of Vajra-speech was written down without fabrication by Chagpa Dorje. Whosoever wishes to attain Buddhahood for the sake of others through sexual ritual let them look to this teaching! Through the power of its virtue may all appearances and every being and phenomena that arises without exception manifest as the chakra of sexual union, and by mastering the self-cognizing awareness of the natural state may everything and everyone be liberated all at once into the body of light!

This is the chapter detailing the method that was taught by The One and Only Goddess Youthful Sun, Nyima Zhönnu.

Tokden Shakya Shri

The Swift Path of the Great Bliss of Primordial Purity

(Tokden Shakya Shri, 1853-1919)

༄༅། །ཀ་དག་བདེ་ཆེན་སྒྱུར་ལམ་གྱི་ཁྲིད་རིམ་རིག་འཛིན་གྲུབ་པའི་ཐུགས་ཏིག་གསང་ཆེན་
བླ་མེད་ཅེས་བྱ་བ་བཞུགས་སོ།།

Stages of Instruction on the Swift Path of the Great Bliss of Primordial
Purity, the Highest, Great Secret Heart-Essence of the Awareness-
holding, accomplished Siddhas.

དཔལ་གདོད་མའི་མགོན་པོ་དང་གཉིས་སུ་མེད་པའི་བླ་མ་མཆོག་ལ་ཕྱག་འཚལ་ལོ།།
ཨེ་མ། རྩོལ་བཅས་འབད་པའི་དྲི་མས་མ་གོས་པའི།། རབ་ཏུ་རྩོལ་མེད་བདེ་ཆེན་ཀ་དག་
ལམ། །གྲུབ་དབང་རིག་འཛིན་ཆེན་པོའི་ལམ་གྱི་སྲོག། སྟོན་མེད་ཡང་ཟབ་མཐར་ཐུག་འདི་ན་
གསལ།། ཐེག་མཆོག་འོད་གསལ་རྫོགས་པ་ཆེན་པོའི་རྣལ་འབྱོར་གྱི་རྒྱལ་པོ། ཀ་དག་བདེ་
བ་ཆེན་པོའི་ཡེ་ཤེས་ལ་སྦྱལ་སྦྱངས་པའི་ཚུལ། རིག་པའི་བླ་མ་མཆོག་གི་མན་ངག་ཡང་ཟབ་
གསང་བའི་མཐར་ཕྱིན་གི་ཟིན་བྲིས་ཅུང་ཟད་བགྱི་པ་ལ།

I prostrate to the supreme Guru, who is none other than the glorious
Primordial Protector Samantabhadra! How wonderful! This path of the
absolutely effortless Great Bliss Primordial Purity, which is untainted by the
stain of exertion! Here will be made clear the unprecedented, most profound,
and ultimate vital essence of the path of the powerful *siddha*-adepts, of the
great Awareness-Holders! Here I will offer a few notes on the King of Yogas
of the supreme vehicle of the Clear Light Great Perfection - on the means
through which to refine the expression of the wisdom of the Primordial
Purity Great Bliss, on the consummation of the most profound and secret
pith instructions of the revered Guru of primordial awareness.

དང་པོ་བདེ་སྟོང་ཤེས་རབ་ཕྱག་རྒྱ་མཚན་ཉིད་དང་ལྡན་པ་ནི་ལུས་མཛེས་ཤིང་ཡིད་དུ་འོང་བ། སྟོད་སྨད་རྒྱས་ཤིང་སྐད་པ་ཕྲ་བ། ནུ་མ་འབུར་ལ་བྲ་ག་དཀ་ཞིང་རུབ་པ། གསང་གསུམ་ན་སྐུ་གསུང་ཐུགས་ཀྱི་སྐྱེ་བ་ཅན། ཁྱད་པར་མཆན་ཁུང་གཡོན་ན་དཀར་པོ་ཆིག་ཐུབ་ཀྱི་སྐྱེ་བ་ཡོད་པ། ལུས་དང་པདྨ་ལ་དྲི་ཞིམ་དུ་ཞིམ་པར་མནམ་པ། རག་འཛམ་ལ་སྨྲན་པ། དྲང་པོར་སྨྲ་ཞིང་། གསང་སྔགས་ཀྱི་ཆོས་ཟབ་མོ་རྫུང་ཕྱོགས་ཚམ་གཞན་ལ་མི་སྨྲོགས་པ། བློ་ཆེ་ཞིང་ཤེས་རབ་དང་སྙིང་རྗེ་ཆེ་བ། ཁྱད་པར་དུ་སྒྲུབ་པ་པོ་དང་གསང་སྔགས་ཀྱི་ཆོས་ལ་དད་ཅིང་མོས་པ། སྦྱོར་བ་ལམ་མཁས་ཤིང་བདེ་བ་ཆེ་བ། པདྨས་རྡོ་རྗེ་ལ་གཞིབ་པར་ཤེས་པ།

Firstly, the proper consort for Karmamudra practice is beautifully-proportioned and attractive; her upper and lower parts are well developed and her voice is high and fine. Her breasts are perky and her vagina is small, tight and compact. She bears the birth-marks of body, speech, and mind in the three places [i.e. on her head and throat, and at her heart]. In particular, she has a white panacea or 'all-in-one' mark on her left armpit. Her body and lotus are delicious-smelling, her voice is gentle and pleasant. She speaks honestly and doesn't breathe even a word of the profound doctrine of Secret Mantra in the direction of (unqualified) others. She is intelligent, wise and full of great compassion. In particular, she feels devotion towards and has faith in the accomplished masters and doctrine of the Secret Mantra. She is an expert in the path of sexual congress and can experience extreme bliss. She knows how to 'suck', or pull on the vajra with her lotus.

དེ་ལྟ་བུའི་ཕྱག་རྒྱ་མཚན་བཟང་དང་།རང་ཉིད་དབེན་པའི་གནས་སུ་བདེ་བའི་སྟན་ལ་ཁ་ཕན་ཚུན་འཁོད་ནས། རིག་རྩལ་མ་འགགས་པས་སེམས་ཅན་ཐམས་ཅད་ཀྱི་དོན་དུ་བདེ་ཆེན་ཀ་དག་གི་ཟུར་ལས་ཉམས་སུ་བླང་ནས་སྣོ་འདས་ཆོས་ཟད་ཆེན་པོར་ལ་བཙ་བར་བྱ་སྙམས་པའི་ཀུན་སློང་སྐྱོན་དུ་སོང་ནས། དེ་ནས་རིག་པ་ཀ་དག་གི་རང་ལས་མ་གཡོས་བཞིན། དང་པོ་ཕྱག་རྒྱ་མའི་གཟུགས་དང་གདོང་ལ་འཛུམ་པ་དང་ཆགས་པའི་ཉམས་འགྱུར་གྱིས་བལྟ་ཞིང་། རིག་གདངས་བདེ་བའི་སྦྱོར་ཆ་མ་འགགས་པའི་རང་སྒྲོ།

Sitting across from each other on a comfortable seat in your secluded place (of practice), without blocking the creative expression of primordial awareness, you and an excellently qualified mudra (consort) as described should practice this swift path of Great Bliss Primordial Purity for the sake of all sentient beings. Move forward with the intention to be liberated and pass beyond into the great dissolution of phenomena that transcends all conceptual thought. Then, without having stirred from the state of the primordial purity of *rigpa* [do as follows]:

Firstly: gaze upon the consort's body and face with a smiling and desirous expression, and sustain the natural glow of awareness without blocking your experience of bliss.

དེ་ནས་ཐུག་རྒྱ་མས་སྒྱུ་གར་སོགས་སྣ་ཚོགས་སྙན་པའི་དབྱངས་དང་ཆགས་པའི་གཏམ་སྣ་ཚོགས་སྣ་
བ་ལ། རིག་པ་རང་བབ་ཀྱི་གཤིས་ལས་རིག་གདངས་བདེ་བའི་སྐྱོང་ཆ་མ་འགགས་པའི་རང་
སྐྱོང་། དེ་ནས་ཐུག་རྒྱ་མའི་ལུས་རྟེ་ཞིམ་པོ་སྣོམ་སྟེ་རིག་པ་རང་བབ་ཀྱི་གཤིས་ལས་བདེ་བའི་
སྐྱོང་ཆ་མ་འགགས་པའི་རང་སྐྱོང་། དེ་ནས་ཐུག་རྒྱ་མའི་ལྕེ་འཛིན་དང་མཆུ་སོགས་གཞིབ་ཅིང་
ཉུ་ནས། རིག་གདངས་བདེ་བའི་སྐྱོང་བ་མ་འགགས་པའི་རང་བསྐྱངས། དེ་ནས་ཐུག་རྒྱ་མའི་
ལུས་ལ་རིག་པ་དང་། གཡན་ཟའི་གནས་དང་ནུ་མ་ལ་སེན་མོ་འདེབ་པ་དང་། རྡོ་རྗེ་པད་མའི་
ཕྱི་ལ་རིག་པར་བྱས་ཏེ། རིག་གདངས་བདེ་བ་མ་འགགས་པའི་རང་བསྐྱངས། དེ་ལྟར་སྟོན་
འགྲོའི་རིམ་པ་ལ་བརྟེན་པ་ཆེར་ཐོབ་ནས། གནས་ལུགས་ཀྱི་ལྟ་བའི་རང་ནས་གཟུགས་སྣ་རེ་
རོ་རིག་ཏུ་ཐབས་ཆད་སྐྱ་མ་མཁན་གྱི་སྐྱ་མའི་ཚོ་འཕུལ་ལ་ལུ་བུར་རྩལ་ཡང་ཡང་སྦྱར་ནས།

Then, with the consort singing and dancing, expressing all kinds of sweet melodies and sexy talk, maintain and nurture the glow of awareness that shines forth from the original ground of natural and innate *rigpa*, without blocking the bliss you're experiencing. Then, while sustaining rigpa but without blocking your experience of its bliss-aspect which comes from its very ground or nature, smell the delicious fragrance of the consort's body. Next, sucking on the consort's tongue, lips, and so on, sustain *rigpa* without blocking the blissful experience of the natural glow of awareness. Then, touch the consort's body, scratch your fingernails across her sensitive, ticklish spots and her breasts, touch the outside of her lotus with your vajra, and maintain *rigpa* without blocking the bliss of the natural glow of awareness. Rely like this on the stages of 'foreplay' or preliminary practices and gain greater and greater bliss. Maintaining the View of the ultimate reality or nature of phenomena, work with the creative energy of the senses and train repeatedly [to perceive] every form, sound, smell, taste and tactile sensation as the magician's illusory display [that they truly are].

དེ་ནས་དངོས་གཞི་རིག་པ་ཀ་དག་གི་ངང་ལས་མ་གཡོས་བཞིན། རིག་གདངས་ཀུན་བཟང་
ཡབ་ཡུམ་གྱི་ལྷ་སྐུར་མ་འགགས་པའི་རང་ངས་རང་དང་ཕྱག་རྒྱ་མཉམ་པར་སྦྱོར་ཏེ། རྡོ་རྗེ་
པདྨ་ལ་བསྣུན་ཏེ་གཉིས་ཀས་དལ་བུས་བསྐྱོད་པའི་ཐིག་ལེ་རིམ་གྱིས་བབ་པ་ན། བསྐྱོད་པ་རྗེ་
དལ་བྱེད་དེ། ཐིག་ལེ་གསང་བར་བབ་པ་ན་བསྐྱོད་འཕྲོ་བཅད། ཐ་མལ་གྱི་ཤེས་པའམ། རིག་
པ་དོ་བོ་ཀ་དག་སྟོང་གསལ་ཡིད་དཔྱོད་བློས་བྱས་མཚན་མའི་སྒོམ་གྱིས་མ་གོས་མ་བསླད་
པས་རྗེན་པ། ཕུང་ཁམས་སྐྱེ་མཆེད་གང་གིས་མ་སྒྲིབ་པ། ཕྱི་ནང་བར་གསུམ་རིས་མེད་ཟང་
ཐལ་ལེ་བའི་རང་ངས། སྣུགས་རྗེའི་ཆ་ལས་བདེ་བའི་མྱོང་ཆ་མ་འགགས། དེ་གའི་གཤིས་དང་
ལས་མ་གཡོས་བཞིན། བདེ་བ་ཡལ་གྲབ་ན་ཡུམ་གྱིས་དལ་བུས་རེ་བསྐྱོད། འཚོར་གྲབ་ན་
བསྐྱོད་འཕྲོ་བཅད་དེ། ཤིག་ནས་མཁའ་ལ་བཞག་ནས། དེ་ལྟར་རིག་པ་རང་བབ་ཀྱི་གཤིས་
ལས་མ་གཡོས་བཞིན། རིག་རྩལ་བདེ་བ་མ་འགགས་པ་ལ་རྩལ་ཡང་ཡང་སྦྱང་ཞིང་། མཐར་
ཐིག་ལེ་གྱིན་དུ་སྤྱོག་པ་དེ། ཤིག་གི་དབང་པོ་གྱིན་དུ་སྤྱོག་ནས།

Next, for the main practice:

Without wavering from the state of primordially pure *rigpa* and without blocking your perception of yourself and the consort manifesting from the glow of awareness in the divine appearance of Samantabhadra and Samantabhadri in union, unite together. Push the vajra into the lotus. As both of your gently vibrating *thiglé* or energy-drops gradually descend, move more and more slowly. When it comes down to the secret [place], stop moving.

[Rest in] the state of 'ordinary awareness', the essence of *rigpa* which is primordially pure emptiness-clarity, in that naked state untainted and unadulterated by any meditation involving distinctions assumed by the mind, unobscured by any aggregates, constituents or sensory bases *skanhdas, dhatus, ayatanas* whatsoever. Abide in this wholly unobstructed state of being and awareness, free from any distinction between outside, inside, and everything in-between. Without blocking your experience of *rigpa*'s bliss-aspect which comes from its compassionate aspect, rest unwavering in the [ultimate, unconditioned] nature of these. If you [feel that] your bliss is on the verge of subsiding, the consort should move a little, slowly and gently. If you feel like you're about to lose control [i.e. and ejaculate], stop all movement. Relax your gaze into space and in this way (rest) unwavering in the basic, naturally present state of *rigpa*. Train again and again in working with the creative expression of *rigpa* without blocking your bliss. Then finally, to reverse the *thiglé*, roll your vision upwards and send the drop back up.

རིག་པ་ཀ་དག་སྟེང་གི་ནས་མཁའི་དབྱིངས་ལ་འཛིན་མེད་དུ་གཏད་པས། ཐིག་ལེ་རྩོལ་མེད་དུ་ལྡོག་པར་འགྱུར་རོ། དེ་ནས་དགྲམ་པ་ནི། རང་ཉིད་ཕྱག་རྒྱ་དང་བྲལ་ཏེ། ལག་གཉིས་པུས་མགོ་ལ་བཀབ་ནས། ལུས་ཐམས་ཅད་ཤིན་ཏུ་ལྷོད་ནས། རིག་པ་ཀ་དག་སྟེང་འོག་ཕྱི་ནང་གང་དུའང་གཏད་སོ་མེད་པར། རང་བབ་ཏུ་ལྷོད་དེ་ཡུན་ཅི་རིང་མཉམ་པར་བཞག་པས། ཐིག་ལེ་རྩ་མིག་ཐམས་ཅད་དུ་རྩོལ་མེད་རང་སར་འགྲིམ་པར་འགྱུར། དེ་ལྟར་རིག་པ་ཀ་དག་ཆེན་པོའི་རང་ལས་མ་གཡོས་པས། དེ་ཁོ་ན་ཉིད་ཀྱིས། ཐིག་ལེ་དབབ་བཟུང་ལྡོག་དགྲམ་ཐམས་ཅད་རྩོལ་མེད་དུ་རང་གིས་འབྱུང་རོ།

By focusing without clinging to the upper expanse of the space of the primordial purity of awareness, the *thiglé* will reverse [direction] without effort. Next, to spread the *thiglé* out: separating from the consort, cover the top of your knees with both hands and completely relax your whole body. Relax into the naturally present state of the primordial purity of awareness which is without any fixed reference point of above, below, outside or inside. Rest like this for however long you like. The *thiglé* will travel about through the 'eyes' of the channels of its own accord, without any effort. In this way, solely through this, by resting without distraction in the state of the great primordial purity of awareness, all of [the movements of] the *thiglé* – bringing it down, holding, reversing and spreading it out – will occur effortlessly.

དེ་ལྟར་རྒྱུན་དུ་ཐིག་ལེ་མ་ཉམས་པ་བྱ་ཞིང་། བོགས་འདོན་གྱི་སྐབས་སུ་ཐིག་ལེ་དྭངས་སྙིགས་ལན་བཞི་ཚམ་ཕྱིས་ནས། མཐར་ཡུམ་གྱི་མཁའ་ལ་ལྷག་མེད་དུ་བཏང་སྟེ། དེ་ཚེ་རྟོག་ཤེས་དུམ་པ་རེ་འདུག་ན། རིག་པ་རང་སོ་མ་ཉམས་པའི་ངང་ལ་ཟད་པར་ལ་བཟླར་བྱའོ། དེ་ལྟར་ལམ་གྱི་སྲོག་ཏུ་བཟུང་ནས་ཉམས་སུ་བླངས་བས། ཚོགས་ཆིག་གི་གཟུང་འཛིན་གྱིས་བསྡུས་པའི་ཆོས་ཐམས་ཅད་ཟད་སར་འཁྱོལ་ཏེ། མཐར་ཕྱག་རིག་པ་འཕོ་འགྱུར་མེད་པར་ཀ་དག་གི་ནང་དབྱིངས་སུ་བཙན་ས་ཟིན་པར་འགྱུར་རོ།

[Work with] the *thiglé* in this way continuously and [prevent] it from deteriorating. After distilling the pure essence of the *thiglé* from the dregs about four times during the enhancement practices, finally send [it] out without remainder into the sky-like womb of the consort. If at that time some residual [conceptual] thought still remains, liberate it by dissolving it utterly in the state of un-deteriorated innate awareness. Thus, having grasped the vital heart of the path, and having put it into practice, all of the collected phenomena of subject-and-object [duality] will be resolved and brought to extinction within a single lifetime. At last, you will seize the stronghold within the inner realm or expanse of the primordial purity of motionless and changeless *rigpa*.

དེའི་རང་ལས་ག་ཏིང་གསལ་ལ་ཕུ་བའི་ཡེ་ཤེས་ལས། ཕྱི་གསལ་ལ་གཟུགས་སྐུ་རྣམ་པ་གཉིས། གདུལ་བྱའི་མོས་རོར་རྒྱུ་རྐྱེའི་རོལ་གར་བཞིན་དུ་སྐྱེད་ཅིག་རེར། བྱེ་བ་ཕྲག་བརྒྱར་འགྱེད་པར་འགྱུར་རོ། ཨེ་མ་ཤིན་ཏུ་སྐལ་བཟང་སྙིས་བུ་དག །རྩོལ་བཅས་དལ་བའི་ལམ་ལ་འབད་པ་ཅི། རྩོལ་མེད་སྒྱུར་ལས་སེང་གེའི་འཕྱོང་སྟབས་ཅན། འདི་ལ་འཇུག་ན་སྐྱེད་ཅིག་ཏུ་གྲུབ་ཕྱིད། ཐབས་ཀྱི་ཐབས་གྱུར་བདེ་ཆེན་ཀ་དག་ལས། །གསང་བའི་གསང་བ་མཁའ་འགྲོའི་སྙིང་གི་ཁྲག །ཟབ་པའི་ཟབ་པ་དམ་པའི་ཕུགས་ཀྱི་བཅུད། སྙིང་པོ་རོ་མཚན་ལས་ཀྱི་རྒུད། དེ་ལྟར་ཟབས་ཀྱི་ལས་ཟབ་རྒྱ་མཚོའི་བཅུད། །རིག་འཛིན་ཀླུ་ཡི་དབང་པོའི་སྙིང་གི་ནོར།། གསང་ཆེན་གྱུར་ལས་ཡིད་བཞིན་དབང་གི་རྒྱལ།། ཨྱུ་ཡུ་ཨི་ཧྲིའི་སྲིད་པོའི་རྒྱན་དུ་ཤོག །སྣར་ཡང་དབང་པོ་རབ་དང་ལྲུན་པ་ཡི།། ཐེག་མ་ཚོག་མཆོག་གི་རྣམ་འབྱོར་མ་གཏོགས་པ། །ཐེག་དམན་དམན་པའི་གང་ཟག་འཇུག་རོག་མིན། །ཟབ་གསང་བསྒྱུར་བར་གཏད་དོ་སྤྲས་སུང་མ༔ ༔

From the primordial wisdom of the subtle luminous profundity [which comes from] this dimension [of being], two body-aspects or manifestations of outer luminosity will shine forth like the playful dancing and revelry or magical display of the moon reflecting in water! In an instant, they will send out one billion [emanated forms] in response to the devotion and needs of disciples! Oh! Such amazingly fortunate ones! Why exert yourselves on the path of effort and toil, if when you enter this effortless, swift path of the Lion's Leap [the nature of all things] will be discerned and distinguished in an instant?

[This I have] obtained - this means of means, this path of Great Bliss Primordial Purity, this secret of secrets, this life-blood of the Dakinis, this most profound of profound [teachings], this essence of the mind of the holy ones! It is the wonder of the quintessential, miraculous path, the essence of the deepest ocean of such methods, the heart-jewel of the Vidyadhara Nagarjuna, the Lord of the Nagas, the Great Secret of the swift path, the king of all wish-fulfilling jewels and the crown of Ayu Indra. It is nothing short of the supreme path of the highest yoga for those endowed with the highest capacities, it is not a point-of-entry for less capable individuals of the lower vehicles.

Tantric Protectress, direct yourself to the protection of (this) Most Profound Secret!"

ཞེས་པ་བདེ་ཆེན་ཀ་དག་གི་ལམ་ཟབ་ཡང་གསང་མཐར་ཐུག་འདི་ནི། སྤྲུལ་དབང་འཇའ་ལུས་
རྡོ་རྗེ་རྩལ་གྱི་ལམ་གྱི་སྲོག་དགོངས་པའི་མཐིལ་ལྷ་བུ་ཡིན་ཏེ། གཞན་གསར་རྙིང་གི་རྒྱུད་སྡེ་
ཕལ་མོ་ཆེར། རྩལ་བཅས་ཀྱི་ཞིག་སློ་བདེ་བ་ཆེན་པོའི་ཐབས་ལམ་ཅེ་རིགས་ཤིག་བརྩོལ་ཡོད་
ཀྱང་། སློ་འདས་རིག་པ་ཀ་དག་གི་རང་ལས་ཤིན་ཏུ་རྩོལ་མེད་ཀྱི་གནད་འདི་ལྷ་བུ་ནི། སྤར་
གད་གིས་བསྐྱགས་མ་ནུས་པའི། གསང་ཆེན་གྱི་ལམ་ཁྱད་པར་མཆོག་ཏུ་འཕགས་པ་ཡིན་
པས། ཕྱི་རབས་རྡོ་རྗེ་ཐེག་པ་རང་ལུགས་ཏེ་མ་མེད་པའི་རྣལ་འབྱོར་རྒྱལ་པོ་མ་བཏོགས། །
གཞན་གང་གིས་སྟོད་ཡུལ་མ་ཡིན་པས། སྲུགས་སྲུང་ནག་མོས་དཔལ་བའི་མིག་བཞིན་ཏུ་
བཅེས་སྲུས་ཀྱིས་སྲུངས་ཤིག། །།

This path of the Great Bliss Primordial Purity, this profound, utmost secret consummation is like the very life-force of the path of Drubwang Jalü Dorje Tsal, is like the very depths of his mind. Although all sorts of other Lower Gate Great Bliss [i.e. Karmamudra] methods have been compiled in most of the classes of Tantras in the New and Old schools, these have all been ones involving effort. No one before now has been able to proclaim an essential teaching like this, one which is totally effortless and which [emerges] from the state of primordially pure *rigpa* that goes beyond all conceptual thought. Being distinctly and supremely exalted this Great Secret path is the pristine King of Yogas of our own tradition of Vajrayana, [meant for] future generations, and is not something to be practiced by any other.

O Black Tantric Protectress, [with your one] forehead eye, watch over this teaching closely and lovingly!

Sera Khandro

Teaching Song

(Sera Khandro Kunzang Dekyong Wangmo, 1892 - 1940)

 སེ་ར་མཁའ་འགྲོའི་གསུངས་མགུར། { འོག་སྒོ་བདེ་ཆེན་ལམ་གྱིས་ལམ་ལྔ་དང་ས་བཅུ་
གསུམ་རྫོགས་ཚུལ་གསུངས་པ་གཤམ་ལྟར། }

*(What follows below is a teaching on how the Five Paths and Thirteen
Bhumi, the 'grounds' or stages of realization are perfected through
the Path of Great Bliss of the Lower Gates, or Karmamudra)*

{ ཚོགས་ལམ }

The First Path: The Path of Accumulation

གཅིག་ཏུ་འཕོད་ཅིང་གཉིས་ཀྱིས།། དགའ་བཞིའི་ཡེ་ཤེས་འབར་ནས།།
བདེ་བ་ཆེན་པོའི་རྩ་བསྐྱངས།། དགའ་མགུར་སྤྱོད་པ་སྤྱོར་ལམ།།

The Daka of Great Bliss' magical song-and-dance display,
The Queen of the Wisdom of the Expanse of Emptiness
[i.e. the male and female Karmamudra partners]
Who delight one another through their many outer and inner celebrations,
This is the Path of Accumulation.

{ སྤྱོར་ལམ }

The Second Path: The Path of Union

གཅིག་ཏུ་འཕོད་ཅིང་གཉིས་ཀྱིས།། དགའ་བཞིའི་ཡེ་ཤེས་འབར་ནས།།
བདེ་བ་ཆེན་པོའི་རྩ་བསྐྱངས།། དགའ་མགུར་སྤྱོད་པ་སྤྱོར་ལམ།།

Seated alone and together,
A flame with the primordial wisdom of the Four Joys
Their channels of Great Bliss made erect,
Their joyful dalliance together – this is the Path of Union

{ མཐོང་ལམ }

The Third Path: The Path of Seeing

༡ ཞི་བ་པད་མའི་དཀྱིལ་འཁོར།། འདབ་བཞི་པོ་ཡིག་མཚན་པར།།
ཁྲོ་བོ་རྡགས་ཀྱི་རྡོ་རྗེ།། དཀར་པོ་ཧཱུྃ་ཡིག་ཕྱུར་བསྒྱན།། མཆོག་གི་དངོས་གྲུབ་རོལ་ཕྱིར།།
བསྣུབས་སློར་ལས་སློར་དང་པོ།།
རབ་ཏུ་དགའ་བའི་ས་ཐོབ།། ཡུམ་གྱི་རྩ་མཆོག་གཞུབས།།
དཔའ་པོའི་སེམས་འཕིན་སྐུལ་ནས།། བདེ་ཆེན་འཁོར་ལོར་གཡོས་པས།།
དགའ་བའི་ཡེ་ཤེས་མཐོང་སྟེ།།

1) The peaceful mandala of the Lotus, its four petals decorated
with BAM syllables,
The wrathful sign of the Vajra, a white HUNG syllable revealed
on its downward sloping side [i.e. the female and male genitals]
To revel in the supreme siddhi, you practice the procedures
of churning and bringing these together
Through which you will attain the first stage of exceeding joy.

Through the Dakini's supreme bliss channel
The Daka's *thiglé* [31] is incited,
It vibrates in the crown chakra of Great Bliss
And the primordial wisdom of bliss is seen.

{ བསྒོམ་ལམ }

The Fourth Path of Meditation

༢ ཉོན་སྒྲིབ་རགས་པ་བཅོམ་ནས།། དྲི་མ་མེད་པའི་ས་ཐོབ།།

2) Having conquered the gross afflictive emotions and obscurations,
you will attain the second stage of stainlessness, of being free
from all impurities.

[31] Sera Khandro refers to the male consort's *thiglé* poetically here, as the '(Tantric) hero's clouds of bodhicitta'. Dr. Nida notes in his fifth section in Chapter One on perceptions of Karmamudra practice as patriarchal that "even when a (Karmamudra) text is revealed by a woman, its instructions may still be phrased in terms of men's bodies and perspectives. My own belief is that if Karmamudra is only designed for men or pitched at men's needs then Karmamudra practice is not yet perfect." Sera Khandro's autobiographical and instructional texts stand out for the way in which they suggest a more female-centric approach to Karmamudra practices. The description the *thiglé* circulating through the different chakras producing states of ecstasy which correlate with the different *bhumi* or stages of enlightenment aligns with a similar scheme that was imparted to Sera Khandro in a dream-vision by the Tantric saint Kukkuripa (whose consort she had been in a previous life) when she was fourteen years old. Analyzing this vision, scholar Sarah Jacoby notes how Kukkuripa's Karmamudra instructions, very unusually, present Karmamudra procedures from the perspective of a female body and practitioner. In that transmission, as part of heterosexual physical union practice involving the exchange of *thiglé*, the female practitioner is advised to stimulate the male consort's 'cloud of Bodhicitta' or *thiglé*, have him eject this into her vagina/womb and then pull this up to circulate through her chakras. Jacoby notes that, in contrast to more standard portrayals of Karmamudra practice which advise male practitioners to refrain from ejaculating and draw the female consort's *thiglé* up through their penis, Kukkuripa's instructions to Sera Khandro:

"...invert the Tantric reversal of ordinary sex, for Sera Khandro describes the man's cloud of semen raining into the woman's secret center and pervading upward in a process that at least initially mirrors the flow of conventional heterosexual intercourse. Kukkuripa's words strongly suggest that if Buddhist sexual yoga is about arousing vital nuclei [i.e. thiglé], retaining them, and "sucking them up like water in a bamboo shoot" along the energy centers of the body, then the cloud of bodhicitta raining into the wisdom lady's secret center in Sera Khandro's vision cannot be about her male partner's spiritual advancement. Rather, this instruction is oriented toward her liberation, despite the tomes of Tantric literature that leave women's subjectivity unexplored." (2014, 203-204).

In this text as well, Sera Khandro describes the daka's 'clouds of bodhicitta' being incited by the dakini's bliss channel. Here again, we catch a glimpse of Karmamudra through a female practitioner's eyes. Just like Yeshe Tsogyal, countless dakinis have no doubt sought out male consorts with which to practice over the centuries but specifics about their practices and experiences as female-bodied practitioners have rarely made their way into print. As a prolific writer and prominent yogini and treasure-revealer who taught and practiced Karmamudra within living memory, Sera Khandro thus represents an important exception to the rule.

༣ སེམས་སྐྱེན་ལོངས་སྤྱོད་འཁོར་ལོ།།
ཁྱབ་སྐྱེལ་མཆོག་དགའི་ཡེ་ཤེས།།
གསུམ་པ་འོད་འཕྲོས་ས་ཐོབ།།

3) When the *thiglé* reaches the chakra of enjoyment and richness
(at the throat),
the primordial wisdom of supreme joy pervades and increases,
And you attain the third stage of radiating light.

{ མི་སློབ་པའི་ལམ }

The Fifth Path of No More Learning/Training/Purifying

ང ཉོན་སྒྲིབ་ཕྲ་བ་བཅོམ་ནས།། བཞི་བ་འོད་བྱེད་ས་ཐོབ།།

4) Having conquered the subtle afflictive emotions and obscurations,
you will attain the fourth stage of illumination.

ཿ སེམས་སྐྱེན་ཆོས་ཀྱི་འཁོར་ལོར།། ཁྱབ་སྐྱེལ་གཏི་མུག་སྒྲིབ་དག།
ལྷུན་སྐྱེས་ཡེ་ཤེས་མངོན་གྱུར།། རླུང་ལྔ་ཡེ་ཤེས་སྒྲིན་པས།། ལྟ་པ་སྦྱང་དཀའི་ས་ཐོབ།།

5) With the *thiglé* in the Chakra of Dharma or Ultimate Reality
[in the heart center],
The obscuration of the haze of all-pervading
and proliferating confusion is purified,
Spontaneous, innate primordial wisdom is made directly manifest,
The five [worldly] winds are ripened into their wisdom forms,
And through this you will attain the fifth stage of that
which is difficult to learn.

༦ སེམས་སྐྱེན་བདུད་རྩི་ཐིག་ལེ་མ།།
སྤྲུལ་པའི་འཁོར་ལོར་ཁྱབ་པས།།
ཁྱད་དགའི་ཡེ་ཤེས་མངོན་གྱུར།།
ཤེས་སྐྱེན་ཕྲ་བ་བཅོམ་ནས།།
མངོན་གྱུར་དྲུག་པའི་ས་ཐོབ།།

6) When the splendour of the *thiglé* nectar,
Pervades the [navel] Chakra of Manifestation,
The primordial wisdom of the Distinctive or Special Joy directly manifests,
Having conquered the subtle obscurations of consciousness,
You will attain the sixth stage of direct or explicit attainment.

༧ བདེ་སྟོང་གཉིས་སུ་མེད་པའི།། འོད་གསལ་ཁོར་ཡུག་འབྱམས་ཀླས།།
བདག་གཞན་དམིགས་སུ་མེད་པའི།། བདུན་པའི་ས་མཆོག་ཐོབ་སོང་།།

7) When you perceive the infinite, limitless Clear Light of indivisible,
nondual Bliss-Emptiness,
Then you will have obtained the supreme seventh stage that is wholly
without fixation on any self or other.

༨ འདུས་མདོར་རླུང་ཐིག་ཁ་སྦྱོར།། སྣང་གསུམ་བག་ཆགས་བཅོམ་པས།།
མི་གཡོ་བ་ཡི་ས་ཐོབ།།

8) With the winds and drops united, joined together as one,
The mental imprints of the Three Visions or Appearances are conquered,
And you will attain the eighth stage of unwavering-ness.

༩ སེམས་སྐྱེན་བདུད་རྩིའི་ཆུ་རྒྱུན།། བདེ་སྟོང་འཁོར་ལོར་ཁྱབ་པས།།
དགའ་བྲལ་ཡེ་ཤེས་མངོན་གྱུར།། ཡོན་ཏན་ཡོངས་རྫོགས་ས་དགུ།།

9) When the flowing stream of the nectar of the *thiglé*,
Pervades the Bliss-Sustaining chakra [at the genitals]
The primordial wisdom that is without or beyond joy directly manifests,
And you attain the ninth stage of Complete Qualities.

༡༠ གཟུང་འཛིན་གཉིས་རྟོགས་སངས་ནས།།
བློ་བྲལ་གཤུག་མའི་གཤིས་སུ།། འཁྲུལ་སྣང་ཆོས་སྐུར་སྦྱོར་པས།།
རྩ་རླུང་ཕྱིག་ལེའི་ཁམས་རྣམས།། དག་རྫོགས་སྨིན་པ་ས་བཅུ།།

10) Having cleared away the dualistic mind which apprehends
subject and object,
Unifying all mental delusions and appearances in the Dharma or Absolute
Reality Body, in the ground of your ultimate, underlying nature
beyond all intellectual concepts,
You will attain the tenth stage of purifying, perfecting and ripening
the elements of the channels, winds and drops.

༡༡ བསྒོམ་པའི་ལམ་གནད་མཐར་ཕྱིན།། སེམས་སྙིན་བདུད་རྩིའི་ཞལ་མཇལ།།
སྐད་ཅིག་འོད་གསལ་ནུས་པས།། སྒྲིབ་གསུམ་བག་ཆགས་རབ་བཅོམ།།
མི་སློབ་ལམ་མཆོག་མཐར་ཕྱིན།། ཀུན་ཏུ་འོད་ཀྱི་ས་ཐོབ།།

11) With the essential points of the Path of Meditation consummated,
You see directly the face of the *thiglé*-nectar,
In an instant, through the power of the Clear Light of consciousness,
The three obscurations and imprints are thoroughly conquered,
The supreme path of No More Learning is consummated,
and you attain the stage of Universal Light.

༡༢ རང་གསལ་སྒྲིབ་མེད་ཆེན་པོའི།།
སྐུ་དང་ཡེ་ཤེས་ཡོན་ཏན།། རྩོལ་སྒྲིབ་བྲལ་བ་ཟུང་འཇུག།
ཁ་སྦྱོར་ཡན་ལག་བདུན་ལྡན།། བཅུ་གཉིས་མ་ཆགས་པད་མ།།

12) The bodies, primordial wisdoms and spiritual qualities
of the great Self-Illumination devoid of obscuration,
The unity or indivisibility of being, free from striving or obscuration,
Having the seven qualities of [enlightened] union,
is the twelfth Stage of the Lotus of no desire or attachment.

ཕྱིས་ལ་མ་རྨུག་འོད་གསལ།། བསམ་བརྗོད་ཕྱོགས་ལྷུང་བྲལ་བ།།
སྐུ་དང་ཡེ་ཤེས་བདག་ཉིད།། རྡོ་རྗེ་ཉིད་སྐྱེར་བྱུང་ཆུབ།།

13) Dissolved into the Clear Light free from the haze of obscuration,
free from succumbing to any thought, expression or bias,
You will become the embodiment of the bodies and wisdoms,
And attain the very body of a Buddha, wholly purified and perfected.

བཅུ་གསུམ་རྡོ་རྗེ་འཛིན་པའི།། ས་ལམ་བགྲོད་པའི་ཤིང་རྟ། བདེ་སྟོང་གྲོལ་ཐབས་ཆེན་པོ།།
རྒྱུ་དང་འབྲས་བུའི་ས་ཆོད།། ལམ་འབྲས་རིམ་པར་མ་སྤྱོས།། ཞོག་སློ་བདེ་བ་ཆེན་པོ།།
ཁམས་གསུམ་རོལ་བའི་ཁྱད་ཆོས།། མདོར་བསྡུས་བྱར་ཚམ་བརྗོད་པས།། གནས་ཆོས་བྲག་
ལ་བརྟེན་པའི།། བྱ་རྒྱལ་ཐང་དཀར་ཉོད་པོ།། ཐྱལ་གསུམ་ { ལྟ་བསྒོམ་སྤྱོད་པ་མཐར་ཕྱིན }
ལུས་ལ་ཐོགས་ཆེ།། དེ་བཞིན་ཐྱགས་ལ་བྲངས་མཆོད།། བྱ་ཐུན་ཐྱལ་མེད་རྣམས་ལ།།
རྣུང་ཕྱོགས་ཚམ་ཡང་མ་སྨྲ།། ཀུན་མཐབང་བདེ་སྟོང་དབང་མོས་བྲིས་སོ།།

The chariot that travels through the paths
and thirteen stages of the Vajra-holder
Is the great liberating means of Bliss-Emptiness,
And the karmic distance it covers
Does not depend on going through the paths and results gradually.
This is the special feature of Karmamudra, the Great Bliss
of the Lower Gates, in which all the three realms delight.
Like the great King of Birds, the white vulture whose (retreat-like)
home is fixed firmly on the rocky crags,
And who achieves in his own body the great perfection of the
consummation of the three skills (Looking, Meditation and Conduct),
Speak of this only in a brief, indirect way,
And hold it in your heart without even breathing a word of it in the
direction of those who lack such skills and are trifling in their actions!

Written by Kunsang Dekyong Wangmo.

Dr. Nida Chenagtsang

Excerpts from the Treatise on Desire

(Dr. Nida Chenagtsang) [32]

ལམ་གྱི་སྐོར།

དབང་སྐབས་དབང་རོ་འཕྲོད་པའམ།།

ཁྲིད་སྐབས་གོ་བ་ལོན་པ་དང་།།

བྱིན་རླབས་དབང་གིས་རྟོགས་པ་བཅས།།

རྟེན་མ་ནོར་ཤིན་ཏུ་གལ།།

The Path:

One can be shown empowerment in the context of
Tantric empowerment (*wang*)
Or can come to some undersdanding when receiving oral instructions (*tri*),
Or one can gain realizations as a result of the blessings received –
Having a basis without error is extremely important.

རིག་མ་རིགས་ལར་བསྟན་པ་ནི།།

པད་མ་དུང་ཚན་རི་དྭགས་དང་།།

གླང་ཆེན་མ་དང་རི་མོ་ཡིན།།

དེ་ལ་ཕྱི་ནང་གསང་རྟགས་གལ།།

The different types of women of awareness [female consorts]
relied on in the practice
Are the lotus, the conch, deer, elephant and design [artistic] consort.
For these both outer and inner secret signs or marks are important. [33]

---

[32] Dr. Nida started writing this poem in Rome on the 24th of April 2012, completed its final sections in Washington on the 13th of June, and did further edits in Beijing on the 6th of September.

[33] Here Dr. Nida reminds us that a good consort is not just somebody who looks a certain way or who possesses certain auspicious birthmarks. The inner qualities and capacities of one's partner are just as important as any outer signs or their exterior appearance.

དཔའ་བོ་རེ་བོང་རི་དགས་རེགས།།
རྟ་མཆོག་དང་ནི་བ་གླང་བཞི།།
ཕྱག་རྒྱ་དཔའ་བོའི་གནས་ལུགས་ཡིན།།
སྔགས་མོ་རྣམས་ཀྱིས་མ་ནོར་འཚོལ།།

There are four types of male consort or 'hero':
The rabbit, deer, stallion, and ox.
These are the basic anatomical types of male mudra
So Tantric yoginis, look for the right one! [34]

ཕྱི་རྟགས་ལུས་དང་གཟུགས་བཟང་ལ།།
ནང་རྟགས་རྩ་བཟང་རག་སྐད་བཟང་།།
གསང་རྟགས་དད་བཙུན་ཤེས་རབ་ཆེ།།
སྔགས་ལ་ཚོམ་མེད་དམ་ཚིག་བསྲུང་།།

The outer signs are that the consort's body and form are good
The inner signs that their channels and voice are good,
And the secret signs that their faith is firm and wisdom great.
So Tantric practitioners, protect your vows without doubt or hesitation!

ཁྱད་པར་གསང་སྔགས་ཁོང་དུ་ཆུད།།
ལོག་བལྟ་ཞེ་ཚོམ་མེད་པ་དང་།།
གསང་བར་མཁས་ཞིང་འདོད་པ་ཆེ།།
གསང་སྔགས་རྟེན་གྱི་མཆོག་གྱུར་ཡིན།།

---

[34] These four-fold typologies of sexual partner line up with those introduced in a later Medieval iteration of Kamasutra teaching by Kokkoka called the Ratirahasya, and eventually found their way from there into Ju Mipham and other Tibetan experts' texts. These classifications are associated with different female and male body types, sexual constitutions, psychological temperaments and genital shapes and sizes. The builds of each partner are explained to be more or less compatible with one another in different ways.

More specifically though, the best consort to rely
on as a physical support for Tantric practice
Is one who has really internalized and understood the Secret Mantra,
Who has no doubts about erroneous views,
And who is skilled in secret knowledge and great in desire.

བཅུ་གཉིས་བཅུ་དྲུག་ལོ་གསུངས་ཀྱང་།།
སྨན་རྒྱལ་གཡུ་ཐོག་ཆེན་པོ་ཡིས།།
ཉམས་རྟོགས་གོང་དུ་སྤེལ་བ་ལ།།
རྒན་གཞོན་གང་ཡིན་བསྟེན་བྱ་གསུངས།།

Even though texts might state that consorts should
be very young in age,
The great master Yuthok, the King of Doctors
Taught that [the consort] you should rely on
Is the one who elevates and increases your meditative
experiences and realization,
However old or young they may be.

དབེན་གནས་ཡང་ན་རང་ཁྱིམ་དང་།།
བདེ་བའི་གདན་དང་འཇམ་གོས་སོགས།།
འདོད་ཡོན་ཅི་འབྱོར་བྱ་བ་དང་།།
ཁྱད་པར་བར་ཆད་མེད་གནས་གལ།།

In either an isolated retreat-spot or in your own home,
Prepare your seat or bed of bliss, set up soft fabrics
and whatever materials to delight the senses you prefer
And most importantly, make sure that your place of practice
is free of any obstacles or disruptive influences.

ལུས་རྒྱས་རྩ་ཁམས་དྭངས་པ་དང་།།

མངར་གསུམ་ཁྱད་པར་སྦྲང་རྩི་བསྟེན།།

རྩ་རླུང་ལས་སུ་རུང་བ་ལ།།

ཤ་བཅུད་སྣུམ་བཅུད་ཟ་བ་ཤིས།།

Use substances like the 'three sweets' (sugar, molasses, honey)
but especially honey
Which (when eaten) increase bodily vigor and make the channels
and subtle elements pure and bright
To make the *tsa* (channels) and *loong* (winds) serviceable,
It is good to consume nutritious foods like meat broths and oil extracts

ཐིག་ལེ་དཀར་དམར་འཕེལ་བ་ལ།།

དཀར་གསུམ་ཁྱད་པར་འོ་མ་བསྟེན།།

གང་མཁོའི་རོ་ཚའི་སྨན་སོགས་ཀྱང་།།

ཆོལ་མཐུན་དམིགས་བསལ་བསྟེན་པར་བྱ།།

To increase the white and red *thiglé* (essential drops),
Use the 'three whites' (yoghurt, butter and milk) and milk in particular.
Use whatever libido-enhancing medicines you require,
Or whatever appropriate or special treatments you need.

ལུས་སྟོང་རྩ་སྟོང་འཁོར་ལོ་སྟོང་།།

དཀར་དམར་ཐིག་ལེའི་དམིགས་པ་བརྟན།།

བོགས་འདོན་འཁྲུལ་འཁོར་ཟབ་མོས་བྱ།།

རྟེན་འབྲེལ་སྟོབས་ཀྱིས་རྟོགས་པ་འཆར།།

Stabilize your visualization of your body, channels and chakras as hollow,
And of your red and white *thiglé*
To enhance your practice perform the physical yoga exercises thoroughly.
And through the power of the auspicious, inter-dependent links [35]
realization will arise

རང་ལུས་ཐབས་ལྡན་ཐོག་མར་གཅེས།།
ལུས་ཀྱི་སྟོང་ར་ཕྱི་བསྒོམ་དང་།།
རྩ་ཡི་སྟོང་ར་ནང་བསྒོམ་ཡིན།།
རྩ་འཁོར་ལྔ་ནི་གསང་བསྒོམ་གྲགས།།

Diligently practicing the solo practice with your own body
is most important in the beginning –
Visualizing the hollow enclosure of one's body is
called the 'outer meditation' or cultivation,
Visualizing the hollow structures of the channels is known
as the 'inner meditation'
And visualizing the five chakras
is the 'secret meditation'.

ཐིག་ལེ་དཀར་པོ་ཧཾ་གཟུགས་དང་།།
ལྟེ་འོག་ཨ་ཤད་བསྒོམ་པར་བྱ།།
དེ་ནས་རྡོ་རྗེ་བཟླས་པ་ཡིས།།
རྩ་རླུང་ཉིད་ལ་གོམས་པར་བྱ།།

Imagine that the white *thiglé* takes the form of a HAM syllable
And that there is a tiny triangle below your navel
Then, through practicing Vajra breathing and recitation
Familiarize yourself with the essential nature of the channels and winds

---

[35] *Tendrel*, the term used here can refer to both the Buddhist concept of 'inter-dependent original' or inter-connectivity, or more colloquially an auspicious karmic occurrence or ominous event. In the context of Tantric yoga and ritual however, this word specifically referred to the careful alignment and linking up of gross and subtle elements and outer, inner, and secret phenomena and conditions. When done thoroughly and correctly, powerful and auspicious resonances are created and solidified through this 'co-incidence' of levels of being and transformation is possible.

རྡོ་རྗེ་བཟླས་པ་བྱུས་ནས་ནི།།
རླུང་གི་གནད་ལ་གདེང་ཐོན་ཞིང་།།
གཏུམ་མོ་བརྟན་པར་གྱུར་བ་ཡིས།།
འོག་སྒོའི་ལམ་ལ་འཇུག་པར་བྱ།།

Having practiced the Vajra recitation and breathing,
You will gain confidence in the essential points of subtle energy
or *loong* practice
Enter onto the Path of the Lower Gates [i.e. Karmamudra]
With a stable foundation in *Tummo* or inner heat practice.

བལྟ་དགོད་ལག་བཅིང་སྦྱོར་བ་བཞི།།
ཐབས་ལམ་འོག་སྒོའི་ཐེམ་སྐས་འདྲ།།
དམིགས་པ་ཡང་ན་མཁའ་འགྲོ་བཅས།།
རིམ་གྱིས་བསྒོམ་པ་གནད་འགག་ཡིན།།

The four stages of 'looking, talking or laughing, holding, and uniting'
Are like the steps or rungs leading you up the ladder of Karmamudra,
the Path of Means of the Lower Gates
Whether you practice with a visualized consort or an actual dakini
The most essential thing is to meditate gradually, in stages

བལྟ་བ་ཞེས་པ་བལྟ་ཞིང་བསྒོམ།།
ཕན་ཚུན་བལྟ་ཞིང་བལྟ་ཞིང་བསྒོམ།།
ཆགས་སེམས་སྐྱེས་ན་བདེ་བ་བསྒོམ།།
དེ་ལྟར་ཆགས་སྐྱོང་བདེ་བ་བསྐྱེད།།

For 'looking', you look at each other and meditate
You look at one another and meditate or focus on what you see
When you find yourself getting aroused, you meditate
on the pleasure that you feel –
Turn yourself on and generate bliss like that

འདོད་ཆགས་རྒྱས་ཞིང་སྐྱོང་བའི་དུས།།
ཉོན་མོངས་རྣམ་གཡེང་གཞན་མི་འཕེལ།།
ལུས་དང་སེམས་ནི་བདེ་བར་མཐོང་།།
བདེ་བའི་ངང་དུ་གློད་ལ་ཞོག།།

When your desire increases and you experience bliss,
Afflictive emotions, mental states and other distracting thoughts
will not proliferate
Just perceive the pleasure in your body and mind
And let go and relax into your blissful state.

དང་པོ་གདོང་དང་མཆུ་སྨིན་དང་།།
མིག་བྱུང་ཚལ་ལ་བལྟ་བར་བྱ།།
དེ་ནས་བྱང་དང་ནུ་མ་དང་།།
བརླ་སོགས་སྨྲས་གནས་བལྟ་ཞིང་བསྒོམ།།

First, just look at each other's face, lips, and eyes
Then look at each other's chest and breasts,
One another's thighs, private parts and so on,
and meditate on what you see.

དགོད་པ་ཞེས་པ་འཛུམ་ལྡངས་ཞིང་།།
འདོད་ཆགས་བལྟ་འཛུམ་སྐྱགས་བྱས་ནས།
མིག་གི་བྱུར་མདའ་འཕེན་པ་དང་།།
ལུས་ཀྱི་རྣམ་འགྱུར་སྣ་ཚོགས་སྟོན།།

For 'talking or laughing', smile at each other
Look at and smile at each other with desire
Then shoot pointed glances at each other like arrows
from the corner of your eyes
And display all kinds of different bodily expressions for one another.

དགོད་ཅིང་འདོད་པའི་གཏམ་སྨྲ་ཞིང་།།
ཕན་ཚུན་བདེ་བ་བསྐྱེད་པ་གཅེས།།
མ་ཡེངས་མ་སྒྲིམ་ཤེས་པ་ལྷོད།།
བདེ་བའི་ངོ་ལ་ཡང་ཡང་བལྟ།།

Focus carefully on laughing or expressing yourself spontaneously,
on saying arousing things,
And generating pleasure in each other
But do this with a relaxed awareness – without getting distracted or
without trying too hard or concentrating too tightly –
just keep looking at the basic essence or nature of your bliss over and over.

དཔའ་བོ་དཔའ་མོ་གཉིས་ཀ་ཡིས།།
མཉམ་དུ་བསྒོམ་ན་ནུས་པ་སྐྱུར།།
ངོ་ཚ་ཞེད་དངངས་ཡོངས་སྤང་ནས།།
བདེ་བའི་སེམས་རོ་བསྐྱང་པར་བྱ།།

If both the daka and dakini
Meditate together they will quickly become powerful
and capable in the practice
Abandon all shame, fear, and anxiety
And nurture and maintain the essence of the mind of bliss!

དགའ་བདེའི་ངག་ཚིག་སྣ་ཚེ་འབྱིན།།
མ་འགོག་རང་ལུགྔ་རང་སོར་ཞོག།
བདེ་བས་དགོད་པ་བསྒོམ་དུ་གསུངས།།
དུ་སྐྱེད་བདེ་བ་བསྐྱེད་པར་བྱ།།

Call out whatever sounds or words of joy and bliss arise –
Don't block these, simply rest in your spontaneously arising
natural state of being.
It is taught that these spontaneous expressions of pleasure

are a form of meditation
So generate bliss through your crying and wailing!

ཨ་ཨང་ཨུ་ཧེ་ཧི་ཧང་ཧ།།
ཨོ་ཧོ་ཡ་ཧོ་ཨ་ཡ་སོགས།།
མ་བཅོས་ཆགས་པའི་རང་སྒྲ་ནི།།
 རྩུན་སྨྲེས་རྩ་ཡི་སྔགས་སྒྲ་ཡིན།།

AH! ANG! UM! HE! HI! HANG! HA!
OH! HO! YA! HO! AH! YA!
And other uncontrived, spontaneous sounds of desire like these
Are the spontaneously produced mantra-sounds of the channels

ཁྱེད་མཛེས་ཁྱེད་ནི་དཔའ་མོ་དང་།།
དཔའ་བོ་ཡིན་པས་སྒྲ་མེད་ཅེས།།
བསྟོད་ཚིག་བཟང་ཚིག་གང་བྱུང་སྨྲ།།
མཐོང་མེད་ཚིག་གིས་བདེ་བ་སྟེར།།

Say 'You're beautiful! You're a dakini, a daka, and there is
no one greater in power and beauty than you!'
Speak words of praise, good words, say whatever comes to mind –
Give each other pleasure through speaking words freely, without regard
for what you're saying.

ལག་བཅངས་ཞེས་པ་ཕན་ཚུན་རེག།
ཐོག་མར་ལག་པ་སོར་མོ་རེག།
བདེ་བ་བྱུང་དུས་ཆུང་ཙམ་བསྒོམས།།
རིམ་གྱིས་གཡའ་བའི་གནས་སུ་རེག།

For 'holding', touch each other
First, touch fingers and hands,
When pleasure arises, concentrate or meditate a little on it
And touch each other's sensitive areas gradually, in stages.

ཁྱད་པར་བླ་ཡི་གསང་གནས་སུ།།
སྣུམ་ཕྲུན་ཡང་ན་མེད་ཀྱང་རུང་།།
རེག་ཅིང་བདེ་བའི་དམིགས་པ་བྱ།།
མཆོག་གི་བདེ་བ་རྒྱས་ཞེས་གསུངས།།

In particular, touch and massage each other's special *la* energy points,
with or without oil
And focus on the bliss that arises
This is said to increase the most supreme bliss

གུང་མོས་པད་རྩ་མཉེ་བ་དང་།།
ཡུམ་གྱི་སོར་མོས་རྡོ་རྗེ་མཉེ།།
གང་དུ་གཡའ་དང་བདེ་བ་ཆེ།།
དེ་རུ་སྐྱོ་མེད་རེག་ལ་བསྒོམ།།

The daka massages the channels of the dakini's lotus [the clitoris]
with his middle finger,
And the dakini rubs his vajra with her fingers
Wherever is most sensitive and gives the most pleasure
Happily and enthusiastically meditate on the sensations there.

བལྟ་དང་རེག་པ་དགོད་པ་གསུམ།།
མཉམ་དུ་ཉམས་ལེན་བྱས་ཀྱང་འགྲིག།
ཁམས་དཀར་འཕོར་སྙམ་ཚེ་འཕྲོ་འཇོག །
བདེ་སྟོང་རོ་བོའི་གནས་ལུགས་བསྒོམ།།

It is fine as well if you practice
The three stages of looking, touching, and talking together simultaneously
If you think that you're going to ejaculate, stop playing together,
And meditate on the basic nature of the essence of bliss-emptiness.

སྦྱོར་བ་ཞེས་པ་དབང་པོ་སྦྱོར།།
འདོད་བསྟན་གོམས་པའི་གང་ཟག་ནི།།
འདི་ཡི་ཐབས་ལ་མཁས་གྱུར་ཡང་།།
གཞན་རྣམས་རིམ་གྱིས་འཇུག་པ་གལ།།

'Union' is the uniting of the genital organs
Those individuals who are familiar with and practiced in the Kamasutra
Will be skilled in this method,
Whereas for others it is important to enter into it in stages

མི་ཕམ་འདོད་བསྟན་གཞུང་དུ་ནི།།
འཇིག་རྟེན་རྗེས་སུ་ཡེ་ཤེས་གསུངས།།
དེ་ཕྱིར་འཇིག་རྟེན་སྦྱོར་ཐབས་པ།།
མཁས་བྱས་ཡེ་ཤེས་སྦྱོར་ཐབས་བསྟེན།།

Mipham's Kamasutra text
States that [one should] practice 'wisdom' [i.e. Tantric]
sex after one has practiced worldly sex:
"Thus, having become skilled in the worldly methods of union,
employ the wisdom ones."

ལུས་ཀྱི་འདུ་ཤེས་ཡི་དམ་ལྷ།།
ངག་ནི་སྔགས་ཀྱི་འདུ་ཤེས་དང་།།
ཡིད་ནི་ཆོས་ཉིད་འདུ་ཤེས་བཅས།།
སུམ་ལྡན་འདུ་ཤེས་རྟག་ཏུ་གཅེས།།

Conceive of your body as the meditational deity
Your speech as mantra
And your mind as dharmata, ultimate reality –
Carefully and constantly maintain this threefold conception.

འདུ་ཤེས་སུམ་ལྡན་རྟོགས་གྱུར་ན།།
བསྐྱེད་པའི་རིམ་པ་མཐར་ཕྱིན་ལ།།
དེ་ནས་བསྐྱེད་རྫོགས་ཟུང་འཇུག་དང་།།
རིམ་གྱིས་རྫོགས་ཆེན་གནད་ཀྱང་རྟོགས།།

If you can realize this threefold conception
This is the consummation of the Creation Stage
After this, you can realize the integration of the Creation
and Completion Stages
And gradually, the essential points of the Great Perfection as well.

ཕྱི་ལུས་སྟོང་ར་བསྒོམ་པ་ལ།།
ཕོ་རྣམས་ཡི་དམ་ཕོ་རུ་བསྐྱེད།།
མོ་རྣམས་ཡི་དམ་མོ་རུ་བསྐོམ།།
གསལ་ལ་མ་ནོར་བརྟན་པར་བསྒོམ།།

Meditating on the outer body as a hollow enclosure
The man generates himself as the male yidam
And the female generates herself as the female yidam –
Meditate on this clearly, firmly and without error.

ནང་གི་རྩ་ཡི་སྟོང་ར་ནི།།
དབུ་མ་ཕྱི་དཀར་ནང་དམར་བ།།
ཐིག་ལེ་དཀར་པོ་སྤྱི་བོ་དང་།།
ཨ་ཤད་དམར་མོ་གསལ་དུ་བསྒོམ།།

The inner enclosures of the channels are hollow
The central channel is white on the outside and red on the inside,
Cultivate the white *thiglé* at the crown of the head
And the tiny red triangle[below the navel] clearly and brightly.

གསང་བ་འཁོར་ལོའི་སྟོང་ར་ནི།།
རྩ་འཁོར་ལྔ་ཡང་རྩ་འདབ་བཅས།།
སོ་གཉིས་བཅུ་དྲུག་བརྒྱད་པ་དང་།།
རེ་བཞི་སོ་གཉིས་གསལ་དུ་བསྐྱེད།།

Produce the secret hollow forms of the chakras,
Which are the five chakras and the channel-petals
Thirty two, sixteen, eight, sixty four, and thirty two,
Generate them clearly [with their correct proportions and positions].

རྡོ་རྗེ་བྱིན་རླབས་ཧཱུྃ་གིས་བཀག།
པད་མ་བྱིན་རླབས་ཕཊ་ཀྱིས་བཀག།
འདི་ལ་སྔགས་དམིགས་མི་འདྲ་བ།།
ཡོང་སྲིད་བསྒོམ་རྩའི་གནས་ལུགས་ཡིན།།

Bless and bind the vajra with a HUNG syllable
Bless and bind the lotus with a PHET syllable
There are many possible mantra visualizations for this
But this is the basic root-structure of the meditation.

ཅལ་ནས་སྦྱོར་བ་མི་ཡི་ཚུལ།།
དེ་ལ་སྟེང་སྦྱོར་ནོག་སྦྱོར་གཉིས།།
ཟུར་དུ་སྦྱོར་བ་ལྷ་མ་ཡིན།
གཡས་གཡོན་མདུན་དང་རྒྱབ་ནས་སྦྱོར།

When you lie down [facing each other] this is the 'human style' of union
For this, both of you unite one atop the other
When you penetrate 'from the side' or obliquely,
it is the demi-god position:
You unite straddling one another side by side, from the front and behind

ཚིག་པུར་སྐྱུར་བ་ཞི་བའི་ལུ།།
ལངས་ཏེ་སྐྱུར་བ་ཁྲོ་བོའི་ཆུལ།།
རྒྱབ་ནས་སྐྱུར་བ་ཀླུ་ཡི་འམ།།
དུད་འགྲོའི་ཆུལ་ཞེས་བཤད་པ་ཡིན།།

Seated, crossed legged union is the peaceful deity position
While uniting while standing is the wrathful deity style
And uniting from behind is described as naga or four-legged animal style

པད་མ་ཅན་ལ་སྟེང་སྐྱུར་ལེགས།།
དུང་ཅན་མ་ནི་འོག་ནས་བགྲོད།།
རི་དྭགས་མ་ལ་སྐྱིལ་དྲུང་དང་།།
གླང་ཆེན་མ་ནི་རྒྱབ་ནས་སྐྱོར།།

Being on top is good for lotus consorts
Having sex while under the man is good for the conch consort
Uniting cross-legged is for the deer consort,
Having sex from behind is for the elephant consort

ཐོག་མར་རང་ལུས་ཐབས་ལ་བརྟེན།།
ཆུལ་ཁྲིམས་ཅན་ལ་འདིས་ཆོག་གསུངས།།
དམིགས་པ་ཁོ་ན་བྱ་བའམ།།
ལག་སོར་བསྐྱོད་པའི་ཐབས་ཀྱང་བྱ།།

At first, rely on the solo practice with your own body
It is taught that using this method is sufficient for monastics
You just visualize
Or make use of your fingers and hand as well.

མཛུབ་ལྟ་རིགས་ལྔའི་མཁའ་འགྲོ་བསྒོམ།།
རྡོ་རྗེ་ཞེ་བ་དལ་བས་ཚུལ།།
སྟེ་བོའི་ཏི་དཀར་བབ་པ་ལས།།
མགྲིན་པར་དགའ་བ་རོས་བརྒྱུད་སྐྱུང་།།

326

Meditate on your five different fingers as the five kinds of dakini,
Let them wander gently and slowly across your vajra
And practice recognizing the bliss that comes from the white HAM
of the *thiglé* descending from the crown of your head to your throat.

ཞག་གསུམ་ཞག་བདུན་ཉེར་གཅིག་སོགས།།
ཆད་དང་ལྡན་པ་བསྒོམ་རྗེས་སུ།།
སྙིང་གར་མཆོག་དགའར་རོས་བཟུང་བསྒོམ།།
དེ་ཡང་ཉམས་ཕོན་གལ་ཆེན་ཡིན།།

Once you've meditated properly and effectively for
A period of say, three, seven or twenty-one days
Meditate on recognizing and capturing the supreme joy
or bliss in your heart chakra
It is very important to gain experience with this as well.

ལྟེ་བར་ཁྱད་དགའར་རོས་བཟུང་བསྒོམ།།
རྡོ་རྗེའི་རྩབར་བབས་པ་དང་།།
བསྐྱོད་འཕོ་བཅད་ལ་འོག་རླུང་གློད།།
བདེ་བ་མི་འཆོར་ལྷུན་ནེ་ཟིན།།

Meditate on identifying the special or distinctive bliss in your navel
Bring it down to the root of your vajra
Stop moving and let go of your hold on the lower winds
Without losing your bliss, stay completely relaxed.

ཐིག་ལེ་མགྲིན་བབས་དགའར་བ་དང་།།
སྙིང་གར་བབས་པས་མཆོག་དགའར་སྐྱེ།།
ལྟེ་བར་བབས་ནས་ཁྱད་དགའར་དང་།།
གསང་གནས་ལྷུན་སྐྱེས་དགའར་བ་ཡིན།།

When the *thiglé* drops down to the throat it is 'joy'
When it descends to the heart chakra the 'supreme joy' is born
Dropping to the navel it is the 'special joy or bliss'
And in the genitals it is the 'innately, spontaneously generated joy'.

དེ་ལ་ཡས་བབ་དགའ་བཞི་ཟེར།།

དགའ་བ་རེ་ནས་བྱང་པར་སྒྲུངས།།

 རིམ་གྱིས་གོམས་ན་བརྟན་པར་འགྱུར།།

བྱེལ་མེད་བསྒོམ་དང་ཉམས་སྐྱོང་སྐྱེ།།

These are called the 'four joys that descend from above'
If you train and become accomplished in each of these joys and habituate
yourself to them gradually you will become stable in your practice.
Meditate unhurriedly and meditative experience(s) will arise.

ཐིག་ལེ་སྟེང་ནས་འོག་ཏུ་འབེབ།།

དབབ་པ་ཞེས་སུ་གྲགས་པ་ཡིན།།

བདེ་སྐྱོང་རྩ་ནས་གྱེན་དུ་འདྲེན།།

བཟུང་བཟློག་ཅེས་བྱ་དེ་ནས་དགྲམ།།

The *thiglé* drops down below from above
And this is known as 'bringing the *thiglé* down'.
You should then pull it upwards through the bliss-sustaining channel,
'retain', 'reverse' and then 'spread it out'.

བདེ་སྐྱོང་རྩ་ནས་སྤྱལ་འཁོར་ལ།

རྒྱུ་མཐུན་ཆུལ་གྱི་དགའ་བ་དང་།།

དེ་ནས་ཆོས་ཀྱི་འཁོར་ལོ་ལ།

རྣམ་སྨིན་གྱི་ཆུལ་གྱི་དགའ་བ་ཟེར།།

From the bliss-sustaining chakra to the magical emanation chakra
(i.e. from the genitals to the navel)
It becomes the 'mode of joy or bliss in accordance with the cause'

Then, in the Dharma or reality chakra (the heart)
It is known as the 'mode of joy of complete ripening'.

སྙིང་གའི་རྩ་ནས་མགྲིན་འཁོར་ལ།།
སྐྱེས་བུ་བྱེད་པའི་ཆུལ་དགའར་བ།།
ལོངས་སྤྱོད་འཁོར་ནས་བདེ་ཆེན་རྩ།།
རྡི་བྲལ་འབྲས་བུའི་དགའར་བའོ།།

From the heart chakra to the throat chakra
It becomes the 'mode of joy of individual effort'
Then from the enjoyment chakra to the great bliss channel
[i.e. throat to crown],
It becomes 'the joy of the wholly stainless result'.

མས་བརྟན་དགའར་བ་གནད་ཆེ་བས།།
ཡས་བབས་ལས་ཀྱང་ལྷག་ཅེས་གསུངས།།
མས་བབ་རིམ་པར་དགའར་བ་ནས།།
གྱེན་དུ་མིང་གཅིག་ལུགས་ཀྱང་མཆིས།།

It is taught that "the joys that come from stabilizing from below are
extremely essential, even more supreme than those which descend
from above."
'bringing or stabilizing from below' is another name for this same
process of successive, ascending joys produced from dropping the *thiglé*
downwards in stages upwards.

རང་དང་ཕྱག་རྒྱ་བདེ་བ་བསྐྱེད།།
རྣམ་གཡེང་མ་ཕྱར་བསྒོམ་པ་གཅེས།།
རིག་པ་མ་བཅོས་རང་སོར་འཇོག།
བདེ་སྟོང་གཉིས་མེད་ཡང་ཡང་བསྒོམ།།།

Generate bliss, you and your consort,
Take care to meditate without succumbing to distracting thoughts
Rest in uncontrived pure awareness, in your natural state of being
And meditate repeatedly on the non-duality of bliss and emptiness.

བདེ་སྐྱེད་དགྱེར་མེད་ཟེར་བ་ཡང་།།
དགའ་བཞི་སྟོང་བཞི་དགྱེར་མེད་ཡིན།
དགའ་སྟོང་མཉམ་དུ་བསྒོམ་པ་ནི།།
གནད་ཀྱི་སྙིང་པོ་ཡིན་པའོ།།

The so-called 'indivisible bliss-emptiness'
Is the same as the 'indivisible four joys and four emptinesses'.
Meditating on joy and emptiness together
Is the most absolutely essential point.

དང་པོའི་དགའ་བ་སྟོང་ཉིད་དང་།།
ཁྱད་དགའ་སྟོང་པ་ཆེན་པོ་ཡིན།།
མཆོག་དགའ་ཤིན་ཏུ་སྟོང་པ་དང་།།
ལྷན་སྐྱེས་དགའ་བ་ཐམས་ཅད་སྟོང་།།

With the first joy, there is the 'emptiness itself' or the 'intrinsic emptiness'
With the special joy, it is the great emptiness'
For the supreme joy, the 'extreme or most exceeding emptiness'
And for the innate, spontaneous joy there is 'everything empty'.

བསླ་བ་དགོད་པ་འཆུད་སྟོར་བཞི།
མགྲིན་སྙིང་ལྟེ་གསང་རྩ་བཞིར་སྦྱར།།
སྤུང་བ་དྲག་གསུམ་རྣམ་རྟོག་སྤུང་།།
ཐོབ་བྱ་བདེ་སྟོང་བདེ་རྟོག་མེད།

The four stages of looking, smiling, embracing, and uniting
Are connecting with the four chakras of the throat, heart, navel,
and secret chakra.
What is renounced are the three poisons and conceptual thoughts
What is gained is bliss-emptiness and non-conceptual bliss.

བདེ་སྟོང་བློ་འདས་མཐར་ཕྱུག་ཡིན།།
ཐོབ་བྱ་སྐུ་བཞིར་འཛིག་པ་འང་ཡོད།།
དེ་རྣམས་བསྒོམ་པའི་ཉམས་ལེན་ལ།།
དགའ་བ་བཅུ་དྲུག་ཅེས་སུ་གསུངས།།

Bliss-emptiness is the ultimate consummation that transcends concepts
and the thinking mind
Through it there is also the attainment of entering into the four bodies
It is taught that "practicing all these together
[brings] the sixteen joys".

 hུ་ཚད་ཆགས་པས་གཡོ་གྱུར་ན།
སྙིང་གར་བ་མ་པོ་ཡིག་ལས།།
ཆགས་བྲལ་བདུད་རྩི་ལུས་གང་ནས།།
བསིལ་སྙིམ་སོང་བས་ཆགས་དབལ་ཞི།།

If you get too aroused and over-stimulated,
Imagine that the guru emerges from a BAM syllable in your heart
And fills your body with nectar, free of desire or arousal –
The heat of your desire will be pacified as you cool down
and get it under control.

དམར་མདངས་རྣམས་ནི་ནས་མཁའ་ལ།།
འཇའ་ཚོན་བཞིན་དུ་ཡལ་བར་གྱུར།།
རྣམ་གཡེང་བྱ་ཞིང་སྒོར་བ་སྤང་།།
ཡང་ན་རྩ་གྱང་ཁྲུས་ཀྱང་བྱ།།

For those hot and ruddy with arousal, your desire
Will disappear like rainbows dissolving into space
Allow yourself to get distracted and give up penetration,
Or douse yourself with cold water.

ཐིག་ལེ་དབབ་དང་འཛིན་པ་དང་།།
གྱེན་དུ་བརྙོག་དང་ལུས་ཀུན་བཁྲམ།།
དབབ་བཟུང་བརྙོག་བཁྲམ་རིམ་པ་བཞི།།
མེད་དུ་མི་རུང་རྩ་བ་ཡིན།།

Bringing down the *thiglé*, holding it,
Reversing its flow upwards and spreading it throughout your body –
These are the four stages of bringing down, retaining,
reversing and spreading,
Which are the indispensable basis of practice.

ཕློག་འདྲེན་འཕུལ་འཁོར་རྟོགས་ཆེན་པས།།
གསུངས་བཞིན་ལྱུང་དུ་འདྲེན་པ་ལ།།
ཡིད་ཆེས་དང་དུ་ཉམས་ལེན་བྱོས།།
ལས་སླ་བྱིན་རླབས་ཆེན་ཁ་ཆེ།།

To quote what is taught by Dzogchen Chöying Tobden Dorje
On reversing and pulling up the *thiglé* :
"Practice with a state of conviction
And you will easily attain great power of blessings." (Dorje 2010)

བདེ་ཆེན་སྐྱེས་འཕྲོ་བཅད་ལ་བསྐྱིལ།།
མིག་གཉིས་གྱེན་བསྒྲད་སྐྱལ་དང་བསྲང་།།
རྩ་བཞི་བསྐུམ་ལ་ཉོག་རླུང་འཐེན།།
ཉོག་སྦྲོ་བཅུམ་ལ་རྒྱ་སྐྱལ་སྐྱུར།།

To stop the generation of Great Bliss hold your breath,
Roll your eyes upwards and straighten your spine,
Contract the muscles of both your calves, pull in the lower winds
And suck your intestines in towards your spine as you constrict your anus.

སྤྱི་ནི་སྦུར་ཞིང་ཁོང་འདྲེན་བྱ།།
རིག་པ་ནས་མཁར་ཐད་ཀར་གཏད།
ཐིག་ལེ་གནས་སུ་སྤྲོག་པར་བྱེད།
ལན་མང་སྐྱར་བ་གལ་ཆེན་ཡིན།།

Connect the tip of your tongue to your palate and pull in your belly
Focus your awareness straight ahead into space
Pull the *thiglé* back into your perineum area –
It is important that you repeat this many times

ཧྲག་ཏུ་བདེ་བ་ལྟེ་སྙིང་དང་།
མགྲིན་པ་སྤྱི་བོར་རིམ་བཞིན་དུ།།
མས་བརྟན་དགར་བཞི་ཡེ་ཤེས་སྐྱོང་།།
རྡོ་རྗེའི་དར་འཚོར་བདེ་བ་འཆར།།

Repeatedly and continually bring the bliss to the navel, heart,
throat and crown chakras in stages,
Experience the primordial wisdom of the four joys produced
by stabilizing from below and bringing the *thiglé* upwards
And the intensity in your vajra will subside and bliss will manifest.

ཁོང་འདྲེན་མང་པོ་བྱས་པའི་མཐར།།
མཐེ་བོང་སྙིན་ལག་ཏུ་ཚུར་བཅིང་།།
གསང་གནས་མཚམས་ནས་སྤྱི་བོར་འཕར།།
ཐིག་ལེ་དྲུ་མར་ཡར་ལ་འདྲེན།།

After you pull in your abdomen many times
Press your thumbs to the base of your ring fingers to make a (Vajra) fist
And shoot the *thiglé* from your perineum to your crown
Rolling it upwards through the central channel.

སྐྱེ་པོ་ཧཱུྃ་ལ་ཐིམ་བསམ་དྲག་ཏུ་སྒུལགས།།
ཧཱུྃ་ལས་ཐིག་འཕེལ་ལུས་ཀུན་ཁྱབ།།
བདེ་བས་ལུས་རྒྱས་དམིགས་མེད་བཞག།
དེ་རྗེས་བུམ་ཅན་རླུང་ལ་སྦྱང་།།

Imagine that it dissolves into the HAM at the crown and vibrates fiercely
Thiglés proliferate from the HAM and pervade your entire body
Bliss expands throughout your body and you rest without
focusing on any object
Then, after this, purify your *loong* by doing *bumbachen* [vase-breathing].

བགེགས་རྣམས་མི་འབྱུང་ཞིམས་པར་འགྱུར།།
ག་དག་རང་ལ་བཞག་པ་གཅེས།།
བགེགས་རྣམས་གཏིང་ནས་འབྱུང་མི་སྲིད།།
དགེ་བ་བླ་མེད་བྱང་ཆུབ་བསྔོ།། ༼ ཞེས་སོ ༽

Spiritual obstacles will not arise and will dissolve
Take care to rest in a state of primordially pure awareness
Such obstacles cannot possibly arise from such profundity
Dedicate the merit to unparalleled Buddhahood.

རྩབ་དང་དགང་དང་གཞིལ་བ་དང་།།
མདའ་ལྱར་འཕངས་དང་རྣམ་པ་བཞི།།
བུམ་པ་ཅན་རླུང་ཆེ་ཆུང་འབྱིད།།
གསུམ་ལས་གང་རུང་ཉམས་ཐོན་བྱ།།

Practice the four aspects of breathing
– inhaling, filling the abdomen, churning,
And shooting it out like an arrow
And whichever of the three levels of vase-breather –
lesser, greater or average – suits you.

གཡུ་ཐོག་ལུགས་ལ་རླུང་ཅན་ནས།།
གཏུམ་མོ་མཐར་ཕྱིན་ལས་རྒྱ་བསྟེན།།
ཡང་ན་རླུང་ལ་མ་གོམས་པས།།
རིམ་གྱིས་བསྒོམ་ན་ཆོག་པར་གསུངས།།

In Yuthok's system, it is taught that
One can make use of Karmamudra practice 'with the yogic winds',
having perfected *Tummo*,
Or one can cultivate the practice gradually,
Without any training or familiarity in channel-and-winds yogic practice.

བསྒོམ་པ་མ་ཡིན་གོམས་པ་ཡིན།།
གོམས་པ་སྐྱོང་དུ་གྱུར་བ་ཡིན།།
རྡོ་རྗེའི་གསུངས་འདི་ཕུན་མིན་དུ།།
ཕྱིན་ཅན་ཡིན་པ་ཤེས་དགོས་སོ།།

You should understand that (the practices in the verses above)
Are the cultivation or meditation which is not meditation,
The meditation through which one realizes the expanse (of reality) –
You should appreciate that this vajra-speech or teaching is uncommon,
And imbued with blessings.

མཐར་ཐུག་ཁམས་འཛིན་གདམས་པ་ནི།།
བླ་མའི་ཉམས་མྱོང་གསང་ཁྲིད་བྱ།།
རིགས་རྒྱུད་སྤེལ་ན་གདམས་ངག་ལྟར།།
བྱང་ཆུབ་སེམས་ཀྱིས་སེམས་དཔའ་སྐྱེད།།

Finally, when it comes to the oral teachings on drawing up the *thiglé*
You should follow the esoteric instructions which are based on the
experience of your gurus.
If you (wish) to expand your lineage (and produce a child),
then as these instructions say,
Generating bodhicitta, you should make a (baby) Bodhisattva. [36]

[36] The above stanzas are excerpted from Dr. Nida's verses on Karmamudra from his
three-part 'treatise on Desire'. The part that precedes this section on Tantric practice
focuses on sexual health and discusses sex, sexuality, and desire from the perspective
of both Tibetan medicine and biomedicine. These preceding stanzas dealing with the
worldly side of sex discuss in considerable detail such topics as STIs, regular STI testing,
contraception, puberty, management of arousal and desire for teenagers, sexual health
advice for homosexual individuals, menstruation, menopause, options for having sex
during pregnancy, treatments for low libido, erectile dysfunction, premature ejaculation,
vaginismus, vulvodynia, and much else besides. Lest readers misunderstand Nida la's final
verse here about how it is permissible for the daka to ejaculate at the close of Karmamudra
practice when Tantric partners wish to have a child, it is worth noting that Nida
advocates for regular sexual health check-ups and the use of contraception in the earlier
sections of his poem. While discussing ovulation and conception, Nida explains that:

"The primary form of contraception is to wear male or female condoms;
Or else to be careful to ejaculate outside by pulling out one's penis
There's also surgery to insert an IUD (intra-uterine device)
And contraceptive drugs that can be used
But after using a lot of drugs
There's a danger that women will become infertile or will develop other disorders
After (unplanned) conception
Women might turn to abortions through drugs or aggressive surgery but these are
dangerous
(If at all possible) expectant parents should keep this most precious human child
And try to get along harmoniously with each other."

While discussing sexually transmitted diseases he notes:

"Contagious diseases that are transmitted through blood
Include viruses that infect the liver and blood (i.e. such as Hepatitis B and C),
Sicknesses transmitted from mother to child,
And many cases where husbands infect their wives –
Thus condoms, so-called 'penis' and 'genital covers'
Are an indispensable protection charm
So wear one that's the right size
And check it from time to time when you enter a woman
To state that condoms stop you from having children
Is certainly true, but more than this, they prevent bad diseases
Diseases which come from the vagina and penis
Are the root of fighting and regret."

These quotations should hopefully make it clear how important communication and honesty between partners, regular sexual health check-ups and sensible use of contraceptive measures can be for all forms of sexual activity, worldly or otherwise. The full verses of the medical part of Dr. Nida's Kamasutra poem can be found in Tibetan here: http://bod.sorig.net/?p=158 (last accessed, March 2018).

Yuthok the younger and the four dakinis

Yuthok's Song

When Yuthok the Younger reached the age of seventy-six he summoned all his disciples to offer a teaching and presented them with many gifts. On that occasion, he briefly recounted his life story in the following song:

Hey! Listen fortunate ones!
Listen well, people of the world!
In particular, you who are gathered here,
Even though you have listened much before,
All those were meaningless illusory words.
Today you will listen to what is really meaningful.
Even though you have seen much before,
They were just designs of false and deceptive visions.
Today, that which you see will purify the two obscurations.

If you do not know who I am,
I am the emissary of all the Buddhas,
I am the refuge of all beings.
All the animate and inanimate world is pervaded by my body,
voice, and mind.

The illusory form of this body is of the nature of a host of sacred deities,
Its materiality is instrinsically pure.
Like a rainbow it cannot be grasped,
Yet like the moon's reflection on the water, it appears everywhere.

The empty sound of my voice is the song of the echo,
Reverberating with the sound of the eighty-four thousand dharmas.
It manifests as a rain of teaching for those who need to be guided,
And sets all beings on the path that ripens and liberates.

In the clarity and emptiness of my mind, the ineffable authentic state,
Bliss is omni-pervasive, arising unceasingly,
And emptiness and compassion are undifferentiated.
Hence, the phenomena created by mind are naturally liberated
through the shortest instant of time.

In an instant I am a fully awakened Buddha;
In an instant I travel to hundreds of Buddha fields;
In an instant I encounter hundreds of Buddhas;
In an instant I manifest hundreds of emanations;
In an instant I guide hundreds of beings,
And I accomplish the totalities and masteries.

With a faith that does not know uncertainties,
Pray without having any doubt!
Even though the cataract of impure vision prevents you from
seeing all these qualites of mine,
In the ordinary perception shared by everyone:

I am the doctor who, with the medicine of skillful compassion,
Cures the inner mental illness of the three emotions,
And the outer illnesses of the three humors, wind, bile, and phlegm.
The title 'doctor' applies to me.

I explain the Buddhist canon and its commentaries by heart.
With logic I overcome the challenges of fundamentalists,
I issue the banner of victory of the Buddhist doctrine.
The title 'scholar' applies to me.

I went to Sri Parvata and robbers created obstacles on my way,
But with a gaze I paralyzed them all.
The title 'siddha' applies to me.

On my way to Odiyana, flesh eating dakinis sent meteorites
and lightning to strike me.
I made the threatening gesture and all the dakinis collapsed.
The title 'siddha' applies to me.

On my way to Ceylon the boat fell apart in the midst of the waves.
I flew like a bird and also saved my companions.
The title 'siddha' applies to me.

When I went to the Kali forest, a vapor of venomous snakes
spread like dark fog.
I meditated on compassion and the fog quickly vanished.
The title 'siddha' applies to me.

When I went to Persia I encountered the army of the Mongols,
So I penetrated the rocky mountains back and forth.
The title 'siddha' applies to me.

When I visited Swayambhu I competed with the Bonpos in magic.
For half a day I remained sitting in space.
The title 'siddha' applies to me.

I went from Bodh Gaya to Tibet taking only a single day,
Carrying a fresh flower as a gift.
The title 'siddha' applies to me.

At the place of Tshongdu Kormoru in Western Tibet,
I prevented the sun from setting and caused a rain of Aruras,
golden in color, to fall.
The title 'siddha' applies to me.

It would be endless to recount all the events of my life.
For one who has gained mind freedom,
There are no disturbances caused by earth, water, fire and wind,
gods and demons, etc,
And by animate and inanimate enemies.

He flies in the sky swifter than birds,
He dives in the waters with nothing to stop him,
He penetrates mountains like a meteorite or lightning,
In the midst of fire he is the fire god.

The beings of the degenerate age are of little merit,
And few are those who meet and listen to me.
Those who see, listen, think, touch me, and have faith in me,
Create the sprout of the spirit of enlightenment,
Purify negativities accumulated throughout eons,
Overcome obstacles and adverse conditions of this life,
Liberate themselves, liberate others, liberate both, and liberate
all their followers.

I will connect to happiness even those,
who harboring negative views, harm me.
Hence, I will lead them from (ordinary) happiness to (ultimate) happiness.
There is no doubt about this.

If you give up your heart and mind to me, beseech me in a sincere way,
Overcome your lack of faith and hope in me
as a refuge throughout your life,
Immediately your two obscurations will diminish.
Upon meeting me in reality, in vision, or in dream,
I will reveal the path to the temporal and ultimate goal.

All of you present now and the students to come,
My sons, and disciples, remember this!
For the time being, my work of training beings in this world is complete.
I will now go to the pure land of the Medicine Buddha.

After he had said this and had given a lot of advice to the doctors, he exhibited enlightened bodily activities that were perceived by beings in many diverse ways, surpassing what each of them could conceive of. The expanse of the sky was completely covered by a net of rainbow light, in the center of which, in the midst of hundreds and thousands of deity-princes bearing an array of flower-garlands and offering substances, were ten thousand wisdom-dakinis. From the tips of their fingers manifold rays of rainbow light emanated. This rainbow light touched the body of the great being Yuthok and he drifted off into the heavens. It is said that people saw many different things: some saw him ride off on a lion, some saw him fly away on a garuda, while yet others saw him ride off on a bull, and so on.

BIBLIOGRAPHY

ABOUT THE AUTHOR

The Yoga of Bliss

Tibetan Language Texts:

'Phrin las, dung dkar blo bzang. *Dung dkar tshig mdzod chen mo.*
Pe cin: krung go'i bod rig pa dpe skrun khang, 2002.

Bzang po, yon tan (ed.) "Rang bzhin brgyab cu'i rtog pa ngos 'dzin."
In Sa skya'i lam 'bras, Vol. 21, Kathmandu, Guru Lama Sachen
International, 2008 (TBRC Resource ID W1KG13617): 279 – 287.

Chos bzang, ye shes. "Gong sa mchog gis kha che tshogs par bka' slob stsal
ba." *Sham bha la'i pho nya.* August 5th, 2009. Accessed March 29th, 2018.
http://www.shambalapost.com/2009-08-05-12-53-57/11083-2014-08-28-04-
29-14

He ru ka (lce nag tshang), nyi zla. " 'dod pa'i bstan bcos 'dod chags sum
sbyor ma yi gleng gzhi."*Rgyal spyi'i bod kyi gso rig khang (bod kyi gso rig
dra ba,* blog). August 15th, 2014a. Accessed March 29th, 2018.
http://bod.sorig.net/?p=152

He ru ka (lce nag tshang), nyi zla. "'dod pa'i bstan bcos 'dod chags sum
sbyor ma las gnyis pa gso rig 'dod bstan (2)." *Rgyal spyi'i bod kyi gso rig
khang (bod kyi gso rig dra ba,* blog). August 15th, 2014b.
Accessed March 29th, 2018.
http://bod.sorig.net/?p=160

He ru ka, nyi zla and ye shes sgrol ma. *Rten 'brel sngags bcos rig pa.*
Pe cin: mi rigs dpe skrun khang, 2015.

Mgon po, g.yu thog yon tan. *G.yu thog snying thig*
(edited by HUNG chen and nyi zla). Pe cin: mi rigs dpe skrun khang, 2005.

Mgon po, g.yu thog yon tan. *Bdud rtsi snying po yan lag brgyad pa gsang ba
man ngag gi rgyud (dpal ldan rgyud bzhi).*
Shin hwa: pod ljongs mi dmangs dpe skrun khang, 2006.

Mkha' 'gro, dbus bza'. "Gsung mgur." In *Gsung 'bum*, Vol. 3, Ca khrong, si khron mi rigs dpe skrun khang, 2009.

Rdo rje, 'jigs bral ye shes. "Dge 'dun rig 'dzin 'dus sde'i bca' yig blang dor gsal ba'i me long." In *Gsung 'bum*, Vol. 22, Kalimpong, Dupjung Lama, 1979-1985 (TBRC Resource ID: W20869): 615 – 636.

Rdo rje, bzhad pa'i. "Lha gcig nyi ma gzhon nus dag snang du stsal ba'i thabs lam nyi zla'i bcud len dang brgyud 'debs." In Gsung 'bum, Vol. 12, Leh, T. Sonam & D.L. Tashigang, 1983 – 1985 (TBRC Resource ID: W22130): 379-386.

Rdo rje, chos dbyings thob ldan. Yang sang rta phag yid bzhin nor bu'i rdzogs chen khri yig. Pe cin: mi rigs dpe skrun khang, 2006.

Rgya mtsho, mi pham. "'dod pa'i bstan bcos 'jig rten kun tu dga'i ba'i gter." In *Gsung 'bum*, Vol. 13, Paro, Bhutan, Lama Ngodrup and Sherab Drimey, 1984–93 (TBRC W23468): 525 – 590.

Shri, Sha kya. "Ka dag bde chen myur lam gyi khrid rim rig 'dzin grub pa'i thugs tig gsang chen bla med." In *Gsung 'bum*, Kathmandu, Khenpo Shedup Tenzin & Lama Thinley Namgyal, 1998 (TBRC W23563): 885 – 894.

Staff Writer. "Sdom pa shor na gsang sngags yin mdog ma byed." *Bod kyi dus bab*. July 17th, 2014. Accessed March 29th, 2018. http://tibettimes.net/2014/07/17/137315/

English Language Texts:

Allione, Tsultrim. *Women of Wisdom*. I thaca: Snow Lion Publications, 2000.

Aryadeva. Aryadeva's Lamp that Integrates the Practices (Caryamelapakapradipa): The Gradual Path of Vajrayana Buddhism According to the Esoteric Community Noble Tradition. Translated by Christian Wedemeyer. New York: American Institution of Buddhist Studies/Tibet House US, 2007.

Bailey, Cameron. "*A feast for scholars: the life and works of Sle lung Bzhad pa'i rdo rje.*" PhD diss., University of Oxford, 2017.

Biernacki, Loriliai. *Renowned Goddess of Desire: Women, Sex, and Speech in Tantra.* New York: Oxford University Press, 2008.

Chenagtsang, Nida. *The Tibetan Art of Good Karma: The hidden treasure of the Turquoise Way.* Sorig Publications Australia, 2011.

Chenagtsang, Nida. *The Tibetan Art of Dream Analysis.* Sorig Press U.K., 2013.

Chenagtsang, Nida. *Path to Rainbow Body: Introduction to Yuthok Nyingthig.* Sorig Press U.K., 2014.

Chenagtsang, Nida. *Mirror of Light: A Commentary on Yuthok's Ati Yoga, Volume One.* Translated by Ben Joffe. Portland: Sky Press, 2016.

Chenagtsang, Nida and Nguyen, Tam. *Sowa Rigpa Points: Point Study in Tradtional Tibetan Medicine.* Portland: Sky Press, 2017

Chenagtsang, Nida. *The Tibetan Book of Health: Sowa Rigpa, the Science of Healing.* Portland: Sky Press, 2017.

Chenagtsang, Nida. *Weapon of Light: Introduction to Ati Yoga.* Portland: Sky Press, 2017.

Chöphel, Gendun. *Tibetan Arts of Love: Sex, Orgasm, and Spiritual Healing.* Translated by Jeffrey Hopkins. Ithaca: Snow Lion Publications, 2000.

Dalton, Jacob. "*The Development of Perfection: The Interiorization of Buddhist Ritual in the Eighth and Ninth Centuries.*" Journal of Indian Philosophy 32 (2004): 1-30.

Dalton, Jacob. *The Taming of the Demons: Violence and Liberation in Tibetan Buddhism.* New Haven: Yale University Press, 2011.

Davidson, Ronald. *Indian Esoteric Buddhism: A Social History of the Tantric Movement.* New York: Columbia University Press, 2002.

Davidson, Ronald. Tibetan Renaissance: *Tantric Buddhism in the Rebirth of Tibetan Culture.* New York: Columbia University Press, 2005.

Bibliography

Dorje, Rangjung. The Profound Inner Principles (With Jamgön Kongtrul Lodrö Taye's Commentary Illuminating "The Profound Principles." Translated by Elizabeth Callahan. Boston: Snow Lion Publications, 2014.

Dorji, Jagar. "Śākya Śrī." *In The Treasury of Lives.* May, 2011. Accessed March 29, 2018. https://treasuryoflives.org/biographies/view/Shakya-Shri/8782

Gayley, Holly. *Love Letters from Golok: A Tantric Couple in Modern Tibet.* New York: Columbia University Press, 2018.

Hatley, Shaman. *"Erotic Asceticism: The Knife's Edge Observance (asidhārāvrata) and the Early History of Tantric Coital Ritual."* The Bulletin of the School of Oriental and African Studies 79, 2 (2016): 329 – 45.

Jacoby, Sarah. *Love and Liberation: Autobiographical Writings of the Tibetan Buddhist Visionary Sera Khandro.* New York: Columbia University Press, 2014.

Jacoby, Sarah. *"The science of sensual pleasure according to a Buddhist monk: Ju Mipam's contribution to kāmaśāstra literature in Tibet."* The Bulletin of the School of Oriental and African Studies 80, 2 (2017): 319 –337.

Joffe, Ben. *"Reaching the Rainbow with Your Feet on the Ground: An Essay on the Importance and Special Characteristics of the Yuthok Nyingthig."* *A Perfumed Skull* (blog). April 2, 2016a. Accessed March 29, 2018. https://perfumedskull.com/2016/04/02/reaching-the-rainbow-with-your-feet-on-the-ground-an-essay-on-the-importance-and-special-characteristics-of-the-yuthok-nyingthik/

Joffe, Ben. *"Tantric Sex Partners, Actual and 'Imagined': Tibetan Karmamudra, and the Life and Times of Lelung Jedrung Zhepai Dorje."* *A Perfumed Skull* (blog). May 16, 2016b. Accessed March 29, 2018. https://perfumedskull.com/2016/05/16/Tantric-sex-partners-actual-and-imagined-tibetan-karmamudra-and-the-life-and-times-of-lelung-jedrung-zhepai-dorje/

Joffe, Ben. *"The White-Robed, Dreadlocked Community: Dr Nida Chenagtsang's Introduction to and Defense of the Ngakpa Tradition."* *A Perfumed Skull* (blog). May 30, 2017. Accessed March 29, 2018.

https://perfumedskull.com/2017/05/30/the-white-robed-dreadlocked-community-dr-nida-chenagtsangs-introduction-to-and-defense-of-the-ngakpa-tradition/

Mingyur Rinpoche, Yongey. *The Joy of Living: Unlocking the Secret & Science of Happiness.* New York: Harmony Books, 2007.

Onians, Isabelle. "*Tantric Buddhist Apologetics or Antinomianism as a Norm.*" PhD diss., University of Oxford, 2003.

Samuel, Geoffrey. *Civilized Shamans: Buddhism in Tibetan Societies.* Washington, DC: Smithsonian Institute Scholarly Press, 1995.

Samuel, Geoffrey. *The Origins of Yoga and Tantra: Indic Religions to the Thirteenth Century.* New York: Cambridge University Press, 2008.

Shaw, Miranda. *Passionate Enlightenment: Women in Tantric Buddhism.* New Jersey: Princeton University Press, 1994.

Snellgrove, David. *Indo-Tibetan Buddhism: Indian Buddhists and Their Tibetan Successors.* London: Serindia, 1987.

Szántó, Péter-Dániel. "*The Case of the Vajra-Wielding Monk.*" Acta Orientalia Academiae Scientiarum Hungaricae 63, 3 (2010): 289-299.

Tiso, Francis. *Rainbow Body and Resurrection: Spiritual Attainment, the Dissolution of the Material Body, and the Case of Khenpo A Chö.* Berkeley: North Atlantic Books, 2016.

Wedemeyer, Christian. *Making Sense of Tantric Buddhism: History, Semiology, and Transgression in the Indian Traditions.* New York: Columbia University Press, 2014.

White, David Gordon. *Kiss of the Yogini: "Tantric Sex" in its South Asian Contexts.* Chicago: Chicago University Press, 2003.

Dr. Nida Chenagtsang

Dr. Nida Chenagtsang was born in Amdo, in North Eastern Tibet. Interested in Sowa Rigpa, the traditional healing science of his people, he began his early medical studies at the local Tibetan Medicine hospital. Later he gained scholarship entry to Lhasa Tibetan Medical University, where he completed his medical education in 1996. He completed his practical training at the Tibetan Medicine hospitals in Lhasa and Lhoka.

Alongside his medical education, Dr. Nida trained in Vajrayana with teachers from every school of Tibetan Buddhism, especially in the Longchen Nyingthig of the Nyingma school from his root teacher Ani Ngawang Gyaltsen and in the Dudjom Tersar lineage from Chönyid Rinpoche and Sremo Dechen Yudron. He received complete teachings in the Yuthok Nyingthig lineage, the unique spiritual tradition of Tibetan Medicine, from his teachers Khenpo Tsultrim Gyaltsen and Khenchen Troru Tsenam, and was requested to continue the lineage by Jamyang Rinpoche of the Rebkong *ngakpa* (non-monastic yogi/ini) tradition.

A well-known poet in his youth, Dr. Nida later published many articles and books on Sowa Rigpa (Traditional Tibetan Medicine) and the Yuthok Nyingthig tradition both in the Tibetan and English languages which have been translated into several languages. He has extensively researched ancient Tibetan healing methods, and has gained high acclaim in the East and West for his revival of little known traditional Tibetan external healing therapies. Dr. Nida is the Co-Founder and Medical Director of Sorig Khang International (formerly the International Academy for Traditional Tibetan Medicine), the largest organization of Tibetan Medicine in the West, and Co-Founder of the International Ngakmang Institute, established to preserve and maintain the Rebkong *ngakpa/ma* culture within modern Tibetan society. In addition to his work as a physician, he trains students in Sowa Rigpa and the Yuthok Nyingthig tradition in over forty countries around the world.

For more information about Dr. Nida Chenagtsang and his teaching activities, please visit www.sorig.net. For information about his publications, visit www.skypressbooks.com

CPSIA information can be obtained
at www.ICGtesting.com
Printed in the USA
BVHW08s2151270918
528674BV00019B/692/P